FOCUS ON COMPUTATIONAL NEUROBIOLOGY

FOCUS ON COMPUTATIONAL NEUROBIOLOGY

LEI LI (EDITOR)

Nova Science Publishers, Inc.
New York

Senior Editors: Susan Boriotti and Donna Dennis
Coordinating Editor: Tatiana Shohov
Office Manager: Annette Hellinger
Graphics: Wanda Serrano
Editorial Production: Vladimir Klestov, Matthew Kozlowski, Alexandra Columbus and Maya Columbus
Circulation: Ave Maria Gonzalez, Vera Popovic, Luis Aviles, Raymond Davis, Melissa Diaz, Marlene Nunez and Jeannie Pappas
Communications and Acquisitions: Serge P. Shohov
Marketing: Cathy DeGregory

Library of Congress Cataloging-in-Publication Data
Available upon Request

ISBN 1-59033-915-0

400 Oser Ave, Suite 1600
Hauppauge, New York 11788-3619
Tele. 631-231-7269 Fax 631-231-8175
e-mail: Novascience@earthlink.net
Web Site: http://www.novapublishers.com

Printed in the United States of America

Contents

Preface

The most distinctive feature in the development of information science and life science is the gradual and growing interlacing of these two fields. As a result, many new disciplines and technologies have emerged from the overlap of these two areas of science. Today, information science and life science depend on each other so closely that they can no longer exist and grow independently.

The interaction and interdependence between the information and life sciences is expected to grow exponentially in the 21st century. Development of the life sciences based on information science and computation will reveal many significant challenges in the life sciences, as well as lead to many new and important discoveries, including targeted and break-through drugs. Application of these discoveries extends to such areas as biotechnology, genomics, proteomics, e-health, pharmaceuticals, and the agricultural sciences.

Xiaojun Chen presents a brief view of recent applications of smoothing methods in the area of numerical analysis and optimization. He describes various nonsmooth problems and illustrates how to apply smoothing methods to these problems. He summarizes properties of smoothing methods which are useful for the convergence analysis and error estimation of smoothing methods.

Two stochastic programming models for vehicle routing problems with stochastic demands and travel times, including chance-constrained programming models and dependent-chance programming models are presented in *Stochastic Programming Models for Vehicle Routing Problems*. A genetic algorithm is also designed for solving the proposed stochastic programming models and the effectiveness of genetic algorithm is illustrated by some numerical examples.

Recently, some criteria for generalized diagonally dominant matrix (GDDM) have been proposed. Many researchers howed an iterative criterion for GDDM. Lei Li and Katsuhisa Someya present an improved algorithm to decrease the number of iterations. The new method is also effective for a class of Non-GDDM.

Jinfang Wang develops third-order asymptotic theories for the jackknife method under the multivariate smooth function model. Both unstudentized and studentized versions are studied. The focus is on the latter case since studentization often results in better accuracy in estimation such as estimating the distribution function.

In the paper by Qing Fang, Yukihiro Shogenji and Tetsuro Yamamoto consideration is given to adaptive finite difference methods using polynomial and exponential stretching functions for Dirichlet boundary value problems in a domain Ω, whose solutions have singular derivatives near a part or the whole of the boundary of Ω. In the case where Ω is the unit square, it is shown that the methods are convergent and the convergence can be accelerated by varying parameters in the stretching functions. Numerical examples are given to illustrate how the effect of stretching functions depends on the choice of parameters.

Tsutomu Ansai, Hiroaki Matsuyama and Kunikatsu Kobayashi propose a public key cryptosystem using the traveling salesman problem that is a NP-complete problem. First, they show the outline on the traveling salesman cryptosystem, then investigate sequences used as the secret key in the traveling salesman cryptosystem. Next, they consider the public key generation for the traveling salesman cryptosystem and further propose the new encryption using the mixed sum and product operations. Finally, they examine the security of this cryptosystem against the attack using Shamir algorithm and LLL algorithm.

Techniques for improving the imaginary-distance full-vectorial beam-propagation method based on Yee's mesh are presented for the eigenmode analysis of optical waveguides. Fourth- and sixth-order accuracies are achieved for the analysis of a graded-index waveguide. For a step-index waveguide, the conventional scheme is used together with a permittivity-averaging technique. Numerical results demonstrate a second-order accuracy even in the analysis of a rib waveguide. The effective index and the field profiles of major and minor components are presented and discussed by Junji Yamauchi, Naofumi Morohashi and Hisamatsu Nakano

A large variety of information processing applications deal with natural language texts. Many such applications require extracting and processing the meanings of the natural language texts, in addition to processing their syntactic forms. In order to extract meanings from texts and manipulate them, a natural language processing system must have a significant amount of knowledge about the world and the domain of discourse. However, different kinds of knowledge are required for different languages, for different functions, and for different media. Fuji Ren and Shingo Kuroiwa design a new general ontology based natural language processing system referred to as Multi-lingual Multi-function Multi-media Intelligent System (MMM-IS). MMM-IS is a big project, it is a complex system with multiple functions that can deal with multiple languages and multiple media. The general ontology consists of a static layer and a dynamic layer, and it provides a real world knowledge model for the natural language processing system. This paper presents the concept of MMM-IS and how to build MMM-IS for real applications, and describes some new advances on the project.

Two experiments were designed by Sheng Ge, Jing-Long Wu, Shunichi Kawano and Takashi Saito in order to investigate the relationship between the subjective contours strength and the curvature of the illusory form. Both of the two experiments used the partial eclipse disc as the inducing elements, while the illusory form was an ellipse. Experimental stimuli are those figures whose one inducing element is randomly omitted from the standard figure. In Experiment 1, the area of the inducing element was bigger where the curvature of the illusory form was smaller. The findings show that the mean subjective contours strength is stronger when the curvature of illusory form of omitted inducing element is smaller. In Experiment 2, the area of the inducing element is bigger where the curvature of the illusory form is bigger. The experimental results show that the conclusion of experiment 1 is still tenable in this different case.

The Asian comma butterfly, *Polygonia c-aureum*, exhibits seasonal dimorphism, i.e. summer and autumn morphs, whose development is determined by photoperiod and temperature during the larval stages. The physiological mechanism of *P. c-aureum* underlying the photoperiodic control of seasonal morph development involves a cerebral factor, named summer-morph-producing hormone (SMPH). Autumn-morph females of *P. c-aureum* as well as females of univoltine butterfly, *Nymphalis xanthomelas japonica*, do not start ovarian maturation after adult emergence and enter reproductive diapause. Diapausing female adults of these two butterfly species started ovarian maturation, a sign of the termination of reproductive diapause, when they were injected with juvenile hormone-I (JH-I). With the injection of JH-I, ovarian maturation of decapitated females and isolated female abdomens was also stimulated in both of *P. c-aureum* and *N. xanthomelas japonica*. In diapause females of *P. c-aureum* and *N. xanthomelas japonica* ovarian maturation also started when they were injected with 2% NaCl extracts of the adult brain-suboesophageal ganglion (Br-SG) complexes of their own species. However, acetone and 80% ethanol extracts of their adult Br-SG complexes failed to stimulate ovarian maturation. Female adults of *P. c-aureum* and *N. xanthomelas japonica*, corpora allata (CA) of which remain inactive after adult emergence to enter reproductive diapause in the absence of JH as has been demonstrated in *Leptinotarsa decemlineata* (De Wilde, 1954). A factor(s) stimulating ovarian maturation in diapausing female adults may exist in the adult Br-SG complexes of *P. c-aureum* and *N. xanthomelas japonica*. The Br-SG factor(s) extracted with 2% NaCl may stimulate the CA *in vivo* to secrete the JH essential for ovarian maturation. The results are presented in the paper, *Presence of Cerebral Factors Terminating Adult Reproductive Diapause in Two Species of Nymphalid Butterflies*.

A brief but concise review by Michael J. Tsatsomeros of methods to generate P-matrices (i.e., matrices having positive principal minors) is provided and motivated by open problems on P-matrices and the desire to develop and test efficient methods for the detection of P-matrices. Also discussed are operations that leave the class of P-matrices invariant. Some new results and extensions of results regarding P-matrices are included in the paper.

The paper by Hongxia Liu and Tao Pan is concerned with global error estimates for the viscosity methods to Riemann initial-boundary problems for scalar conservation laws $u_t+f(u)_x=0$ on R_+, with the boundary data $u(0,t) = u_-$ and the initial data $u(x,0) = u_+$, where $u_\pm$ are two constants, $u_- \neq u_+$. The error of the viscosity solution to the inviscid solution is bounded by $O(\varepsilon + \varepsilon |\ln \varepsilon|$ in the L^1-norm for all cases with convex fluxes and some cases with non-convex fluxes, respectively. If there is no central rarefaction wave included in the inviscid solution, the error bound is improved to $O(\varepsilon)$. The proof is given by a matching method and the traveling wave solutions.

When DCT (discrete cosine transform) method as a standard transform coding is used to extend images at higher compression ratio, it is difficult to eliminate degradation of image quality due to blocking effect. Kanae T. Kobayashi and Hideo Sawami quantify and analyze blocking effect for the DCT and OBDCT(overlapping block DCT) methods corresponding to four bases as degradation of image quality caused by quantization error. They clarify theoretically that the OBDCT method with type-I, III bases show the least blocking effect. It is concluded that the OBDCT method is more effective transform coding than the DCT method with data compression and image extension since it did not occur blocking effect visually from results of subjective comparison and enough image quality is kept.

Microlocal filtering is performed with adapted orthonormal multiwavelets and smooth frame multiwavelets in $\mathbb{R}^n$. The values of the wavelet coefficients of a function give a rough estimate of its microlocal content, as shown by an example in *Microlocal Analysis, Smooth Frames and Denoising in Fourier Space*. Multidirectional denoising of images is presented as the action of a pseudodifferential operator which is the product of directional diffusion equations.

In *On the Bounds of (0,1) Matrix Permanents*, Lei Li and Wakana Tamada show some new bounds for the permanent of n-order (0,1) matrices with the row sums and the column sums are all a positive integer k, where $1 \leq k \leq n$. Especially, for case *of (0,1) circulant* matrix, they propose some better bounds of the permanent.

Zhao Feng-ji, Guo Hai-jiao and Ken-ichi Abe describe an efficient method for estimating long distance navigation of a mobile robot, by fusing dead reckoning and the combining sensors which consist of sonar and infrared. A corridor with interval convex edges is applied as the mobile robot's moving space, and the convex edges are accepted as good landmarks for robot's position estimation. The robot detects the convex edges using combined sensor system, and navigates in this corridor by fusion the information from the dead reckoning and combined sensor based on the Extended Kalman Filter(EKF). The experimental result has shown that the method is effective for estimating of long distance navigation of the mobile robot.

Guifa Teng and Xiaodong Liu advocate that reengineering is an effective means of legacy system evolution. Extracting formal specification semantically consistent to the original legacy system will facilitate further redesign and forward engineering greatly. The key technology is abstraction, which is often interpreted as the act of hiding irrelevant details. Programming knowledge refers to the "technique" or "convention" that a programmer used to implement an application. The structure of an existing program was heavily affected by this kind of knowledge. A set of programming knowledge patterns are developed to discover the programming knowledge embedded in legacy systems. Implementation details can be eliminated effectively with these patterns and relevant abstraction rules. A unified reengineering approach with a focus on reverse engineering is proposed. The approach is based on three points: the construction of a wide spectrum language based reengineering framework, the development of abstraction rules and programming knowledge patterns.

Generally, an IPCS should reconcile two contradictory properties: reacting in "real time" to the solicitations of the environment and operating out some evolved reasoning in order to meet these solicitations. Aziz El Fazziki proposes an approach where the system is considered as composition of three sub-systems. A reactive sub-system taking into account the control, the surveillance of the IP. An evaluating sub-systems that watch out for the functioning safety and the breakdowns prediction. A supervising sub-system taking into account the diagnosis and the supervision of the IP. This approach proposes a diagnosis architecture using the Data Mining techniques. These techniques enable to answer different tasks of the diagnosis such as the selection of pertinent indicators, the generation of breakdown cases, the prediction and more particularly, the temporal and spatial dependencies of the IP.

Tsutomu Ansai, Takahiro Hayata and Kunikatsu Kobayashi show a factoring algorithm based on a new idea that using Jacobi's symbol in regard to the composite number of $n = p^2q$ The complexity of this method is about $\boldsymbol{O}(n^{1/3.7})$.

In: Focus on Computational Neurobiology
Editor: Lei Li, pp. 1-12
ISBN 1-59033-915-0

APPLICATIONS OF SMOOTHING METHODS IN NUMERICAL ANALYSIS AND OPTIMIZATION

XIAOJUN CHEN*

Abstract. This paper presents a brief view of recent applications of smoothing methods in the area of numerical analysis and optimization. We describe various nonsmooth problems and illustrate how to apply smoothing methods to these problems. We summarize properties of smoothing methods which are useful for the convergence analysis and error estimation of smoothing methods.

Key words. nonsmooth function, smoothing method, differentiability, variational inequality, complementarity problem, approximation.

AMS subject classifications. 90C30, 65H10

1. Introduction. In the last decade smoothing methods have been successfully applied to many important problems in the area of numerical analysis and optimization. These problems include

- complementarity problems [7, 9, 10, 11, 12, 13, 14, 15, 16, 17, 21, 29, 32, 38, 39, 47, 49, 51, 52, 56, 62, 63, 68, 71, 72],
- variational inequality problems [6, 30, 31, 44, 55, 61, 64, 76],
- optimal control problems with bound constraints on the control [46, 53],
- nonsmooth Dirichlet problems [23, 26, 28],
- computational fluid dynamics [34],
- shape preserving approximation [35],
- nonsmooth convex programs [8, 24],
- comformal mapping [73],
- semi-infinite programs [70],
- mathematical programs with equilibrium constraints [25, 36, 41, 42, 48],
- the unbounded in optimization [2],
- stochastic programs [5, 22],
- minimizing a sum of Euclidean norms [65],etc.

A common feature shared by these problems is that each problem or its reformulation involves functions which are not differentiable in the sense of Fréchet or Gâteaux [58]. These functions are said to be nonsmooth, and the problems are called nonsmooth problems. Traditional algorithms lack robustness for solving these problems [58].

There has been a growing interest in the study of nonsmooth functions in finite dimensional spaces or functional spaces [27, 28, 33, 43, 45, 50, 59, 63, 69, 75]. A number of numerical methods for solving nonsmooth problems based on the theory of nonsmooth analysis have been developed [1, 18, 19, 20, 29, 37, 40, 57, 60, 62, 74, 77]. Among these methods, smoothing methods approximate the nonsmooth functions by parameteried differentiable functions. By updating the parameters in the numerical methods, many traditional algorithms for smooth problems can be modified to efficiently solve these nonsmooth problems.

This paper presents a brief illustration on how to apply smoothing methods to some typical problems. In Section 2 various problems and smoothing approximations for the problems are described. In Section 3 the properties of the smoothing approximations are

* Department of Mathematics System Science, Hirosaki University, Hirosaki 036-8561, Aomori, Japan

summarized which are useful for the convergence analysis and error estimation of smoothing methods.

A few words about notations. For two vectors $x, y \in R^n$, $x \geq y$ and $x \geq 0$ denote $x_i \geq y_i$ and $x_i \geq 0$ for $i = 1, 2, \ldots, n$, respectively. Let e_i be the ith column of the identity matrix $I \in R^{n\times n}$. Let $R_+ = \{\epsilon \,|\, \epsilon > 0, \epsilon \in R\}$.

2. Problems and Smoothing Approximations. In this section, we consider seven important problems in numerical analysis and optimization. We show how to define smoothing functions to approximate these problems.

2.1. Complementarity problems. Let $f : R^n \to R^n$ be a continuously differentiable function. The complementarity problem is to find a vector x such that

$$x \geq 0, \quad f(x) \geq 0 \quad \text{and} \quad x^T f(x) = 0. \tag{2.1}$$

This problem is called a nonlinear complementarity problem if f is a nonlinear function, or a linear complementarity problem if f is an affine mapping of the form

$$f(x) = Mx + q,$$

where $M \in R^{n\times n}$ and $q \in R^n$.

There are several ways to formulate the complementarity problems as a system of nonsmooth equations. Among these reformulations, the following two functions F and $\tilde{F}$ are well-known, whose components are defined by

$$F_i(x) = \min(x_i, f_i(x))$$

and

$$\tilde{F}_i(x) = \frac{1}{2}\left(x_i + f_i(x) - \sqrt{x_i^2 + (f_i(x))^2}\right).$$

The two functions have the same growth rate by the following inequalities [71]:

$$\frac{1}{\sqrt{2}+2}|F_i(x)| \leq \frac{1}{2}|\tilde{F}_i(x)| \leq \frac{\sqrt{2}+2}{2}|F_i(x)|.$$

Each F_i can be written as

$$F_i(x) = x_i - \max(0, x_i - f_i(x)),$$

which is piecewise smooth whose nondifferentiable points form the set:

$$\{x \,|\, x_i = f_i(x) \text{ and } e_i \neq f_i'(x)\ \}.$$

The function $\tilde{F}_i$ is differentiable everywhere except at the point

$$\{x \,|\, x_i = f_i(x) = 0\}.$$

Two typical smoothing functions H and $\tilde{H}$ approximating to these two nonsmooth functions have the components

$$H_i(x, \epsilon) = \frac{1}{2}\left(x_i + f_i(x) - \sqrt{(x_i - f_i(x))^2 + 4\epsilon^2}\right)$$

and

$$\tilde{H}_i(x, \epsilon) = \frac{1}{2}\left(x_i + f_i(x) - \sqrt{x_i^2 + (f_i(x))^2 + 2\epsilon^2}\right).$$

For every $\epsilon > 0$, the functions H and $\tilde{H}$ are continuously differentiable with respect to x in R^n. Moreover, for all $x \in R^n$ we have

$$0 \le F_i(x) - H_i(x, \epsilon) \le \epsilon$$

and

$$0 \le \tilde{F}_i(x) - \tilde{H}_i(x, \epsilon) \le \frac{1}{\sqrt{2}}\epsilon.$$

The smoothing approximations for complementarity problems can also be applied to the problems which involve complementarity problems. For example, mathematical programs with equilibrium constraints [25, 36, 41, 42, 48].

2.2. Variational inequality problems with box constraints. Let $l \in \{R \cup \{-\infty\}\}^n$ and $u \in \{R \cup \{\infty\}\}^n$ be two vectors which satisfy $l \le u$ and $l \ne u$. Then

$$X = \{x \in R^n \,|\, l \le x \le u\}$$

is called a box in R^n. Let $f : D \subset R^n$ be a continuously differentiable function defined on the open set $D \subset R^n$ containing X. This problem is to find a vector $x^* \in X$ such that

$$(y - x^*)^T f(x^*) \ge 0 \quad \text{for} \quad y \in X. \tag{2.2}$$

When $l_i = -\infty$, $u_i = \infty$,for $i = 1, 2, \ldots, n$, this problem reduces to the system of nonlinear equations

$$f(x) = 0.$$

When $l_i = 0$, $u_i = \infty$ for $i = 1, 2, \ldots, n$, this problem reduces to the nonlinear complementarity problem (2.1). Moreover, if f is the gradient of a function $\phi : R^n \to R$, this problem becomes the stationary point problem of the following minimization problem with box constriants:

$$\begin{array}{ll} \text{minimize} & \phi(x) \\ \text{subjcet to} & x \in X. \end{array}$$

We can define two reformulations of this problem as a system of nonsmooth equations:

$$F(x) = x - \Pi_X(x - f(x)) = 0$$

or

$$\tilde{F}(x) = f(\Pi_X(x - f(x))) + x - f(x) - \Pi_X(x - f(x)) = 0,$$

where $\Pi_X(z)$ denotes the projection of the vector z onto X, which can be written as

$$(\Pi_X(z))_i = \begin{cases} l_i, & z_i \le l_i \\ z_i, & l_i < z_i < u_i \\ u_i, & z_i \ge u_i \end{cases} \quad i = 1, 2, \ldots, n.$$

It is easy to verify that x is a zero of F if and only if x solves (2.2). Moreover, if x is a zero of F, then x is a zero of $\tilde{F}(x)$. Conversely, if x is a zero of $\tilde{F}$, then $\Pi_X(x - f(x))$ is a zero of F.

The projection is the only nonsmooth term in F and $\tilde{F}$. Hence we can derive a smoothing function for this problem by smoothing the projection. In particular, we have

$$H(x,\epsilon) = x - P(x - f(x), \epsilon)$$

and

$$\tilde{H}(x,\epsilon) = f(P(x - f(x), \epsilon)) + x - f(x) - P(x - f(x), \epsilon)$$

where

$$P_i(z,\epsilon) = \frac{1}{2}\left(\sqrt{(l_i - z_i)^2 + 4\epsilon^2} - \sqrt{(u_i - z_i)^2 + 4\epsilon^2} + l_i + u_i\right) \quad i = 1, 2, \ldots, n.$$

For every $\epsilon > 0$, P is continuously differentiable with respect to x in R^n, and so are H and $\tilde{H}$. Moreover, there are two positive constants c_i and $\tilde{c}_i$, which are only dependent of l_i and u_i, such that

$$|F_i(x) - H_i(x,\epsilon)| \le c_i\epsilon,$$

and

$$|\tilde{F}_i(x) - \tilde{H}_i(x,\epsilon)| \le \tilde{c}_i\epsilon.$$

2.3. Optimal Control Problems with Bound Constraints on the Control. Let $\Omega \subset R^m$ be a closed and bounded convex set. Let K be a completely continuous map from $L^\infty(\Omega)$ to $C(\Omega)$, and Φ be the map on $C(R^m)$ given by

$$\Phi(K(x))(t) = \begin{cases} l(t), & K(x)(t) \le l(t) \\ K(x)(t), & l(t) \le K(x)(t) \le u(t) \\ u(t), & K(x)(t) \ge u(t), \end{cases}$$

for given l and u in $C(\Omega)$. This problem is to find $x \in C(\Omega : R^m)$ such that

$$F(x) = x(t) - \Phi(K(x))(t) = 0, \quad \text{on} \quad \Omega. \tag{2.3}$$

A paradigm for problems of the form (2.3) is the integral equation with

$$K(x)(t) = \int_\Omega k(t,s)x(s)ds,$$

where $k \in C(\Omega \times \Omega)$ is a smooth kernel function. Discretization of this problem gives the variational inequality problem (2.2).

2.4. Nonsmooth Dirichlet Problems. Let Ω be a bounded domain in R^2 with a Lipschitz boundary $\partial\Omega$. Given a real number λ, this problem is to find u such that

$$\begin{cases} -\Delta u + \lambda\xi(u) = f(x,y) & \text{in } \Omega \\ u = g(x,y) & \text{on } \partial\Omega, \end{cases}$$

where

$$\xi(u) = \begin{cases} u^p, & u \geq 0 \\ 0, & u < 0 \end{cases}$$

and $p \in (0, 1]$ is a positive number. Such problem is related to reaction-diffusion problems [3, 4] and to MHD(magnetohydrodynamics) equilibria [66]. If $p = 1$, the term $\xi(u) = \max(0, u)$ is Lipschitz continuous. We can define two smoothing approximations for $\max(0, u)$ as

$$\phi(u, \epsilon) = \frac{1}{2}(u + \sqrt{u^2 + 4\epsilon^2})$$

and

$$\tilde{\phi}(u, \epsilon) = \begin{cases} \frac{1}{2\epsilon}(\frac{\epsilon}{2} + u)^2, & |u| \leq \frac{\epsilon}{2} \\ \max(0, u), & \text{otherwise.} \end{cases}$$

For $p \in (0, 1)$, ξ is not Lipschitiz continuous. To use the smoothing approximations ϕ and $\tilde{\phi}$, a Lipschitz reformulation was introduced in [23]:

$$\begin{cases} -\Delta u + \lambda \max(0, v) &= f(x, y) & \text{in } \Omega \\ u &= \psi(v) & \text{in } \Omega, \\ u &= g(x, y) & \text{on } \partial\Omega \end{cases}$$

where

$$\psi(v) = \begin{cases} v^{1/p}, & v \geq 0 \\ 0, & v < 0, \end{cases}$$

which is continuously differentiable.

2.5. Computational Fluid Dynamics. We consider Euler equations for flow through a nozzle of length L. The nozzle is a surface of revolution about the x axis with cross section area $S(x)$.

The governing equations for Quasi-One Dimensional Euler flow in conservative variables are

$$\frac{\partial(\rho S)}{\partial t} + \frac{\partial(\rho u S)}{\partial x} = 0$$

$$\frac{\partial(\rho u S)}{\partial t} + \frac{\partial[(\rho u^2 + p)S]}{\partial x} = p\frac{dS}{dx}$$

$$\frac{\partial(\rho E S)}{\partial t} + \frac{\partial(\rho u H S)}{\partial x} = 0$$

where $\rho(x, t)$ is density, $p(x, t)$ is pressure, $u(x, t)$ is velocity,

$$E(x, t) = \frac{c^2}{\gamma(\gamma - 1)} + \frac{u^2}{2},$$

is total energy and

$$H(x, t) = \frac{1}{\rho}(\rho E + p)$$

is stagnation enthalpy. Here $c = \sqrt{\gamma p/\rho}$ is the speed of sound, and γ is the ratio of the specific heat at constant pressure to the specific heat at constant volume.

In many applications, the cross-sectional area of the flow domain is nonsmooth. For instance, we consider the following example [34]:

$$S(x) = \begin{cases} 1 + 4(x-1)^2, & 0.5 < x < 1.5 \\ 2, & \text{otherwise.} \end{cases}$$

The boundary conditions are supersonic flow in the inlet. It is easy to find that

$$S(x) = \min(2, 1 + 4(x-1)^2).$$

Since $1 + 4(x-1)^2$ is continuosuly differentiable, we can define the smoothing functions in the similar way as for complementarity problems. In particular, we have

$$\tilde{S}(x,\epsilon) = \frac{1}{2}\left(3 + 4(x-1)^2 - \sqrt{(1-4(x-1)^2)^2 + 4\epsilon^2}\right).$$

Replacing $S(x)$ by $\tilde{S}(x,\epsilon)$ in the governing equations, we obtain a smoothing approximation for this problem.

2.6. Shape Preserving Approximation. This problem arises from practical applications in computer aided geometric design where one has not only to approximate data points but also to achieve a desired shape of a curve or surface. A special case of shape preserving approximation is one-dimensional convex best interpolation, which is to find a real valued function that is convex and passes through given points in R. We write this problem as a constrained minimization problem:

$$\begin{cases} \text{minimize} & \|f''\|_2 \\ \text{subject to} & f(t_i) = y_i, i = 0, 1, \cdots n+1 \\ & f \text{ is convex on } [a,b] \\ & f \in W^{2,2}[a,b], \end{cases}$$

where $a = t_0 < t_1 < \cdots < t_{n+1} = b$ and $y_i, i = 0, 1, \cdots, n+1$ are given numbers, $\|\cdot\|_2$ is the Lebesgue $L^2[a,b]$ norm, and $W^{2,2}[a,b]$ denotes the Sobolev space of functions with absolutely continuous first derivatives and second derivatives in $L^2[a,b]$, and equipped with the norm being the sum of the $L^2[a,b]$ norms of the function, its first and its second derivatives.

Empolying the normalized B-splines B_i of order two associated with $(t_i, y_i), i = 0, 1 \ldots n+1$, and the corresponding second divided differences d_i, the problem can be rewritten as nonsmooth equations

$$F(x) = G(x) - d = 0 \tag{2.4}$$

where

$$G_i(x) = \int_a^b \left(\sum_{i=1}^n x_j B_j(t)\right)_+ B_i(t)dt.$$

Here $(z)_+$ denotes $\max(0, z)$.

Using the solution x^* of (2.4), we can define the second derivative of the desired function as

$$f''(t) = \left(\sum_{i=1}^n x_j^* B_j(t)\right)_+.$$

It is well-known that a function f is convex if and only if the second derivative f'' is nonnegative. The function G is nonsmooth. To see it, we consider the following example. Let $t_i = i+1, i = 0, 1, 2, 3$. The B-splines are defined by

$$B_1(t) = \begin{cases} t-1, & t \in [1,2] \\ 3-t, & t \in [2,3] \end{cases}$$

and

$$B_2(t) = \begin{cases} t-2, & t \in [2,3] \\ 4-t, & t \in [3,4] \end{cases}$$

In this case, the function G is given by

$$G(x) = G(x_1, x_2) = \begin{pmatrix} \int_1^2 (x_1 B_1(t))_+ B_1(t)dt + \int_2^3 (x_1 B_1(t) + x_2 B_2(t))_+ B_1(t)dt \\ \\ \int_2^3 (x_1 B_1(t) + x_2 B_2(t))_+ B_2(t)dt + \int_3^4 (x_2 B_2(t))_+ B_2(t)dt \end{pmatrix}.$$

The function G is not differentiable at $(x_1, x_2) = (0, 0)$. If we replace the term $(\cdot)_+$ by a smoothing approximation as we have done for $\max(0, u)$, we can get a smoothing function for F.

2.7. Stochastic Programs. A version of two-stage stochastic program with recourse is

$$\begin{array}{ll} \text{mimimize} & c^T x + F(x) \\ \text{subject to} & Ax = b, \quad x \geq 0 \end{array}$$

where

$$F(x) = \sum_{i=1}^{N} Q(x, w_i)\rho_i.$$

Here $\rho_i \geq 0$, $\sum_{i=1}^N \rho_i = 1$ and Q is calculated by finding for given decision x and even w, an optimal recourse $y \in R^{n_2}$, namely

$$Q(x, w) = \max\{(h(w) - T(w))^T z \,|\, W^T z \leq q\}.$$

The cost coefficient vector $c \in R^n$, the constrianed matrix $A \in R^{m \times n}$ and the vector $b \in R^m$ in the first stage (a master problem), and the associated cost coefficient vector $q \in R^{n_2}$ and the recourse matrix $W \in R^{m_2 \times n_2}$ in the second stage (a recourse problem) are assumed to be deterministic. In the second stage, the demand vector $h(\cdot) \in R^{n_2}$ and the technology matrix $T(\cdot) \in R^{m_2 \times n_2}$ are allowed to depend on the random vector $w \in \Omega \subset R^s$.

The function F presents the expected value of minimum extra cost based on the first-stage decision and random events, which is convex and nonsmooth. Two smoothing approximations to F were defined in [5, 22]. One of them is given by [22]

$$\tilde{Q}(x, w, \epsilon) = \max\{-\frac{\epsilon}{2} z^T z + (h(w) - T(w)x)^T z \,|\, W^T z \leq q\}$$

and

$$H(x,\epsilon)=\sum_{i=1}^{N}\tilde{Q}(x,w_i,\epsilon)\rho_i.$$

Assume that the feasible set Z of the second stage is bounded. Let

$$\beta\geq\max_{z\in Z}z^Tz.$$

Then we can show that for every $\epsilon>0$, F is continuously differentiable and for every x, there is an $\bar{\epsilon}(x)>0$ such that for any $\epsilon\in(0,\bar{\epsilon}(x)]$

$$H(x,\epsilon)\leq F(x)\leq H(x,\epsilon)+\frac{1}{2}\beta\bar{\epsilon}(x).$$

3. What are Good Smoothing Approximations. For a nonsmooth function $F: R^n\to R^n$, a good smoothing function $H: R^n\times R_+\to R^n$ should have the following three properties.

P1. For every $\epsilon>0$, $H(\cdot,\epsilon)$ is continuously differentiable with respect to $x\in R^n$.

P2. There is a constant $c>0$ such that $\|F(x)-H(x,\epsilon)\|\leq c\epsilon$ for $x\in R^n$ and $\epsilon\in R_+$.

P3. For every $x\in R^n$, the limit

$$\lim_{\epsilon\downarrow 0}H'(x,\epsilon)$$

exists, say $F^o(x)$, and satisfies

$$\lim_{h\to 0}\frac{F(x+h)-F(x)-F^o(x)h}{h}=0.$$

The first property states that H is a smoothing function, the second property implies that the error of $H(x,\epsilon)$ to $F(x)$ is bounded by the smoothing parameter ϵ and the third property is required for designing locally fast convergent algorithms. These smoothing functions discussed in Section 2 satisfy the three properties.

For a nonsmooth problem, we can construct many smoothing approximations of the nonsmooth functions involved in the problem, and design many smoothing algorithms to solve the problem. Using smoothing approximations satisfying the three properties, we can obtain globally and superlinearly convergent algorithms for solving the nonsmooth problems.

The system of nonsmooth equations

$$F(x)=0$$

where $F: R^n\to R^n$, provides the prime candidate for illustrating the methodology of smoothing methods. For this reason, let us end this paper by considering how to use smoothing approximations to design smoothing methods for solving nonsmooth equations.

Most smoothing methods for solving nonsmooth equations include three steps:

S1. Newton Step Find a solution $\hat{d}^k$ of the system of linear equations

$$F(x^k)+F^o(x^k)d=0. \tag{3.1}$$

Use the smoothing parameter ϵ_k to check whether $\|F(x^k+\hat{d}^k)\|/\|F(x^k)\|$ is small enought. If it is true, let $x^{k+1}=x^k+\hat{d}^k$, otherwise perform Step 2.

S2. Global Smoothing Step Find a solution d^k of the system of linear equations

$$F(x^k) + H'(x^k, \epsilon_k)d = 0. \tag{3.2}$$

Let m_k be the smallest nonnegative integer m such that

$$\|H(x^k + \rho^m d^k, \epsilon_k)\|^2 - \|H(x^k, \epsilon_k)\|^2 \leq -\sigma\rho^m \|F(x^k)\|^2, \tag{3.3}$$

where $\sigma, \rho \in (0,1)$. Set $t_k = \rho^{m_k}$ and $x^{k+1} = x^k + t_k d^k$.

S3. Update Smoothing parameter ϵ_k

If F is continuously differentiable, then (P3) implies that $F^o(x) = F'(x)$. Thus, the Newton step (3.1) is a generalization of the Newton method. Hence, the algorithm will have fast local convergent rate. Using the smoothing function H in the second step, which satisfies (P1)-(P2), will ensure that the solution d^k of (3.2) is a descent direction, that is, there exists a finite nonnegative integer m_k such that (3.3) holds. Updating ϵ in Step 3 makes connection between the Newton step and the global smoothing step. We can show that the smoothing methods are globally and superlinearly convergent. Hence these methods are not only fast but are also robust.

REFERENCES

[1] G.E. Alefeld, X. Chen and F.A. Potra, *Numerical validation of solutions of linear complementarity problems*, Numer. Math., 83 (1999), pp. 1-23.

[2] A. Auslender, *How to deal with the unbounded in optimization: theory and algorithm*, Math. Programming, 79 (1997), pp. 3-18.

[3] A.K.Aziz, A.B.Stephens and M. Suri, *Numerical methods for reaction-diffusion problems with non-differentiable kinetics*, Numer. Math., 53 (1988), pp. 1-11.

[4] J.W. Barrett and R.M. Shanahan, *Finite element approximation of a model reaction-diffusion problem with a non-Lipschitz nonlinearity*, Numer. Math., 59 (1991),pp. 217-242.

[5] J.R. Birge, S.M. Pollock and L. Qi, *A quadratic recourse function for the two-stage stochastic program*, Progress in optimization, Appl. Optim., 39, Kluwer Acad. Publ., Dordrecht, 2000, pp. 109–121.

[6] S.C. Billups, S.P. Dirkse and M.C. Ferris, *A comparison of algorithms for large-scale mixed complementarity problems*, Comp. Optim. Appl. 7 (1997), pp. 3-25.

[7] J.V. Burke and S. Xu, *The global linear convergence of a non-interior path-following algorithm for linear complementarity problems*, Math. Oper. Res. 23 (1998), pp. 719-734.

[8] J.V. Burke and M. Qian, *On the superlinear convergence of the variable metric proximal point algorithm using Broyden and BFGS matrix secant updating*, Math. Program., 88 (2000), pp. 157–181.

[9] B. Chen and X. Chen, *A global and local superlinear continuation-smoothing method for P_0 and R_0 NCP or monotone NCP*, SIAM J. Optim., 9 (1999), pp. 624-645.

[10] B. Chen and X. Chen, *A global linear and local quadratic continuation smoothing method for variational inequalities with box constraints*, Comp. Optim. Appl., 17 (2000), pp. 131-158.

[11] B. Chen, X. Chen, and C. Kanzow, *A penalized Fischer-Burmeister NCP-function: theoretical investigation and numerical results*, Math. Programming, 88 (2000), pp. 211-216.

[12] B. Chen and P.T. Harker, *A non-interior-point continuation method for linear complementarity problems*, SIAM J. Matrix Anal. Appl., 14 (1993), pp. 1168-1190.

[13] B. Chen and P.T. Harker, *A continuation method for monotone variational inequalities*, Math. Programming, 69 (1995), pp. 237-253.

[14] B. Chen and P.T. Harker, *Smooth approximations to nonlinear complementarity problems*, SIAM J. Optim. 7 (1997), pp. 403-420.

[15] B. Chen and N. Xiu, *A global linear and local quadratic non-interior continuation method for nonlinear complementarity problems based on Chen-Mangasarian smoothing function*, SIAM J. Optim. 9 (1999), pp. 605-623.

[16] C. Chen and O.L. Mangasarian, *Smoothing methods for convex inequalities and linear complementarity problems*, Math. Programming, 71 (1995), pp. 51-69.

[17] C. Chen and O.L. Mangasarian, *A class of smoothing functions for nonlinear and mixed complementarity problems*, Comp. Optim. Appl., 5 (1996), pp. 97-138.

[18] X. Chen, *Superlinear convergence of smoothing quasi-Newton methods for nonsmooth equations*, J. Comp. Appl. Math., 80 (1997), pp. 105-126.

[19] X. Chen, *A verification method for solutions of nonsmooth equations*, Computing, 58(1997), pp. 281-294.

[20] X. Chen, *Global and superlinear convergence of inexact Uzawa methods for saddle point problems with nondifferentiable mappings*, SIAM J. Numer. Anal., 35 (1998), pp. 1130-1148.

[21] X. Chen, *Smoothing methods for complementarity problems and their applications: a survey*, J. Oper. Res. Soc. Japan, 43 (2000), pp. 32-47.

[22] X. Chen, *Newton-type methods for stochastic programming*, Math. Comp. Modelling, 31 (2000), pp. 89-98.

[23] X. Chen, *A superlinearly and globally convergent method for reaction and diffusion problems with a non-Lipschitzian operator*, Computing[Suppl] 15(2001), pp. 79-90.

[24] X. Chen and M. Fukushima, *Proximal quasi-Newton methods for nondifferentiable convex optimization*, Math. Programming, 85 (1999), pp. 313-334.

[25] X. Chen and M. Fukushima, *A smoothing method for a mathematical program with P-matrix linear complementarity constraints*, The Second International Conference on Nonlinear Analysis and Convex Analysis, Hirosaki, 2001.

[26] X. Chen, N. Matsunaga and T. Yamamoto, *Smoothing Newton methods for nonsmooth Dirichlet problems*, in: M. Fukushima and L. Qi, (eds.), Reformulation - Nonsmooth, Piecewise Smooth, Semismooth and Smoothing Methods, (Kluwer Academic Publisher, Dordrecht, The Netherlands, 1999), pp. 65-79.

[27] X. Chen, M.Z. Nashed and L. Qi, *Convergence of Newton's method for singular smooth and nonsmooth equations using adaptive outer inverses*, SIAM J. Optim., 7 (1997), pp. 445-462.

[28] X. Chen, M.Z. Nashed and L. Qi, *Smoothing methods and semismooth methods for nondifferentiable operator equations*, SIAM J. Numer. Anal., 38(2000), pp. 1200-1216.

[29] X. Chen and L. Qi, *A parameterized Newton method and a Broyden-like method for solving nonsmooth equations*, Comp. Optim. Appl., 3 (1994), pp. 157-179.

[30] X. Chen, L. Qi and D. Sun, *Global and superlinear convergence of the smoothing Newton method and its application to general box constrained variational inequalities*, Math. Comp., 67 (1998), pp. 519-540.

[31] X. Chen and Y. Ye, *On homotopy-smoothing methods for box-constrained variational inequalities*, SIAM J. Control Optim., 37 (1999), pp. 589-616.

[32] X. Chen and Y. Ye, *On smoothing methods for the P_0 matrix linear complementarity problems*, SIAM J. Optim., 11 (2000), pp. 341-363.

[33] F.H. Clarke, *Optimization and Nonsmooth Analysis*, John Wiley, New York, 1983.

[34] T. Coffey, R.J.McMullan, C.T. Kelley and D.S. McRae, *Global convergent algorithms for nonsmooth nonlinear equations in computational fluid dynamics*, International Conference on Recent Advances in Computational Mathematics, Matsuyama, 2001.

[35] A. L. Dontchev, H.Qi and L.Qi, *Convergence of Newton's method for convex best interpolation*, Numer. Math., 87 (2001), pp. 435-456.

[36] F. Facchinei, H. Jiang and L. Qi, *A smoothing method for mathematical programs with equilibrium constraints*, Math. Programming, 85 (1999), pp. 107-134.

[37] F. Facchinei and C. Kanzow, *Beyond monotonicity in regularization methods for nonlinear complementarity problems*, SIAM J. Control Optim. 37(1999),pp. 1150-1161.

[38] A. Fischer, *A special Newton-type optimization method*, Optim., 24 (1992), pp. 269-284.

[39] A. Fischer and C. Kanzow, *On finite termination of an iterative method for linear complementarity problems*, Math. Programming, 74 (1996), pp. 279-292.

[40] M. Fukushima, *Merit functions for variational inequality and complementarity problems*, in: G.Di Pillo and F. Giannessi (eds.), Nonlinear Optimization and Applications (Plenum Press, New York, NY 1996),pp. 155-170.

[41] M. Fukushima, Z-Q. Luo and J.S. Pang, *A globally convergent sequential quadratic programming algorithm for mathematical programming problems with linear complementarity constraints*, Comp. Optim. Appl., 10 (1998), pp. 5-34.

[42] M. Fukushima and J.S. Pang, *Convergence of a smoothing continuation method for mathematical programs with equilibrium constraints*, in: M. Théra and R. Tichatschke(eds), Ill-posed Variational Problems and Regularization Techniques, Lecture Notes in Economics and Mathematical Systems, Vol 477 (Springer-Verlag, Berlin, 1999),pp. 99-110.

[43] M. Fukushima and L. Qi eds, *Reformulation: Nonsmooth, Piecewise Smooth, Semismooth and*

Smoothing Methods, Kluwer Academic Publishers 1999.

[44] S.A. GABRIEL AND J.J. MORÉ, *Smoothing of mixed complementarity problems*, in: M.C. Ferris and J.S. Pang (eds.), Complementarity and Variational Problems: State of the Art (SIAM, Philadelphia, Pennsylvania, 1997),pp. 105-116.

[45] M.S. GOWDA AND R. SZNAJDER, *Weak univalence and connectedness of inverse images of continuous functions*, Math. Oper. Res., 24 (1999), pp. 255-261.

[46] M. HEINKENSCHLOSS, C.T. KELLEY AND H.T. TRAN, *Fast algorithms for nonsmooth compact fixed-point problems*, SIAM J. Numer. Anal., 29 (1992), pp. 1769-1792.

[47] K. HOTTA AND A. YOSHISE, *Global convergence of a class of non-interior-point algorithms using Chen-Harker-Kanzow functions for nonlinear complementarity problems*, Math. Program. 86 (1999), pp. 105–133.

[48] H. JIANG AND D. RALPH, *Smooth SQP methods for mathematical programs with nonlinear complementarity constraints*, SIAM J. Optim. 10 (2000), pp. 779–808

[49] C. KANZOW, *Some noninterior continuation methods for linear complementarity problems*, SIAM J. Matrix Anal. Appl. 17 (1996),pp. 851-868.

[50] C. KANZOW AND M. FUKUSHIMA, *Theoretical and numerical investigation of D-gap function for box constrained variational inequalities*, Math. Programming, 83 (1998), pp. 55-87.

[51] C. KANZOW AND H. PIEPER, *Jacobian smoothing methods for general complementarity problems*, SIAM J. Optim. 9 (1999), pp. 342-373.

[52] C. KANZOW, N. YAMASHITA AND M. FUKUSHIMA, *New NCP-functions and their properties*, J. Optim. Theory Appl., 94 (1997), pp. 115-135.

[53] C.T. KELLEY, *Identification of the support of nonsmoothness*, in W.W. Hager, D.W. Hearn and P.M. Pardalos (eds.), Large Scale Optimization: State of the Art (Boston, Kluwer Academic Publishers B.V. 1993),pp. 192-205.

[54] M. KOJIMA, N. MEGIDDO AND T. NOMA, *Homotopy continuation methods for nonlinear complementarity problems*, Math. Oper. Res. 16 (1991), pp. 754-774.

[55] D.H. LI AND M. FUKUSHIMA, *Smoothing Newton and quasi-Newton methods for mixed complementarity problems*, Comput. Optim. Appl. 17 (2000), pp. 203–230.

[56] Z.-Q. LUO AND P. TSENG, *A new class of merit functions for the nonlinear complementarity problem*, in M.C. Ferris and J.-S. Pang (eds), Complementarity and Variational Problems: State of the Art (SIAM, Philadelphia, PA, 1997),pp. 204-225.

[57] J.M. MARTÍNEZ AND M.C. ZAMBALDI, *Least change update methods for nonlinear systems with non-differentiable terms*, Numer. Funct. Optim., 14 (1993), pp. 405-415.

[58] J.M. Ortega and W.C. Rheinboldt, Iterative Solution of Nonlinear Equations in Several Variables, Academic Press, New York, NY, 1970.

[59] J.-S. PANG, *A B-differentiable equations based, globally, and locally quadratically convergent algorithm for nonlinear problems, complementarity and variational inequality problems*, Math. Programming, 51 (1991), pp. 101-131.

[60] J.-S.PANG AND L. QI, *Nonsmooth equations: motivation and algorithms*, SIAM J. Optim. 3 (1993),pp. 443-465.

[61] H.-D. QI, *A regularized smoothing Newton method for box constrained variational inequality problems with P_0 function*, SIAM J. Optim. 10 (2000), pp. 315–330

[62] L. QI AND X. CHEN, *A globally convergent successive approximation method for severely nonsmooth equations*, SIAM J Control Optim., 33 (1995), pp. 402-418.

[63] L. QI AND D. SUN, *A survey of some nonsmooth equations and smoothing Newton methods*. in: Progress in optimization, (Appl. Optim., 30, Kluwer Acad. Publ., Dordrecht, 1999),pp. 121-146.

[64] L. QI, D. SUN AND G. ZHOU, *A new look at smoothing Newton methods for nonlinear complementarity problems and box constrained variational inequalities*, Math. Programming, 87(2000) pp. 1-35.

[65] L.QI AND G. ZHOU, *A smoothing Newton method for minimizing a sum of Euclidean norms*, SIAM J. Optim, 11 (2000), pp. 389-410.

[66] J. RAPPAZ, *Approximation of a nondifferentiable nonlinear problem related to MHD equilibria*, Numer. Math., 45 (1984), pp. 117-133.

[67] S. ROBINSON, *Normal maps induced by linear transformation*, Math. Oper. Res. 17 (1992), pp. 691-714.

[68] S. SMALE, *Algorithms for solving equations*, Proceedings of the International Congress of Mathematicians (Berkeley, California, 1986),pp. 172-195.

[69] D. SUN AND L. QI, *Solving variational inequality problems via smoothing-nonsmooth reformulations*, J. Comput. Appl. Math. 129 (2001), pp. 37–62.

[70] K.L. TEO, V. REHBOCK AND L.S. JENNINGS, *A new computational algorithm for functional inequality constrained optimization problems*, Automatica, 29 (1993), pp. 789-792.

[71] P. TSENG, *Growth behaviour of a class of merit functions for the nonlinear complementarity problem*, J. Optim. Theory Appl., 89 (1996), pp. 17-37.

[72] P. TSENG, *Analysis of a non-interior continuation method based on Chen-Mangasarian functions for complementarity problems*, in M. Fukushima and L. Qi (eds.), Reformulation - Nonsmooth, Piecewise Smooth, Semismooth and Smoothing Methods (Kluwer Academic Publisher, Nowell, Maryland, 1999), pp. 381-404.

[73] T. TSUCHIYA, *Finite element approximations of conformal mappings*, Numer. Funct. Anal. Optim. 22 (2001), pp. 419-440.

[74] T. YAMAMOTO, *Split nonsmooth equations and verification of solution*, Zeitschrift für Angewandte Mathematik und Mechanik 76 (1996), pp. 199-202.

[75] I. ZANG, *A smoothing-out technique for min-max optimization*, Math. Programming, 19 (1980), pp. 61-71.

[76] G. ZHOU, D. SUN AND L. QI, *Numerical experiments for a class of squared smoothing Newton methods for box constrained variational inequality problems*, in M. Fukushima and L. Qi (eds.), Reformulation - Nonsmooth, Piecewise Smooth, Semismooth and Smoothing Methods (Kluwer Academic Publisher, Nowell, Maryland, 1999), pp. 421-441.

[77] A.I. ZINCENKO, *Some approximate methods of solving equations withe nondifferentiable operators* (Ukrainian), Dopovidi Akad. Nauk. Ukrain. RSR (1963), pp. 156-161.

In: Focus on Computational Neurobiology
Editor: Lei Li, pp. 13-27

ISBN 1-59033-915-0

STOCHASTIC PROGRAMMING MODELS FOR VEHICLE ROUTING PROBLEMS

BAODING LIU* AND K. K. LAI†

Abstract. This paper presents two stochastic programming models for vehicle routing problems with stochastic demands and travel times, including chance-constrained programming models and dependent-chance programming models. A genetic algorithm is also designed for solving the proposed stochastic programming models and the effectiveness of genetic algorithm is illustrated by some numerical examples.

Key words. vehicle routing problem, stochastic programming, genetic algorithm

1. Introduction. Vehicle routing problems (VRP) are concerned with finding the efficient routes, beginning and ending at a central depot, for a fleet of vehicles to serve a number of customers with demands for some commodity. If there are stochastic factors in a VRP, then the problem is called a stochastic VRP (SVRP). Due to its wide applicability and economic importance, VRP has been extensively studied.

Surveys on exact algorithms and heuristic algorithms for solving VRP may be found in Bodin et al. [4], Solomon and Desrosiers [33] and Laporte [23]. In order to solve VRP, Desrochers et al. [7] presented an exact algorithm, called the column generation approach, which is capable of optimally solving 100-customer problems. However, several authors have concluded that a heuristic algorithm may be practically appropriate in tackling problems of a realistic size, even though the limitations of heuristic methods are obvious; such as the deviation of an optimal solution, which may imply a great loss of profit (Koskosidis and Powell [22]).

In addition, Garcia et al. [14] presented a parallel tabu search heuristic for VRP and claimed it very beneficial in solving the problems. Brandão and Mercer [5] gave a tabu search algorithm for the multi-trip vehicle routing and scheduling problem. Potvin et al. [30] designed a tabu search for VRP based on specialized local search heuristics that maintain the feasibility of the solution at all times. Chiang and Russell [6] introduced a simulated annealing metaheuristic for solving VRP. Potvin and Bengio [31] suggested a genetic algorithm which may produce solutions that are competitive with the best solutions reported by other researchers.

In recent years, several researchers have studied different situations of VRP in the real world. For example, Frizzell and Giffin [13] considered split delivery VRP in which customers were visited by more than one vehicle. Hooker and Natraj [20] applied the chain decomposition and tabu search method to solve the problem of permitting pick-up and delivery in a route. Sharma and Paradkar [32] studied the situation in Indian Railways, in which some distinguishing features were identified. Taillard et al. [35] considered VRP in which vehicles may be assigned to several routes.

Practically, there are stochastic factors in VRP. Waters [36] listed various potential uncertainties, such as demands of customers, travel times between customers, customers to be visited, locations of customers, capacities of vehicles, and number of vehicles available. This provides motivation to study SVRP. Bertsimas and Simchi-Levi [3] surveyed the new

*DEPARTMENT OF MATHEMATICAL SCIENCES, TSINGHUA UNIVERSITY, BEIJING 100084, CHINA
†DEPARTMENT OF MANAGEMENT SCIENCES, CITY UNIVERSITY OF HONG KONG, KOWLOON, HONG KONG

developments in the research area of VRP under uncertainty. Gendreau et al. [16] provided a detailed summary of the scientific literature on SVRP. Golden and Yee [18] presented a chance-constrained programming model for SVRP with stochastic demands and provided some analytic results. Stewart and Golden [34] extended and generalized the work of Golden and Yee [18], and gave some computational results. Dror and Trudreau [8] presented a Clarke-Wright heuristic for chance-constrained programming model of SVRP with stochastic demand. Dror et al. [9] modeled SVRP by chance-constrained programming and expected value model, and discussed some mathematical properties. Bertsimas [2] constructed an a priori sequence among all customers of minimal expected total length, and provided closed-form expressions and algorithms to compute the expected length of an a priori sequence under general probabilistic assumptions. Bastian and Rinnooy Kan [1] presented chance-constrained programming models for various situations in SVRP. Dror [10] presented a multistage stochastic model and a Markov decision model for SVRP, and discussed some properties of solutions. Laporte et al. [24] introduced a chance-constrained programming model for SVRP with stochastic travel times. Gendreau et al. [15] designed an integer L-shaped exact algorithm for SVRPs with stochastic customers and demands.

All the above authors only focused on SVRP with a single objective. In this paper, we will present chance-constrained programming, chance-constrained goal programming, dependent-chance multi-objective programming, and dependent-chance goal programming models for SVRP with stochastic demands and travel times. We also design a genetic algorithm for solving the proposed stochastic programming models and illustrate the effectiveness of genetic algorithm by some numerical examples.

2. Assumptions and Notations. In SVRPs, we assume that: (a) each vehicle has a container with a physical capacity limitation and the total loading of each vehicle cannot exceed its capacity; (b) a vehicle will be assigned for only one route on which there may be more than one customer; (c) a customer will be visited by one and only one vehicle; (d) each route begins and ends at the company site (depot); (e) each customer specifies its time window within which the delivery is permitted or preferred to start; and (f) the demands of customers and travel times between customers are assumed to be stochastic.

Let us first introduce the following indices, model parameters and decision variables.

Indices:

$i = 0$: depot;

$i = 1, 2, \cdots, n$: customers;

$k = 1, 2, \cdots, m$: vehicles.

Parameters:

q_i: the demand of customer i, which is assumed to be a stochastic variable, $i = 1, 2, \cdots, n$;

Q_k: the physical capacity of vehicle k, $k = 1, 2, \cdots, m$;

D_{ij}: the travel distance from customers i to j, $i, j = 0, 1, 2, \cdots, n$;

T_{ij}: the travel time from customers i to j, which is assumed to be a stochastic variable, $i, j = 0, 1, 2, \cdots, n$;

S_i: the unloading time at customer i, $i = 1, 2, \cdots, n$;

$[a_i, b_i]$: the time window of customer i, where a_i and b_i are the beginning and end of the time window, $i = 1, 2, \cdots, n$, respectively.

As an alternative to the three-index vehicle flow formulation initiated by Fisher and Jaikumar [12], in this paper, we present a new representation structure to describe the operational plan using the following decision variables $\boldsymbol{x}$, $\boldsymbol{y}$ and $\boldsymbol{t}$, where

$\boldsymbol{x} = (x_1, x_2, \cdots, x_n)$: integer decision variables representing n customers with $1 \leq x_i \leq n$ and $x_i \neq x_j$ for all $i \neq j$, $i, j = 1, 2, \cdots, n$. That is, the sequence $\{x_1, x_2, \cdots, x_n\}$ is a rearrangement of $\{1, 2, \cdots, n\}$;

$\boldsymbol{y} = (y_1, y_2, \cdots, y_{m-1})$: integer decision variables with $y_0 \equiv 0 \leq y_1 \leq y_2 \leq \cdots \leq y_{m-1} \leq n \equiv y_m$;

$\boldsymbol{t} = (t_1, t_2, \cdots, t_m)$: each t_k represents the starting time of vehicle k at the depot, $k = 1, 2, \cdots, m$.

We note that the operational plan is fully determined by the decision variables $\boldsymbol{x}$, $\boldsymbol{y}$ and $\boldsymbol{t}$ in the following way. For each k $(1 \leq k \leq m)$, if $y_k = y_{k-1}$, then vehicle k is not used; if $y_k > y_{k-1}$, then vehicle k is used and starts from the depot at time t_k, and the tour of vehicle k is

$$0 \to x_{y_{k-1}+1} \to x_{y_{k-1}+2} \to \cdots \to x_{y_k} \to 0. \tag{2.1}$$

It is clear that this type of representation is intuitive, and the total number of decision variables is $n + 2m - 1$. We also note that the above decision variables $\boldsymbol{x}$, $\boldsymbol{y}$ and $\boldsymbol{t}$ ensure that: (a) each vehicle will be used at most one time; (b) all tours begin and end at the depot; (c) each customer will be visited by one and only one vehicle; and (d) there is no subtour.

Let $f_i(\boldsymbol{x}, \boldsymbol{y}, \boldsymbol{t})$ be the arrival time function of some vehicles at location i, $i = 1, 2, \cdots, n$. We remind readers that $f_i(\boldsymbol{x}, \boldsymbol{y}, \boldsymbol{t})$ are determined by the decision variables $\boldsymbol{x}$, $\boldsymbol{y}$ and $\boldsymbol{t}$, $i = 1, 2, \cdots, n$. Since unloading can start either immediately, or later, when a vehicle arrives at a customer, the calculation of $f_i(\boldsymbol{x}, \boldsymbol{y}, \boldsymbol{t})$ is heavily dependent on the operational strategy. Here we assume that the customer does not permit a delivery earlier than the time window. That is, the vehicle will wait to unload until the beginning of the time window if it arrives before the time window. If a vehicle arrives at a customer after the beginning of the time window, unloading will start immediately. For each k with $1 \leq k \leq m$, if vehicle k is used (i.e., $y_k > y_{k-1}$), then we have

$$f_{x_{y_{k-1}+1}}(\boldsymbol{x}, \boldsymbol{y}, \boldsymbol{t}) = t_k + T_{0x_{y_{k-1}+1}} \tag{2.2}$$

and

$$f_{x_{y_{k-1}+j}}(\boldsymbol{x}, \boldsymbol{y}, \boldsymbol{t}) = f_{x_{y_{k-1}+j-1}}(\boldsymbol{x}, \boldsymbol{y}, \boldsymbol{t}) \vee a_{x_{y_{k-1}+j-1}} + S_{x_{y_{k-1}+j-1}} + T_{x_{y_{k-1}+j-1}x_{y_{k-1}+j}} \tag{2.3}$$

for $2 \leq j \leq y_k - y_{k-1}$, where $\vee$ denotes the maximum operator. It follows from the stochasticity of travel times T_{ij}'s that the arrival times $f_i(\boldsymbol{x}, \boldsymbol{y}, \boldsymbol{t})$, $i = 1, 2, \cdots, n$ are stochastic variables fully determined by (2.2) and (2.3).

Let $g(\boldsymbol{x}, \boldsymbol{y})$ be the total travel distance of all vehicles, then we have

$$g(\boldsymbol{x}, \boldsymbol{y}) = \sum_{k=1}^{m} g_k(\boldsymbol{x}, \boldsymbol{y}) \tag{2.4}$$

where

$$g_k(\boldsymbol{x}, \boldsymbol{y}) = \begin{cases} D_{0x_{y_{k-1}+1}} + \sum\limits_{j=y_{k-1}+1}^{y_k-1} D_{x_j x_{j+1}} + D_{x_{y_k}0}, & \text{if } y_k > y_{k-1} \\ 0, & \text{if } y_k = y_{k-1} \end{cases} \tag{2.5}$$

for $k = 1, 2, \cdots, m$.

3. Chance-Constrained Programming Models. At first, the total amount of demands in a route cannot exceed the capacity of the associated vehicle. In view of the stochasticity of demands q_i's, for each vehicle k we should assign a confidence level α_k at which the demands served by vehicle k are satisfied, i.e.

$$\Pr\left\{\sum_{j=y_{k-1}+1}^{y_k} q_{x_j} \le Q_k\right\} \ge \alpha_k, \quad k = 1, 2, \cdots, m. \tag{3.1}$$

We also hope that each customer i is visited within its time window $[a_i, b_i]$ with a confidence level β_i, $i = 1, 2, \cdots, n$, respectively. Then we have the following constraints,

$$\Pr\{a_i \le f_i(\boldsymbol{x}, \boldsymbol{y}, \boldsymbol{t}) \le b_i\} \ge \beta_i, \quad i = 1, 2, \cdots, n. \tag{3.2}$$

If we want to minimize the total travel distance of all vehicles subject to constraints (3.1) and (3.2), then we have the following chance-constrained programming model,

$$\begin{cases} \min g(\boldsymbol{x}, \boldsymbol{y}) \\ \text{subject to:} \\ \qquad \Pr\{a_i \le f_i(\boldsymbol{x}, \boldsymbol{y}, \boldsymbol{t}) \le b_i\} \ge \beta_i, \quad i = 1, 2, \cdots, n \\ \qquad 1 \le x_i \le n, \quad i = 1, 2, \cdots, n \\ \qquad x_i \ne x_j, \quad i \ne j, \ i, j = 1, 2, \cdots, n \\ \qquad 0 \le y_1 \le y_2 \le \cdots \le y_{m-1} \le n \\ \qquad \Pr\left\{\sum_{j=y_{k-1}+1}^{y_k} q_{x_j} \le Q_k\right\} \ge \alpha_k, \quad k = 1, 2, \cdots, m \\ \qquad x_i, y_j, \quad i = 1, 2, \cdots, n, \quad j = 1, 2, \cdots, m-1, \quad \text{integers.} \end{cases} \tag{3.3}$$

Sometimes, management goals have the following priority structure set by the decision-maker:

Priority 1: Each customer i should be visited within its time window $[a_i, b_i]$ with a confidence level β_i, $i = 1, 2, \cdots, n$, respectively. We thus have the following goal constraints,

$$\Pr\left\{f_i(\boldsymbol{x}, \boldsymbol{y}, \boldsymbol{t}) + d_i^- - d_i^+ = [a_i, b_i]\right\} \ge \beta_i, \quad i = 1, 2, \cdots, n \tag{3.4}$$

in which $\sum_{i=1}^n \left(d_i^+ + d_i^-\right)$ should be minimized, and the positive and negative deviations should be understood as the minimal non-negative values of d_i^+ and d_i^- such that

$$\Pr\left\{d_i^+ \ge f_i(\boldsymbol{x}, \boldsymbol{y}, \boldsymbol{t}) - b_i\right\} \ge \beta_i, \quad \Pr\left\{d_i^- \ge a_i - f_i(\boldsymbol{x}, \boldsymbol{y}, \boldsymbol{t})\right\} \ge \beta_i \tag{3.5}$$

for $i = 1, 2, \cdots, n$, respectively.

Priority 2: We should minimize the total travel distance of all vehicles, so that we have

$$g(\boldsymbol{x}, \boldsymbol{y}) + d_{n+1}^- - d_{n+1}^+ = 0 \tag{3.6}$$

in which d_{n+1}^+ will be minimized.

We thus have the following chance-constrained goal programming model for SVRP,

$$
(3.7) \quad \begin{cases}
\text{lexmin}\left\{\sum_{i=1}^{n}(d_i^+ + d_i^-), d_{n+1}^+\right\} \\
\text{subject to:} \\
\qquad \Pr\left\{f_i(\boldsymbol{x},\boldsymbol{y},\boldsymbol{t}) + d_i^- - d_i^+ = [a_i, b_i]\right\} \geq \beta_i, \quad i = 1,2,\cdots,n \\
\qquad g(\boldsymbol{x},\boldsymbol{y}) + d_{n+1}^- - d_{n+1}^+ = 0 \\
\qquad 1 \leq x_i \leq n, \quad i = 1,2,\cdots,n \\
\qquad x_i \neq x_j, \quad i \neq j, \; i,j = 1,2,\cdots,n \\
\qquad 0 \leq y_1 \leq y_2 \leq \cdots \leq y_{m-1} \leq n \\
\qquad \Pr\left\{\sum_{j=y_{k-1}+1}^{y_k} q_{x_j} \leq Q_k\right\} \geq \alpha_k, \quad k = 1,2,\cdots,m \\
\qquad x_i, y_j, \quad i = 1,2,\cdots,n, \quad j = 1,2,\cdots,m-1, \quad \text{integers}
\end{cases}
$$

where lexmin represents lexicographically minimizing the objective vector.

4. Dependent-Chance Programming Models. We assume that the management goals have the following priority structure set by the decision-maker:

Priority 1: The probability that all customers are visited within their time windows should achieve a target level α. We thus have a goal constraint,

$$
(4.1) \qquad \Pr\left\{a_i \leq f_i(\boldsymbol{x},\boldsymbol{y},\boldsymbol{t}) \leq b_i, i = 1,2,\cdots,n\right\} + d_1^- - d_1^+ = \alpha
$$

in which d_1^- will be minimized.

Priority 2: The probability that all demands are satisfied should achieve a target level β, then we have a goal constraint,

$$
(4.2) \qquad \Pr\left\{\sum_{j=y_{k-1}+1}^{y_k} q_{x_j} \leq Q_k, k = 1,2,\cdots,m\right\} + d_2^- - d_2^+ = \beta
$$

in which d_2^- will be minimized.

Priority 3: We should minimize the total travel distance of all vehicles, then we have

$$
(4.3) \qquad g(\boldsymbol{x},\boldsymbol{y}) + d_3^- - d_3^+ = 0
$$

in which d_3^+ will be minimized.

We thus have the following dependent-chance goal programming model for SVRP,

$$
(4.4) \quad \begin{cases}
\text{lexmin}\left\{d_1^-, d_2^-, d_3^+\right\} \\
\text{subject to:} \\
\qquad \Pr\left\{a_i \leq f_i(\boldsymbol{x},\boldsymbol{y},\boldsymbol{t}) \leq b_i, i = 1,2,\cdots,n\right\} + d_1^- - d_1^+ = \alpha \\
\qquad \Pr\left\{\sum_{j=y_{k-1}+1}^{y_k} q_{x_j} \leq Q_k, k = 1,2,\cdots,m\right\} + d_2^- - d_2^+ = \beta \\
\qquad g(\boldsymbol{x},\boldsymbol{y}) + d_3^- - d_3^+ = 0 \\
\qquad 1 \leq x_i \leq n, \quad i = 1,2,\cdots,n \\
\qquad x_i \neq x_j, \quad i \neq j, \; i,j = 1,2,\cdots,n \\
\qquad 0 \leq y_1 \leq y_2 \leq \cdots \leq y_{m-1} \leq n \\
\qquad x_i, y_j, \quad i = 1,2,\cdots,n, \quad j = 1,2,\cdots,m-1, \quad \text{integers.}
\end{cases}
$$

5. Stochastic Simulations. In order to solve the proposed stochastic programming models (3.3), (3.7) and (4.4), we have to compute the probability

$$\Pr\left\{\sum_{j=y_{k-1}+1}^{y_k} q_{x_j} \le Q_k, k=1,2,\cdots,m\right\}$$

and the probability

$$\Pr\{a_i \le f_i(\boldsymbol{x},\boldsymbol{y},\boldsymbol{t}) \le b_i, i=1,2,\cdots,n\}$$

as well as to find the positive and negative deviations for the goal constraints like

$$\Pr\left\{f(\boldsymbol{x},\boldsymbol{y},\boldsymbol{t}) + d^- - d^+ = [a,b]\right\} \ge \beta.$$

If the above problems are easy to handle, we may employ numerical integration methods. But if the constraints fail to be regular or are hard to calculate, it is more convenient to deal with them using stochastic simulations.

First, let us compute the probability

$$\Pr\left\{\sum_{j=y_{k-1}+1}^{y_k} q_{x_j} \le Q_k, k=1,2,\cdots,m\right\}$$

using the stochastic simulation. For any given decisions $\boldsymbol{x}$ and $\boldsymbol{y}$, we generate N independent random vectors $(q_1^{(l)}, q_2^{(l)}, \cdots, q_n^{(l)})$, $l=1,2,\cdots,N$, from their probability distributions. Let N' be the number of occasions on which

$$\sum_{j=y_{k-1}+1}^{y_k} q_{x_j}^{(l)} \le Q_k, \quad k=1,2,\cdots,m$$

for $l=1,2,\cdots,N$ (i.e. the number of random vectors satisfying the constraints). Then, by the law of large numbers, the probability

$$\Pr\left\{\sum_{j=y_{k-1}+1}^{y_k} q_{x_j} \le Q_k, k=1,2,\cdots,m\right\}$$

can be estimated by N'/N.

Similarly, we may compute the probability

$$\Pr\{a_i \le f_i(\boldsymbol{x},\boldsymbol{y},\boldsymbol{t}) \le b_i, i=1,2,\cdots,n\}$$

using stochastic simulations.

Now we consider the goal constraint

$$\Pr\left\{f(\boldsymbol{x},\boldsymbol{y},\boldsymbol{t}) + d^- - d^+ = [a,b]\right\} \ge \beta.$$

From the meaning of this goal constraint, we should find the minimal non-negative values of d^- and d^+ such that

$$\Pr\{d^- \ge a - f(\boldsymbol{x},\boldsymbol{y},\boldsymbol{t})\} \ge \beta, \quad \Pr\{d^+ \ge f(\boldsymbol{x},\boldsymbol{y},\boldsymbol{t}) - b\} \ge \beta.$$

We obtain a sequence of $\{f_1^-, f_2^-, \cdots, f_N^-\}$ where $f_l^- = a - f(\boldsymbol{x}, \boldsymbol{y}, \boldsymbol{t})$ by generating $T_{ij}^{(l)}$ from their probability distributions, $l = 1, 2, \cdots, N$, respectively. We take N' as the integer part of βN. Then the N'th least element in $\{f_1^-, f_2^-, \cdots, f_N^-\}$ is regarded as the negative deviation d^- provided that it is non-negative. If the N'th least element is negative, then we set $d^- = 0$. Analogously, we make a sequence $\{f_1^+, f_2^+, \cdots, f_N^+\}$ where $f_l^+ = f(\boldsymbol{x}, \boldsymbol{y}, \boldsymbol{t}) - b$ and $T_{ij}^{(l)}$ are generated from their probability distributions, $l = 1, 2, \cdots, N$, respectively. Then the N'th least element in $\{f_1^+, f_2^+, \cdots, f_N^+\}$ is regarded as the positive deviation d^+. Certainly, if $d^+ < 0$, then we set $d^+ = 0$.

6. Genetic Algorithms. Genetic algorithms have demonstrated considerable success in providing good solutions to many complex optimization problems. They have received growing attention over the past three decades, have been well documented in numerous literature, such as in Holland [19], Goldberg [17] and Michalewicz [29], and have been applied to a wide variety of optimization problems. In particular, Iwamura and Liu [21] provided a genetic algorithm for chance-constrained programming. Liu [25][26] presented a genetic algorithm for solving dependent-chance programming. For detailed expositions, the readers may consult Liu [28] in which numerous genetic algorithms have been suggested to solve stochastic programming models.

The proposed chance-constrained programming and dependent-chance programming models for SVRPs have non-convexity, discontinuity, non-differentiability and multiple objectives, they are thus extremely complicated optimization problems without a traditional algorithm. Since genetic algorithms are capable of solving such complicated problems, we design a genetic algorithm to solve the proposed models in this section.

6.1. Representation Structure. We represent an operational plan by the chromosome $V = (\boldsymbol{x}, \boldsymbol{y}, \boldsymbol{t})$, where the genes $\boldsymbol{x}, \boldsymbol{y}, \boldsymbol{t}$ are the same as the decision variables. Without loss of generality, we also assume that the time window at the depot is $[a, b]$. This means that the gene $\boldsymbol{t}$ will be restricted in the hypercube $[a, b]^m$.

6.2. Initialization Process. We define an integer *pop_size* as the number of chromosomes and initialize *pop_size* chromosomes randomly. For gene $\boldsymbol{x}$, we define a sequence $\{x_1, x_2, \cdots, x_n\}$ with $x_i = i$, $i = 1, 2, \cdots, n$. We repeat the following process from $j = 1$ to n: generating a random position n' between j and n, and exchanging the values of x_j and $x_{n'}$. It is clear that $\{x_1, x_2, \cdots, x_n\}$ is just a random rearrangement of $\{1, 2, \cdots, n\}$. Then we obtain a gene $\boldsymbol{x} = (x_1, x_2, \cdots, x_n)$.

For each i with $1 \le i \le m - 1$, we set y_i as a random integer between 0 and n. Then we rearrange the sequence $\{y_1, y_2, \cdots, y_{m-1}\}$ from small to large. We thus have a gene $\boldsymbol{y} = (y_1, y_2, \cdots, y_{m-1})$.

Finally, for each i with $1 \le i \le m$, we set t_i as a random number on the time window $[a, b]$. Then we get a gene $\boldsymbol{t} = (t_1, t_2, \cdots, t_m)$.

If the generated chromosome $V = (\boldsymbol{x}, \boldsymbol{y}, \boldsymbol{t})$ is proven to be feasible (here the stochastic simulation may be employed), then it is accepted as a chromosome; otherwise we repeat the above process until a feasible chromosome is obtained. We may generate *pop_size* initial chromosomes $V_1, V_2, \cdots, V_{pop\_size}$ by repeating the above process *pop_size* times.

6.3. Evaluation Function. Let $V_1, V_2, \cdots, V_{pop\_size}$ be the *pop_size* chromosomes in the current generation. At first we calculate the objective values of the chromosomes by stochastic simulations. According to the objective values, we can rearrange these chromosomes $V_1, V_2, \cdots, V_{pop\_size}$ from good to bad (i.e. the better the chromosome, the smaller the ordinal number). Now let a parameter $a \in (0,1)$ in the genetic system be given, then we can define the so-called *rank-based evaluation function* as follows,

$$eval(V_i) = a(1-a)^{i-1}, \qquad i = 1, 2, \cdots, pop\_size. \tag{6.1}$$

We mention that $i = 1$ means the best individual, and $i = pop\_size$ means the worst individual.

6.4. Selection Process. The selection process is based on spinning the roulette wheel *pop_size* times; each time we select a single chromosome for a new population in the following way:

Step 1. Calculate the cumulative probability q_i for each chromosome V_i,

$$q_0 = 0, \quad q_i = \sum_{j=1}^{i} eval(V_j), \quad i = 1, 2, \cdots, pop\_size. \tag{6.2}$$

Step 2. Generate a random real number r in $(0, q_{pop\_size}]$.

Step 3. Select the i-th chromosome V_i ($1 \le i \le pop\_size$) such that $q_{i-1} < r \le q_i$.

Step 4. Repeat the second and third steps for *pop_size* times and obtain *pop_size* copies of chromosomes.

6.5. Crossover Operation. We define a parameter P_c of a genetic system as the probability of crossover. In order to determine the parents for a crossover operation, let us do the following process repeatedly from $i = 1$ to *pop_size*: generate a random real number r from the interval $[0, 1]$. The chromosome V_i is selected as a parent if $r < P_c$.

We denote the selected parents as $V_1', V_2', V_3', \cdots$ and split them into the following pairs: $(V_1', V_2'), (V_3', V_4'), (V_5', V_6'), \cdots$ Let us illustrate the crossover operator on each pair by (V_1', V_2'). We denote $V_i' = (\boldsymbol{x}_i, \boldsymbol{y}_i, \boldsymbol{t}_i)$ with $i = 1, 2$, respectively. First, we generate a random number c from the open interval $(0, 1)$ and define

$$\boldsymbol{t}_1' = c \cdot \boldsymbol{t}_1 + (1-c) \cdot \boldsymbol{t}_2, \qquad \boldsymbol{t}_2' = (1-c) \cdot \boldsymbol{t}_1 + c \cdot \boldsymbol{t}_2.$$

The two children V_1'' and V_2'' are produced by the crossover operation as follows: $V_1'' = (\boldsymbol{x}_1, \boldsymbol{y}_2, \boldsymbol{t}_1')$ and $V_2'' = (\boldsymbol{x}_2, \boldsymbol{y}_1, \boldsymbol{t}_2')$. We note that the two children are not necessarily feasible, thus we must check the feasibility of each child (here stochastic simulation may be used) and replace the parents only with feasible children.

6.6. Mutation Operation. We define a parameter P_m of a genetic system as the probability of mutation. In a similar manner to the process of selecting parents for a crossover operation, we repeat the following steps from $i = 1$ to *pop_size*: generate a random real number r from the interval $[0, 1]$. The chromosome V_i is selected as a parent for mutation if $r < P_m$.

For each selected parent, denoted by $V = (\boldsymbol{x}, \boldsymbol{y}, \boldsymbol{t})$, we mutate it in the following way. For the gene $\boldsymbol{x}$, we randomly generate two mutation positions n_1 and n_2 between 1 and n, and rearrange the sequence $\{x_{n_1}, x_{n_1+1}, \cdots, x_{n_2}\}$ at random to form a new sequence $\{x_{n_1}', x_{n_1+1}', \cdots, x_{n_2}'\}$, thus we obtain a new gene $\boldsymbol{x}' = (x_1, \cdots, x_{n_1-1}, x_{n_1}', x_{n_1+1}', \cdots, x_{n_2}', x_{n_2+1}, \cdots, x_n)$.

Similarly, for gene $\boldsymbol{y}$, we generate two random mutation positions n_1 and n_2 between 1 and $m-1$, and set y_i as a random integer number y_i' between 0 and n for $i = n_1, n_1+1, \cdots, n_2$. We then rearrange the sequence $\{y_1, \cdots, y_{n_1-1}, y_{n_1}', y_{n_1+1}', \cdots, y_{n_2}', y_{n_2+1}, \cdots, y_{m-1}\}$ from small to large and obtain a new gene $\boldsymbol{y}'$.

For the gene $\boldsymbol{t}$, we choose a mutation direction $\boldsymbol{d}$ in $\Re^m$ randomly, if $\boldsymbol{t} + M \cdot \boldsymbol{d}$ is not in the time window $[a, b]^m$, then we set M as a random number between 0 and M until it is in $[a, b]^m$, where M is a predetermined step length. If the above process cannot yield a gene $\boldsymbol{t}$ in $[a, b]^m$ in a predetermined number of iterations, then we set $M = 0$. We replace the parent gene $\boldsymbol{t}$ with its child $\boldsymbol{t}' = \boldsymbol{t} + M \cdot \boldsymbol{d}$.

Finally, we replace the parent V with the offspring $V' = (\boldsymbol{x}', \boldsymbol{y}', \boldsymbol{t}')$ if it is feasible (here stochastic simulation may be used). If it is not feasible, then we repeat the above process.

6.7. Genetic Algorithm Procedure. Following selection, crossover and mutation, the new population is ready for its next evaluation. The genetic algorithm will terminate after a given number of cyclic repetitions of the above steps. We now summarize the genetic algorithm for solving the stochastic programming model for the SVRP as follows.

Step 0. *Input parameters pop_size, a, P_c and P_m.*

Step 1. *Initialize pop_size chromosomes in which stochastic simulations may be employed to check the feasibility.*

Step 2. *Update the chromosomes by crossover and mutation operations in which the feasibility of offspring may be checked by stochastic simulations.*

Step 3. *Calculate the objective values for all chromosomes using stochastic simulations.*

Step 4. *Compute the fitness of each chromosome by rank-based evaluation function based on the objective values.*

Step 5. *Select the chromosomes by spinning the roulette wheel.*

Step 6. *Repeat the second to fifth steps for a given number of cycles.*

Step 7. *Report the best chromosome as the optimal operational plan of vehicles.*

7. Computational Experiment. The computer code for the genetic algorithm to the goal programming model of the SVRP has been written in C language. In order to illustrate the effectiveness of the genetic algorithm, we now give some numerical examples performed on a personal computer with the following parameters: the population size is 200, the probability of crossover P_c is 0.3, the probability of mutation P_m is 0.6, the parameter a in the rank-based evaluation function is 0.05. Genetic algorithms are often criticized due to the setting of these parameters. Fortunately, genetic algorithms are very robust in the setting of parameters.

Now we assume that there are 20 customers labeled "$1, 2, \cdots, 20$" in a company and one depot labeled "0". We also assume that the demands of the customers and travel times between customers are all normally distributed with mean μ and standard deviation σ. The time windows and demands of customers are shown in Table 7.1. The travel time and distance matrixes for the depot and customers are listed in Tables 7.2 and 7.3, respectively.

We assume that the unloading times $(S_i, i = 1, 2, \cdots, 20)$ at the 20 locations are 20, 10, 15, 10, 13, 18, 20, 12, 15, 16, 18, 20, 15, 16, 20, 15, 12, 14, 10, 18, and the capacities $(Q_k, k = 1, 2, 3, 4)$ of the four vehicles are 800, 850, 1000, 1200, respectively.

At first, we assign a confidence level 90% at which all customers are visited within their time windows, then we have a chance constraint,

$$\Pr\{a_i \le f_i(\boldsymbol{x}, \boldsymbol{y}, \boldsymbol{t}) \le b_i, i = 1, 2, \cdots, 20\} \ge 0.90.$$

We also assign a confidence level 80% at which all demands of customers are satisfied, then we have a chance constraint,

$$\Pr\left\{\sum_{j=y_{k-1}+1}^{y_k} q_{x_j} \le Q_k, k = 1, 2, 3, 4\right\} \ge 0.80.$$

TABLE 7.1
Time Windows and Demands

Customers	Time Window $[a, b]$	Demand(μ)	Demand(σ)
1	$[08:00, 15:20]$	200	100
2	$[08:20, 14:30]$	100	50
3	$[08:40, 14:40]$	140	70
4	$[08:20, 14:30]$	160	80
5	$[08:00, 15:20]$	200	100
6	$[08:00, 14:20]$	60	30
7	$[08:30, 14:00]$	200	100
8	$[08:00, 15:30]$	135	60
9	$[08:00, 15:50]$	160	80
10	$[08:30, 14:20]$	165	80
11	$[08:40, 13:20]$	140	70
12	$[08:10, 14:20]$	100	50
13	$[08:00, 15:20]$	200	100
14	$[08:20, 15:30]$	80	40
15	$[08:40, 15:00]$	60	30
16	$[08:20, 14:30]$	200	100
17	$[08:00, 14:10]$	90	45
18	$[08:00, 15:20]$	200	100
19	$[08:30, 15:00]$	90	45
20	$[08:30, 15:20]$	100	50

If we want to minimize the total travel distance of all vehicles subject to the above two chance constraints, then we have the following chance-constrained programming model,

$$\begin{cases} \min g(\boldsymbol{x}, \boldsymbol{y}) \\ \text{subject to:} \\ \qquad \Pr\{a_i \le f_i(\boldsymbol{x}, \boldsymbol{y}, \boldsymbol{t}) \le b_i, i = 1, 2, \cdots, 20\} \ge 0.90 \\ \qquad 1 \le x_i \le 20, \quad i = 1, 2, \cdots, 20 \\ \qquad x_i \ne x_j, \quad i \ne j, \ i, j = 1, 2, \cdots, 20 \\ \qquad 0 \le y_1 \le y_2 \le y_3 \le 20 \\ \qquad \Pr\left\{ \sum_{j=y_{k-1}+1}^{y_k} q_{x_j} \le Q_k, k = 1, 2, 3, 4 \right\} \ge 0.80 \\ \qquad x_i, y_j, \quad i = 1, 2, \cdots, 20, \quad j = 1, 2, 3, \quad \text{integers.} \end{cases}$$

A run of the proposed genetic algorithm with 1000 generations shows that the best operational plan is:

Vehicle 1: depot$\rightarrow$ 10 $\rightarrow$ 19 $\rightarrow$ 17 $\rightarrow$ 18 $\rightarrow$depot, starting time: 8:32;
Vehicle 2: depot$\rightarrow$ 13 $\rightarrow$ 8 $\rightarrow$ 2 $\rightarrow$ 16 $\rightarrow$depot, starting time: 8:05;
Vehicle 3: depot$\rightarrow$ 1 $\rightarrow$ 14 $\rightarrow$ 6 $\rightarrow$ 7 $\rightarrow$ 4 $\rightarrow$depot, starting time: 8:14;
Vehicle 4: depot$\rightarrow$ 3 $\rightarrow$ 9 $\rightarrow$ 15 $\rightarrow$ 11 $\rightarrow$ 5 $\rightarrow$ 12 $\rightarrow$ 20 $\rightarrow$depot, starting time: 8:32.

TABLE 7.2
Travel Time Matrix (μ, σ)

LCTs	0	1	2	3	4	5	6	7	8	9
1	(50,25)									
2	(10,5)	(40,20)								
3	(50,25)	(10,5)	(40,20)							
4	(15,7)	(50,25)	(15,7)	(45,22)						
5	(50,25)	(35,17)	(35,17)	(30,15)	(35,17)					
6	(50,25)	(15,7)	(40,20)	(5,2)	(45,22)	(30,15)				
7	(25,12)	(40,20)	(30,15)	(35,17)	(15,7)	(25,12)	(35,17)			
8	(15,7)	(40,20)	(10,5)	(45,22)	(20,10)	(35,17)	(40,20)	(35,17)		
9	(50,25)	(15,7)	(45,22)	(10,5)	(45,22)	(30,15)	(10,5)	(40,20)	(40,20)	
10	(20,10)	(45,22)	(25,12)	(45,22)	(15,7)	(30,15)	(40,20)	(10,5)	(25,12)	(45,22)
11	(50,25)	(10,5)	(35,17)	(30,15)	(35,17)	(10,5)	(30,15)	(10,5)	(35,17)	(35,17)
12	(55,27)	(35,17)	(35,17)	(30,15)	(35,17)	(5,2)	(30,15)	(15,7)	(35,17)	(35,17)
13	(10,5)	(40,20)	(10,5)	(40,20)	(15,7)	(30,15)	(35,17)	(35,17)	(10,5)	(40,20)
14	(50,25)	(10,5)	(40,20)	(5,2)	(45,22)	(30,15)	(5,2)	(35,17)	(35,17)	(10,5)
15	(45,22)	(10,5)	(40,20)	(10,5)	(45,22)	(30,15)	(10,5)	(35,17)	(35,17)	(5,2)
16	(15,7)	(45,22)	(15,7)	(45,22)	(20,10)	(30,15)	(45,22)	(35,17)	(20,10)	(45,22)
17	(30,15)	(40,20)	(25,12)	(40,20)	(20,10)	(25,12)	(35,17)	(5,2)	(25,12)	(40,20)
18	(50,25)	(10,5)	(45,22)	(10,5)	(50,25)	(30,15)	(15,7)	(35,17)	(40,20)	(15,7)
19	(30,15)	(40,20)	(25,12)	(40,20)	(20,10)	(25,12)	(35,17)	(5,2)	(25,12)	(40,20)
20	(25,12)	(40,20)	(25,12)	(45,22)	(20,10)	(30,15)	(40,20)	(10,5)	(25,12)	(45,22)

LCTs	10	11	12	13	14	15	16	17	18	19
11	(30,15)									
12	(25,12)	(15,7)								
13	(40,20)	(35,17)	(35,17)							
14	(40,20)	(30,15)	(30,15)	(40,20)						
15	(40,20)	(30,15)	(40,20)	(40,20)	(5,2)					
16	(30,15)	(35,17)	(15,7)	(15,7)	(45,22)	(45,22)				
17	(10,5)	(25,12)	(25,12)	(25,12)	(35,17)	(35,17)	(25,12)			
18	(40,20)	(30,15)	(40,20)	(40,20)	(15,7)	(15,7)	(40,20)	(40,20)		
19	(10,5)	(25,12)	(25,12)	(25,12)	(35,17)	(35,17)	(25,12)	(5,2)	(40,20)	
20	(10,5)	(30,15)	(20,10)	(20,10)	(40,20)	(40,20)	(40,20)	(10,5)	(45,22)	(10,5)

The total travel distance of the four vehicles is 915. Furthermore, when the obtained operational plan is performed, we have

$$\Pr\{a_i \le f_i(\boldsymbol{x}^*, \boldsymbol{y}^*, \boldsymbol{t}^*) \le b_i, i = 1, 2, \cdots, 20\} = 0.94,$$

$$\Pr\left\{\sum_{j=y_{k-1}^*+1}^{y_k^*} q_{x_j^*} \le Q_k, k = 1, 2, 3, 4\right\} = 0.80.$$

Now let us consider the SVRP from a different angle. At the first priority level, the probability that all customers are visited within their time windows should achieve 95%,

TABLE 7.3
Travel Distance Matrix

LCTs	0	1	2	3	4	5	6	7	8	9	10	11	12	13	14	15	16	17	18	19
1	90																			
2	20	70																		
3	80	30	60																	
4	30	90	25	75																
5	85	65	55	70	75															
6	95	25	70	15	85	60														
7	45	70	65	75	35	45	65													
8	35	80	20	85	40	65	70	65												
9	80	35	85	20	75	60	20	90	70											
10	45	85	45	85	25	60	80	20	35	85										
11	90	20	65	60	65	20	65	20	75	75	60									
12	95	65	65	70	55	15	60	25	65	65	45	35								
13	20	80	20	80	25	60	75	75	20	80	80	75	75							
14	95	20	80	15	85	60	15	75	75	20	80	60	60	80						
15	85	20	80	20	85	60	20	65	75	10	80	60	80	80	15					
16	25	85	25	85	40	60	75	75	40	85	60	65	30	25	85	85				
17	60	80	55	80	40	45	65	15	45	80	20	45	45	45	65	65	45			
18	90	20	85	20	95	60	25	75	80	25	80	60	80	80	25	25	80	80		
19	60	70	45	80	40	55	65	15	45	80	20	45	45	45	65	75	45	15	80	
20	55	80	45	85	40	60	80	20	45	85	20	60	40	40	80	80	80	20	85	20

then we have

$$\Pr\{a_i \le f_i(\boldsymbol{x}, \boldsymbol{y}, \boldsymbol{t}) \le b_i, i = 1, 2, \cdots, 20\} + d_1^- - d_1^+ = 0.95$$

in which d_1^- should be minimized.

At the second priority level, the probability that the total amount of demands are met should achieve 90%, then we have

$$\Pr\left\{\sum_{j=y_{k-1}+1}^{y_k} q_{x_j} \le Q_k, k = 1, 2, 3, 4\right\} + d_2^- - d_2^+ = 0.90$$

in which d_2^- should be minimized.

At the third priority level, we should minimize the total travel distance, then we have

$$g(\boldsymbol{x}, \boldsymbol{y}) + d_3^- - d_3^+ = 0$$

in which d_3^+ will be minimized.

In order to satisfy as many goals as possible in the order specified, we have to employ the following dependent-chance goal programming model:

$$\begin{cases} \text{lexmin}\left\{d_1^-, d_2^-, d_3^+\right\} \\ \text{subject to:} \\ \qquad \Pr\left\{a_i \le f_i(\boldsymbol{x}, \boldsymbol{y}, \boldsymbol{t}) \le b_i, i = 1, 2, \cdots, 20\right\} + d_1^- - d_1^+ = 0.95 \\ \qquad \Pr\left\{\sum_{j=y_{k-1}+1}^{y_k} q_{x_j} \le Q_k, k = 1, 2, 3, 4\right\} + d_2^- - d_2^+ = 0.90 \\ \qquad g(\boldsymbol{x}, \boldsymbol{y}) + d_3^- - d_3^+ = 0 \\ \qquad 1 \le x_i \le 20, \quad i = 1, 2, \cdots, 20 \\ \qquad x_i \ne x_j, \quad i \ne j, \ i, j = 1, 2, \cdots, 20 \\ \qquad 0 \le y_1 \le y_2 \le y_3 \le 20 \\ \qquad x_i, y_j, \quad i = 1, 2, \cdots, 20, \quad j = 1, 2, 3, \quad \text{integers.} \end{cases}$$

A run of the proposed genetic algorithm with 3000 generations shows that the best operational plan is:

Vehicle 1: depot$\to$ 14 $\to$ 18 $\to$ 11 $\to$ 8 $\to$depot, starting time: 8:32;

Vehicle 2: depot$\to$ 13 $\to$ 5 $\to$ 19 $\to$ 20 $\to$depot, starting time: 8:09;

Vehicle 3: depot$\to$ 1 $\to$ 10 $\to$ 3 $\to$ 15 $\to$ 9 $\to$depot, starting time: 8:10;

Vehicle 4: depot$\to$ 2 $\to$ 4 $\to$ 7 $\to$ 12 $\to$ 6 $\to$ 17 $\to$ 16 $\to$depot, starting time: 8:27

which can satisfy the first goal, but the second and third objectives are 0.10 and 1170, respectively. Furthermore, when the obtained operational plan is performed, we have

$$\Pr\left\{a_i \le f_i(\boldsymbol{x}^*, \boldsymbol{y}^*, \boldsymbol{t}^*) \le b_i, i = 1, 2, \cdots, 20\right\} = 0.98,$$

$$\Pr\left\{\sum_{j=y_{k-1}^*+1}^{y_k^*} q_{x_j^*} \le Q_k, k = 1, 2, 3, 4\right\} = 0.80,$$

and the total travel distance of the four vehicles is 1170.

The time complexity of this type of problem is the sum of the time spent for the stochastic simulation and the time spent for the genetic algorithm, where the computation time for the stochastic simulation is exactly proportional to the number of sampling points of SVRPs.

8. Conclusion. In this paper we have contributed to the VRP research area in the following two aspects. First, a spectrum of stochastic programming models for SVRPs are reviewed which are more applicable to a real case; and second, an effective genetic algorithm for solving the proposed stochastic programming models is presented.

Acknowledgment. This work was supported by the National Natural Science Foundation of China Grant No.69804006, City University of Hong Kong Strategic Research Grant 7100075, and Sino-French Joint Laboratory for Research in Computer Science, Control and Applied Mathematics (LIAMA).

REFERENCES

[1] Bastian C. and Rinnooy Kan A.H.G., The Stochastic Vehicle Routing Problem Revisited, *European Journal of Operational Research*, Vol.56(1992), 407-412.

[2] Bertsimas D.J., A Vehicle Routing Problem with Stochastic Demand, *Operations Research*, Vol.40(1992), 574-585.

[3] Bertsimas D.J., and Simchi-Levi D., A new generation of vehicle routing research: Robust algorithms, addressing uncertainty, *Operations Research*, Vol.44, No.2, 286-304, 1996.

[4] Bodin L., Golden B.L., Assad A.A. and Ball M., Routing and Scheduling of Vehicles and Crews: The State of the Art, *Computers & Operations Research*, Vol.10(1983), 63-211.

[5] Brandã J. and Mercer A., A Tabu Search Algorithm for the Multi-trip Vehicle Routing and Scheduling Problem, *European Journal of Operational Research*, Vol.100(1997), 180-191.

[6] Chiang W.-C. and Russell R.A., Simulated Annealing Metaheuristics for the Vehicle Routing Problem with Time Windows, *Annals of Operations Research*, Vol.63(1996), 3-27.

[7] Desrochers M., Desrosiers J. and Solomon M., A New Optimization Algorithm for the Vehicle Routing Problem with Time Windows, *Opns. Res.*, Vol.40(1992), 342-354.

[8] Dror M. and Trudreau P., Stochastic Vehicle Routing with Modified Savings Algorithm, *European Journal of Operational Research*, Vol.23(1986), 228-235.

[9] Dror M., Laporte G. and Trudreau P., Vehicle Routing with Stochastic Demands: Properties and Solution Frameworks, *Transportation Science*, Vol.23(1989), 166-176.

[10] Dror M., Modeling Vehicle Routing with Uncertain Demands as a Stochastic Programming: Properties of the corresponding solution, *European Journal of Operational Research*, Vol.64(1993), 432-441.

[11] Dror M., Note on the Complexity of the Shortest Path Models for Column Generation in VRPTW, *Opns. Res.*, Vol.42(1994), 977-979.

[12] Fisher M.L. and Jaikumar R., A Generalized Assignment Heuristic for Vehicle Routing, *Networks*, Vol.11(1981), 109-124.

[13] Frizzell P.W. and Giffin J.W., The Split Delivery Vehicle Scheduling Problem with Time Windows and Grid Network Distances, *Computers Ops. Res.*, Vol.22(1995), 655-667.

[14] Garcia B.L., Potvin J.Y. and Rousseau J.M., A Parallel Implementation of the Tabu Search Heuristic for Vehicle Routing Problems with Time Window Constraints,*Computers Ops. Res.*, Vol.21(1994), 1025-1033.

[15] Gendreau M, Laporte G. and Séguin R., An Exact Algorithm for the Vehicle Routing Problem with Stochastic Customers and Demands, *Transportation Science*, Vol.29(1995), 143-155.

[16] Gendreau M, Laporte G. and Séguin R., Stochastic Vehicle Routing, *European Journal of Operational Research*, Vol.88(1999), 3-12.

[17] Goldberg D.E., *Genetic Algorithms in Search, Optimization and Machine Learning,* (Addison-Wesley, 1989).

[18] Golden B.L. and Yee J.R., A Framework for Probabilistic Vehicle Routing, *AIIE Transactions*, Vol.11(1979), 109-112.

[19] Holland J.H., *Adaptation in Natural and Artificial Systems*, (University of Michigan Press, Ann Arbor, 1975).

[20] Hooker J.N. and Natraj N.R., Solving a General Routing and Scheduling Problem by Chain Decomposition and Tabu Search, *Transportation Science*, Vol.29(1995), 30-44.

[21] Iwamura K. and B. Liu, A genetic algorithm for chance constrained programming, *Journal of Information & Optimization Sciences*, Vol.17 (1996), No.2, 409-422.

[22] Koskosidis Y.A. and Powell W.B., Application of Optimization based Models on Vehicle Routing and Scheduling Problems with Time Window Constraints, *Journal of Business Logistics*, Vol.11(1990), 101-128.

[23] Laporte G., The Vehicle Routing Problem: An Overview of Exact and Approximate Algorithms, *Eur. J. Opl. Res.*, Vol.59(1992), 345-358.

[24] Laporte G., Louveaux F.V. and Mercure H., The Vehicle Routing Problem with Stochastic Travel Times, *Transportation Science*, Vol.26(1992), 161-170.

[25] Liu B., Dependent-chance goal programming and its genetic algorithm based approach, *Mathematical and Computer Modelling*, Vol.24(1996), No.7, 43-52.

[26] Liu B., Dependent-chance programming: A class of stochastic optimization, *Computers & Mathematics with Applications*, Vol.34(1997), No.12, 89-104.

[27] Liu B. and K. Iwamura, Modelling stochastic decision systems using dependent-chance programming, *European Journal of Operational Research*, Vol.101(1997), No.1, 193-203.

[28] Liu B., *Uncertain Programming*, (John Wiley & Sons, New York, 1999).

[29] Michalewicz Z., *Genetic Algorithms + Data Structures = Evolution Programs,* 3rd ed., (New York: Springer-Verlag, 1996).

[30] Potvin J.-Y., Kervahut T., Garcia B.-L. and Rousseau J.-M., The Vehicle Routing Problem with Time Windows Part I: Tabu Search, *INFORMS Journal on Computing*, Vol.8(1996), No.2, 158-164.

[31] Potvin J.-Y. and Bengio S., The Vehicle Routing Problem with Time Windows Part II: Genetic Search, *INFORMS Journal on Computing*, Vol.8(1996), No.2, 165-172.

[32] Sharma R.R.K. and Paradkar S.S., Modelling a Railway Freight Transport System, *Asia-Pacific J.*

Opl. Res., Vol.12(1995), 17-36.

[33] Solomon M.M. and Desrosiers J., Time Window Constrained Routing and Scheduling Problems, *Transportation Science*, Vol.22(1988), 1-13.

[34] Stewart W.R.Jr. and Golden B.L., Stochastic Vehicle Routing: A Comprehensive Approach, *European Journal of Operational Research*, Vol.14(1983), 371-385.

[35] Taillard E.D., Laporte G. and Gendrean M., Vehicle Routing with Multiple Use of Vehicles, *J. Opl. Res. Soc.*, Vol.47(1996), 1065-1070.

[36] Waters C.D.J., Vehicle-Scheduling Problems with Uncertainty and Omitted Customers, *Journal of the Operational Research Society*, Vol.40(1989), 1099-1108.

In: Focus on Computational Neurobiology
Editor: Lei Li, pp. 29-35

ISBN 1-59033-915-0

AN IMPROVED ITERATIVE CRITERION FOR GDDM WITH ELECTIVE PARAMETERS*

LEI LI† AND KATSUHISA SOMEYA‡

Abstract. Recently, some criteria for generalized diagonally dominant matrix (GDDM) have been proposed in [1-6]. Especially in [5,6], we showed an iterative criterion for GDDM. This paper presents an improved algorithm to decrease the number of iterations. The new method is also effective for a class of Non-GDDM.

Key words. GDDM, H-matrix, M-matrix, criterion

1. Introduction. Let matrix $A = (a_{ij}) \in C^{n,n}$. We call that row i in a diagonally dominant row if row i in A satisfies $|a_{ii}| > \sum_{j \neq i} |a_{ij}|$. And we call that A in a strictly diagonally dominant matrix, if all rows in A are diagonally dominant rows.

DEFINITION 1.1. *Let $A = (a_{ij}) \in C^{n,n}$. We call that A in a generalized diagonally dominant matrix (GDDM for short), if there exists a positive diagonal matrix*

$$D = diag\{d_i | d_i > 0, i = 1, 2, \ldots, n\},$$

which satisfies the all rows in AD are diagonally dominant.

We know that if a matrix A is generalized diagonally dominant, then many iterative methods for system $Ax = b$ of linear equations are convergent [7]. Recently, some criteria for GDDM have been proposed in [1-6]. Especially in [5,6], an iterative criterion for GDDM was shown. In this paper, we present an improved algorithm to decrease the number of iterations. The new algorithm is also effective for a class of Non-GDDM.

2. An Iterative Criterion. In order to introduce our new algorithm, we first summarize the iterative criterion for GDDM shown in [5,6]. Let

$$N = \{1, 2, \ldots, n\}, \qquad N_1 = \{i | |a_{ii}| > \sum_{j \neq i} |a_{ij}| = S_i, i \in N\} \neq \phi,$$

and $N_2 = N - N_1$.

H-Algorithm:

INPUT: a matrix $A = (a_{ij}) \in C^{n \times n}$ and any $\varepsilon > 0$.

OUTPUT: $D = D^{(1)} D^{(2)} \cdots D^{(m)}$ if A is an H-matrix.

1) if $N_1(A) = \phi$ or $a_{ii} = 0$ for some $i \in \{1, 2, \cdots, n\}$, '$A$ is not an H-matrix', STOP; otherwise

2) set $A^{(0)} = A$, $D^{(0)} = I$, $m = 1$

3) Compute $A^{(m)} = A^{(m-1)} D^{(m-1)} = (a_{ij}^{(m)})$

4) If $N_1(A^{(m)}) = N$, 'A is an H-matrix', STOP; otherwise

5) set $d = (d_i)$, where

$$d_i = \begin{cases} \frac{S_i(A^{(m)}) + \varepsilon}{|a_{ii}^{(m)}| + \varepsilon}, & \text{if } i \in N_1(A^{(m)}); \\ 1, & \text{if } i \in N_2(A^{(m)}). \end{cases}$$

*This work was presented in International Conference on Computational Engineering Science'98, Oct. 1998, Atlanta, USA.

†Faculty of Engineering, Hosei University, Kajino-cho 3-7-2, Koganei, Tokyo 184-8584, Japan (lilei@k.hosei.ac.jp).

‡ Faculty of Science, Yamaguchi University, Yoshita 1677-1, Yamaguchi 753-8512, Japan

6) set $D^{(m)} = diag(d_i)$, $m = m + 1$; go to step 3).

Two unsolved problems are remained in the above algorithm. The first problem is that how to choose the parameter ε for obtaining the smallest number of iterations. The second problem is that the method will be divergent when A is not a GDDM. In order to settle these two problems, we present an improved algorithm. Our idea is finding an optimal parameter ε_k in every iterative step k.

3. Conditions for the Parameter ε. For an input matrix A, $a_{ii} \neq 0$, $i = 1, 2, \ldots, n$, let A' be

$$A' = (a'_{ij}), \qquad a'_{ij} = \frac{a_{ij}}{a_{ii}}, \qquad i, j = 1, 2, \ldots, n$$

then it is obvious that A' is GDDM if and only if A is GDDM. In [5], the diagonal matrix D is decided by

$$D = diag\{d_i | d_i = \frac{S_i + \varepsilon}{|a_{ii}| + \varepsilon}, i \in N_1, d_i = 1, i \in N_2\}.$$

Now we define the diagonal matrix D for A' as the follows,

$$D = diag\{d_i | d_i = \frac{S'_i + \varepsilon}{|a'_{ii}| + \varepsilon}, i = 1, 2, \ldots, n\}, \qquad S'_i = \sum_{j \neq i} |a'_{ij}|.$$

Then from the condition $d_i > 0, i = 1, 2, \ldots, n$, we have

$$d_i = \frac{S'_i + \varepsilon}{|a'_{ii}| + \varepsilon} = \frac{S'_i + \varepsilon}{1 + \varepsilon} > 0, \qquad i = 1, 2, \ldots, n$$

If $\varepsilon > -1$, then

$$\varepsilon > -S'_i, \qquad i = 1, 2, \ldots, n$$

and if $\varepsilon < -1$, then

$$\varepsilon < -S'_i, \qquad i = 1, 2, \ldots, n$$

Excluding two cases for all rows are diagonally dominant row and all rows are not diaogonally dominant row, there exists some i and j with satisfying $S'_i < 1$ and $S'_j > 1$. So, if $\varepsilon > -S'_i$, $i = 1, 2, \cdots, n$, then $\varepsilon > -1$, and if $\varepsilon < -S'_j$, $j = 1, 2, \cdots, n$, then $\varepsilon < -1$. It is to say we have

Condition 1.

$$\varepsilon > -min\{S'_i\}, \qquad or \qquad \varepsilon < -max\{S'_i\}$$

Condition 1 must be satisfied for ε. Next, we consider another condition for ε.

If A' is a GDDM, then there exists $d_i > 0$, $i = 1, 2, \ldots, n$ with satisfying

$$|a'_{ii}| d_i > \sum_{j \neq i} |a'_{ij}| d_j, \qquad i = 1, 2, \cdots, n$$

If input $d_i = \frac{S'_i + \varepsilon}{|a'_{ii}| + \varepsilon}$ into the above inequalities, then

$$|a'_{ii}| \frac{S'_i + \varepsilon}{|a'_{ii}| + \varepsilon} > \sum_{j \neq i} |a'_{ij}| \frac{S'_j + \varepsilon}{|a'_{jj}| + \varepsilon}.$$

If ε satisfies this inequality in row i, then row i in matrix $A'D$ is a diagonally dominant row. So, we can increase number of the diagonally dominant rows in every iteration.

From $a'_{ii} = 1$, we have

$$\frac{S'_i + \varepsilon}{1+\varepsilon} > \sum_{j \neq i} |a'_{ij}| \frac{S'_j + \varepsilon}{1+\varepsilon}. \tag{3.1}$$

Solve this inequality about ε. If $\varepsilon > -1$, then

$$S'_i + \varepsilon > \sum_{j \neq i} |a'_{ij}|(S'_j + \varepsilon)$$

$$S'_i + \varepsilon > \sum_{j \neq i} |a'_{ij}| S'_j + \varepsilon S'_i,$$

$$(1 - S'_i)\varepsilon > \sum_{j \neq i} |a'_{ij}| S'_j - S'_i$$

So, if $1 > S'_i$, $i \in N_1$, then

$$\varepsilon > \frac{\sum_{j \neq i} |a'_{ij}| S'_j - S'_i}{1 - S'_i},$$

If $1 < S'_i$, $i \in N_2$, then

$$\varepsilon < \frac{\sum_{j \neq i} |a'_{ij}| S'_j - S'_i}{1 - S'_i}.$$

And if $\varepsilon < -1$, from (3.1),

$$S'_i + \varepsilon < \sum_{j \neq i} |a'_{ij}|(S'_j + \varepsilon)$$

$$S'_i + \varepsilon < \sum_{j \neq i} |a'_{ij}| S'_j + \varepsilon S'_i,$$

$$(1 - S'_i)\varepsilon < \sum_{j \neq i} |a'_{ij}| S'_j - S'_i$$

If $1 > S'_i$, $i \in N_1$, then

$$\varepsilon < \frac{\sum_{j \neq i} |a'_{ij}| S'_j - S'_i}{1 - S'_i},$$

If $1 < S'_i$, $i \in N_2$, then

$$\varepsilon > \frac{\sum_{j \neq i} |a'_{ij}| S'_j - S'_i}{1 - S'_i}$$

The above results can be summarized as the follows.

Condition 2 If $i \in N_1$, then

$$\varepsilon > -1, \qquad and \qquad \varepsilon > \frac{\sum_{j\neq i}|a'_{ij}|S'_j - S'_i}{1-S'_i},$$

or

$$\varepsilon < -1, \qquad and \qquad \varepsilon < \frac{\sum_{j\neq i}|a'_{ij}|S'_j - S'_i}{1-S'_i}.$$

If $i \in N_2$, then

$$\varepsilon > -1, \qquad and \qquad \varepsilon < \frac{\sum_{j\neq i}|a'_{ij}|S'_j - S'_i}{1-S'_i},$$

or

$$\varepsilon < -1, \qquad and \qquad \varepsilon > \frac{\sum_{j\neq i}|a'_{ij}|S'_j - S'_i}{1-S'_i}$$

Now let

$$\varepsilon_i = \frac{\sum_{j\neq i}|a'_{ij}|S'_j - S'_i}{1-S'_i},$$

from the condition 1 and condition 2,

$$\varepsilon > -min\{S_i\}, \tag{3.2}$$

and

$$\varepsilon > \varepsilon_j, \qquad \varepsilon < \varepsilon_k, \tag{3.3}$$

or

$$\varepsilon < -max\{S_i\}, \tag{3.4}$$

and

$$\varepsilon < \varepsilon_j, \qquad \varepsilon > \varepsilon_k, \tag{3.5}$$

where $j \in N_1$, $k \in N_2$.

ε must satisfies conditions (3.2) and (3.4), but it is not necessary to satisfy conditions (3.3) and (3.5) completely in every iterative step. So, we decide ε to satisfy the largest number of condiditions (3.3) or (3.5) by using the following selection method of the parameter ε.

1) For ε_i, $i = 1, 2, \cdots, n$, if $\varepsilon_i > -min\{S_i\}$, then count p_i

$$p_i = car\{j|\varepsilon_i > \varepsilon_j, j \in N_1\} + car\{k|\varepsilon_i < \varepsilon_k, k \in N_2\},$$

If $\varepsilon_i < -max\{S_i\}$, then count p_i

$$p_i = car\{j|\varepsilon_i < \varepsilon_j, j \in N_1\} + car\{k|\varepsilon_i > \varepsilon_k, k \in N_2\},$$

where $car\{\cdot\}$ means the size of set $\{\cdot\}$.

2) If $max\{p_i\} = p_t$, then let $\varepsilon = \varepsilon_t$.

4. An Improved Algorithm. Now, we show an improved algorithm which is based the above ideas.

IH-Algorithm :

1) Compose the matrix

$$A' = (a'_{ij}), \qquad a'_{ij} = \frac{a_{ij}}{a_{ii}}, \qquad i,j = 1,2,\ldots,n$$

2) Compute

$$S'_i = \sum_{j \neq i} |a'_{ij}|, \qquad i = 1,2,\cdots,n$$

3) Compute

$$\varepsilon_i = \frac{\sum_{j \neq i} |a'_{ij}| S'_j - S'_i}{1 - S'_i}, \qquad i = 1,2,\cdots,n.$$

4) Decide ε as the follows. For ε_i, $i = 1,2,\cdots,n$, if $\varepsilon_i > -min\{S_i\}$ then count p_i

$$p_i = car\{j|\varepsilon_i > \varepsilon_j, j \in N_1\} + car\{k|\varepsilon_i < \varepsilon_k, k \in N_2\},$$

If $\varepsilon_i < -max\{S_i\}$, then count p_i

$$p_i = car\{j|\varepsilon_i < \varepsilon_j, j \in N_1\} + car\{k|\varepsilon_i > \varepsilon_k, k \in N_2\}$$

where $car\{\cdot\}$ means the size of set $\{\cdot\}$.

When $max\{p_i\} = p_t$, let $\varepsilon = \varepsilon_t$.

5) Compute a diagonal matrix D as the follows.

$$D^{(1)} = diag\{d_i | d_i = \frac{S'_i + \varepsilon}{|a'_{ii}| + \varepsilon}, i \in N\},$$

6) Compute $A^{(1)} = A'D^{(1)}$.

7) If $A^{(1)}$ is not strictly diagonally dominant matrix, return to step 1) and continue computing.

5. Criterion for Non-GDDM. THEOREM 5.1. *Let $A = \{a_{ij}\} \in C^{n,n}$. If there exists a diagonal matrix*

$$D = diag\{d_i | d_i > 0, \quad i = 1,2,\cdots,n\}$$

which makes all rows in AD to be Non-diagonally dominant rows, then A is not GDDM.

Proof. Let $A = \{a_{ij}\} \in C^{n,n}$. Because there exists a positive diagonal matrix D

$$D = diag\{d_i | d_i > 0, \quad i = 1,2,\cdots,n\},$$

with satisfying

$$|a_{ii}| d_i < \sum_{j \neq i} |a_{ij}| d_j, \quad i = 1,2,\cdots,n$$

So

$$m(A)\cdot d<0, \tag{5.1}$$

where $m(A)$ is the comparing matrix of A, and vector $d=\{d_1,d_2,\dots,d_n\}^T$. We suppose A is GDDM, then $m(A)$ is an M-matrix [7] and $m(A)^{-1}\geq 0$. From (5.1),

$$m(A)(-d)>0,$$

$$m(A)^{-1}m(A)(-d)\geq 0,$$

$$-d\geq 0.$$

This is a contradiction. Therefore A is not GDDM. □

For distinguishing the class of Non-GDDM shown in Theorem 5.1, we just need to compute the following step 4') to instead the step 4) in IH-Algorithm.

4') Decide ε as the follows. For ε_i, $i=1,2,\cdots,n$, if $\varepsilon_i>-min\{S_i\}$ then count p_i

$$p_i=car\{j|\varepsilon_i<\varepsilon_j,j\in N_1\}+car\{k|\varepsilon_i>\varepsilon_k,k\in N_2\}.$$

If $\varepsilon_i<-max\{S_i\}$, then count p_i

$$p_i=car\{j|\varepsilon_i>\varepsilon_j,j\in N_1\}+car\{k|\varepsilon_i<\varepsilon_k,k\in N_2\},$$

where $car\{\cdot\}$ means the size of set $\{\cdot\}$. When $max\{p_i\}=p_h$, let $\varepsilon=\varepsilon_h$.

6. Examples. Example 1. Let the coefficients matrix

$$A=\begin{pmatrix} 1 & -0.2 & -0.1 & -0.2 & -0.1\\ -0.4 & 1 & -0.2 & -0.1 & -0.1\\ -0.9 & -0.2 & 1 & -0.1 & -0.1\\ -0.3 & -0.7 & -0.3 & 1 & -0.1\\ -1 & -0.3 & -0.2 & -0.4 & 1 \end{pmatrix},$$

then the H-Algorithm shown in [6] spend 13 iterations for distinguishing this matrix. But the IH-Algorithm shown in this paper just needs 3 iterations, where ε in every step are as the follows.

$$\varepsilon^{(1)}=0.150000,\qquad \varepsilon^{(2)}=0.344444,\qquad \varepsilon^{(3)}=-0.217411.$$

Example 2. Let the coefficients matrix

$$A=\begin{pmatrix} 1 & -0.3 & -0.1 & -0.3 & -0.1\\ -0.4 & 1 & -0.3 & -0.1 & -0.1\\ -0.8 & -0.2 & 1 & -0.1 & -0.1\\ -0.2 & -0.7 & -0.3 & 1 & -0.1\\ -0.6 & -0.3 & -0.1 & -0.2 & 1 \end{pmatrix},$$

then, IH-Algorithm just spends 2 iterations. ε in every iteration are as the follows.

$$\varepsilon^{(1)}=0.500000,\qquad \varepsilon^{(2)}=0.299997.$$

For using this algorithm, we distinguished 10 input matrices which are 300×300 matrices made by random function. The average of the number of iterations just was 2.6. If use the H-Algorithm shown in [6] with the same input matrices, the average of the number of iterations was 77.8.

Acknowledgments. The authors thank Dr. Kazunari Kuboyama for his kind comments.

REFERENCES

[1] Y. GAO AND X. WANG, *Criteria for Generalized Diagonally Dominant Matrix and M-matrix*, Linear Algebra Appl.,169 (1992), pp. 257–268.

[2] L. LI, *On Some Practical Criteria for the Convergence of Splitting Iterations*, Acta Mathematica Applicatae Sinica, 17(1994), pp. 429–436.

[3] M. HARADA, M. USUI AND H. NIKI, *An Extension of the Criteria for Generalized Diagonally Dominant Matrices*, Inter.J.Computer Math., 60(1996), pp. 115–119.

[4] Y. GAO AND X. WANG, *Criteria for Generalized Diagonally Dominant Matrix and M-matrix II*, Linear Algebra Appl., 248(1996), pp. 339-353.

[5] L. LI, *Criterion for generalized diagonally dominant matrices*, In Proceedings of the 25th Japan Symposium of Numerical Analisis, 1996, pp. 72-74.

[6] B. LI, L. LI, HAMADA, M., NIKI, H. AND TSATSOMEROS M.J., *An Iterative Criterion for H-matrices*, Linear Algebra Appl., 271(1998), pp. 179–190.

[7] A. BERMAN, R.J. PLEMMONS, *Nonnegative Matrices in the Mathematical Sciences, Classics in Applied Mathematics*, SIAM, 1994.

In: Focus on Computational Neurobiology
Editor: Lei Li, pp. 37-48
ISBN 1-59033-915-0

HIGHER-ORDER ASYMPTOTIC THEORIES OF THE JACKKNIFE IN A MULTIVARIATE SETTING*

JINFANG WANG†

Abstract. In this paper we develop third-order asymptotic theories for the jackknife method under the multivariate smooth function model. Both unstudentized and studentized versions are studied. We shall focus on the latter case since studentization often results in better accuracy in estimation such as estimating the distribution function.

Key words. Bootstrap, computer-intensive methods, Edgeworth expansion, higher-order asymptotic theory, jackknife, smooth function model.

AMS subject classifications. 62E20, 62G07, 62G09, 62G20, 62H10.

1. Introduction. Computer-intensive methods such as the jackknife [9], [10] and the bootstrap [4] are popularly employed in applied scientific works in analyzing data for objective decision making. These methods are utilized often because they require very little mathematical manipulations such as asymptotic expansions. There exists a large body of literature on both the jackknife and the bootstrap methods [2], [6]. These methods are expected to be useful alternatives to traditional methods especially in relatively complicated situations. The theoretical properties of these methods in such situations are however less transparent.

In this paper we develop third-order asymptotic theories for the multivariate jackknife methods under the smooth function model. Both unstudentized and studentized versions are studies. Since there are advantages in using studentized statistics, we shall focus on the jackknife-t method. The results obtained not only help in understanding the jackknife methodology but also provide some basic tools for further studies on comparing the jackknife and the bootstrap, the latter attracting more theoretical and practical attention recently. The results presented in this paper generalize the univariate theories studied in [11].

The paper is organized as follows. Section 2 gives a brief review of the jackknife method under the smooth function model. Section 3 studies the third order asymptotic theories for the unstudentized jackknife method. Section 4 studies the third order asymptotic theories for the studentized jackknife method, which is quite involved due to studentization.

2. Jackknifing the smooth function model. In this section the smooth function model and the delete-one jackknife are introduced.

The smooth function model. Let $\{\boldsymbol{Z}_p\}_{p\geq 1}$ be a sequence of i.i.d. r-dimensional random vectors, and $g_1, \cdots, g_d$ be real-valued Borel measurable functions on $I\!R^r$. Define

$$\boldsymbol{X}_p = (X_p^1, \cdots, X_p^i, \cdots, X_p^d) = (g_1(\boldsymbol{Z}_p), \cdots, g_i(\boldsymbol{Z}_p), \cdots, g_d(\boldsymbol{Z}_p)).$$

Let $\eta = E[\boldsymbol{X}_p] = (\eta^1, \cdots, \eta^i, \cdots, \eta^d)$ be the mean of $\boldsymbol{X}_p$. We shall consider inferences for parameters in a form $\theta = h(\eta)$, where h is a $I\!R^k$-valued smooth Borel measurable function on $I\!R^d$. The plug-in principle suggests using the following statistic

$$\hat{\theta} = h(\bar{\boldsymbol{X}}) = (h^1(\bar{\boldsymbol{X}}), \cdots, h^\alpha(\bar{\boldsymbol{X}}), \cdots, h^k(\bar{\boldsymbol{X}})) = (\hat{\theta}^1, \cdots, \hat{\theta}^\alpha, \cdots, \hat{\theta}^k)$$

*This work was supported partially by Grand-in-Aid 12780181 of the Japanese Ministry of Education, Science, Sports and Culture.

†Department of Animal Production and Agricultural Economics, Obihiro University of Agriculture and Veterinary Medicine Inada-cho, Obihiro, Hokkaido 080-8555, Japan (wang@obihiro.ac.jp).

as a natural initial estimator for $\hat{\theta}$, where $\bar{\boldsymbol{X}} = \sum_{p=1}^{n} \boldsymbol{X}_p/n$ and n is the sample size. The class of parameters, $\theta = h(\eta)$, is large enough to include all smooth functions of population moments. The corresponding class of so-called plug-in estimators, $\hat{\theta} = h(\bar{\boldsymbol{X}})$, consists of all smooth functions of sample means.

Example 1. (*regression coefficient*) Let $\boldsymbol{Z} = (V, W)$. Define $\boldsymbol{X} = g(\boldsymbol{Z}) = (V, W, V \times W, (V)^2)$, so the regression coefficient can be written as $\theta \equiv \mathrm{cov}(V, W)/\mathrm{var}\, V = (\eta^3 - \eta^1\eta^2)/(\eta^4 - (\eta^1)^2)$, with $r = 2, d = 4$ and $k = 1$.

Example 2. (*correlation coefficient*) Let $\boldsymbol{Z} = (V, W)$ be a $I\!R^2$-valued random variable and $\boldsymbol{X} = g(\boldsymbol{Z}) = (V, W, V \times W, (V)^2, (W)^2)$, then the correlation coefficient can be expressed as

$$\theta \equiv \rho = \frac{(\eta^3 - \eta^1\eta^2)}{\sqrt{(\eta^4 - (\eta^1)^2)(\eta^5 - (\eta^2)^2)}}$$

with $r = 2, d = 5$ and $k = 1$.

Both the regression coefficient and the correlation coefficient are of the ratio type. Difficulties in using the corresponding plug-in estimators are usually caused by the instability of the denominators.

The jackknife. Omitting the p-th observation, we compute the delete-one-sample mean $\bar{\boldsymbol{X}}_{\not p} = (n\bar{\boldsymbol{X}} - \boldsymbol{X}_p)/(n-1)$ and define the estimator $\hat{\theta}_{\not p} = h(\bar{\boldsymbol{X}}_{\not p})$. The jackknife pseudo-values are defined as ${}_{pv}\hat{\theta}_{\not p} = n\hat{\theta} - (n-1)\hat{\theta}_{\not p}$, average of which

$$\hat{\theta}_J = \frac{1}{n}\sum_{p=1}^{n} {}_{pv}\hat{\theta}_{\not p} = n\hat{\theta} - (n-1)\hat{\theta}_{(\cdot)} \tag{2.1}$$

where $\hat{\theta}_{(\cdot)} = \sum_{p=1}^{n} \hat{\theta}_{\not p}/n$, is called the (delete-one) jackknife bias-adjusted estimator. The jackknife estimator $\hat{\theta}_J$ has a bias $O(n^{-2})$. Since the original estimator $\hat{\theta}$ has a bias $O(n^{-2})$, the jackknife estimator $\hat{\theta}_J$ much improves $\hat{\theta}$ in terms of bias.

A higher order bias reduction can be achieved by iterating the jackknife procedure until the desired order is realized. The over-reduction of bias however sometimes may cause an increase of variance. In some extreme cases when there exists no unbiased estimator, the bias reduction may result in divergence in the mean squared error [3].

Inferences for θ, such as constructing confidence regions or carrying out hypothesis tests, are often based on asymptotic pivots T rather than the plug-in type estimators $\hat{\theta}$ or $\hat{\theta}_J$ directly. A random variable T is called an asymptotic pivot if the distribution of T tends asymptotically to a limit which is completely specified. If the central limit theorem applies then the standard Gaussian distribution is an example of the limit distribution. Studentization is a common technique to use in order to apply the central limit theorem starting from an estimator such as $\hat{\theta}_J$. A good studentization depends on a stable estimate of the variance. The jackknife again provides an estimate of the variance using the same pseudo-values for calculating $\hat{\theta}_J$. The jackknife variance estimate of

$$\tilde{\theta}_J^{\alpha} = \sqrt{n}(\hat{\theta}_J^{\alpha} - \theta^{\alpha}) \tag{2.2}$$

is defined by

$$(\hat{\sigma}_J^{\alpha})^2 = \frac{1}{n-1}\sum_{p=1}^{n}({}_{pv}\hat{\theta}_{\not p}^{\alpha} - \hat{\theta}_J^{\alpha})^2 \tag{2.3}$$

where α runs from 1 to k. At a finite sample size it is not always clear that $(\hat{\sigma}_J^\alpha)^2$ is a good estimator for the variance of $\hat{\theta}^\alpha$ or $\hat{\theta}_J^\alpha$ [5], [8]. Under mild conditions however $(\hat{\sigma}_J^\alpha)^2$ may be shown to consistently estimate the common asymptotic variance of $\hat{\theta}$ and $\hat{\theta}_J^\alpha$. Now we define the jackknife-t statistic by $T_J^\alpha = \tilde{\theta}_J^\alpha/\hat{\sigma}_J^\alpha$.

3. The Jackknifed Estimator.

Now we first discuss the unstudentized version.

3.1. Stochastic expansions. Denote by $\kappa^i = \mathrm{cum}(X^i)$, $\kappa^{i,j} = \mathrm{cum}(X^i, X^j)$, $\kappa^{i,j,k} = \mathrm{cum}(X^i, X^j, X^k)$, the first, second and third cumulant of random variable $\boldsymbol{X} = (X^1, \cdots, X^d)$. Let $\eta^i = \mathrm{E}(X^i)$, $\eta^{ij} = \mathrm{E}(X^i X^j)$, $\eta^{ijk} = \mathrm{E}(X^i X^j X^k)$ be the mean of X^i, $X^i X^j$, $X^i X^j X^k$, respectively; where $i, j, k = 1, 2, \cdots, d$. By definition we have $\kappa^i = \eta^i$, so the two symbols will be used interchangeably wherever we feel convenient.

LEMMA 3.1. *Define* $X_p^{ij} = X_p^i X_p^j$, $\bar{X}^{ij} = \sum_{p=1}^n X_p^{ij}/n$, *and* $\tilde{X}^{ij} = \sqrt{n}(\bar{X}^{ij} - \eta^{ij})$, *then* $\hat{\kappa}^{i,j} = n^{-1}\sum_{p=1}^n (X_p^i - \bar{X}^i)(X_p^j - \bar{X}^j)$ *can be decomposed as follows*

$$\hat{\kappa}^{i,j} = \kappa^{i,j} + \frac{1}{\sqrt{n}}(\tilde{X}^{ij} - \kappa^i \tilde{X}^j[2]_{(ij)}) - \frac{1}{n}\tilde{X}^i \tilde{X}^j, \tag{3.1}$$

where $[2]_{(ij)}$ *denotes symmetrized sum with respect to indices* i, j; *e.g.* $[2]_{(ij)}\eta^i \tilde{X}^j = \eta^i \tilde{X}^j + \eta^j \tilde{X}^i$.

Proof Define random vectors $\boldsymbol{Z}_p = (W_p^1, W_p^2, W_p^3) = (X_p^i, X_p^j, X_p^{ij})$, where $p = 1, \cdots, n$. Let $\bar{W} = n^{-1}\sum_{p=1}^n \boldsymbol{Z}_p = (\bar{W}_p^1, \bar{W}_p^2, \bar{W}_p^3)$ be the sample mean. Let $\xi = \mathrm{E}(\bar{W}) = (\xi^1, \xi^2, \xi^3)$. Let $A(\bar{\boldsymbol{Z}}) = \bar{W}_p^3 - \bar{W}_p^1 \bar{W}_p^2$, then $\hat{\kappa}^{i,j} = A(\bar{\boldsymbol{Z}})$. Expanding $A(\bar{\boldsymbol{Z}})$ at ξ yields

$$A(\xi) + \partial_a A(\xi)(\bar{W}^a - \xi^a) + \frac{1}{2}\partial_{ab}A(\xi)(\bar{W}^a - \xi^a)(\bar{W}^b - \xi^b), \tag{3.2}$$

where $\partial_a A(\xi) = \partial A(\xi)/\partial \xi^a$, and $\partial_{ab}A(\xi) = \partial^2 A(\xi)/\partial \xi^a \partial \xi^b$, $a, b = 1, 2, 3$. Evaluating the differentiations of (3.2) and simplifying then lead to (3.1). □

The following expansion for $\tilde{\theta}_J$ can be obtained by applying Lemma 3.1.

THEOREM 3.2. *Let* $h_i^\alpha = \partial h^\alpha(\eta)/\partial \eta^i$, $h_{ij}^\alpha = \partial^2 h^\alpha(\eta)/(\partial \eta^i \partial \eta^j)$, $h_{ijk}^\alpha = \partial^3 h^\alpha(\eta)/(\partial \eta^i \partial \eta^j \partial \eta^k)$. *Under certain mild regularity conditions, the third order stochastic expansion of jackknife bias-adjusted estimator assumes the following form*

$$\begin{aligned}\tilde{\theta_J^\alpha} &= h_i^\alpha \tilde{X}^i + \frac{1}{2\sqrt{n}}h_{ij}^\alpha(\tilde{X}^i \tilde{X}^j - \kappa^{i,j}) \\ &+ \frac{1}{n}\left\{\frac{1}{6}h_{ijk}^\alpha \tilde{X}^i \tilde{X}^j \tilde{X}^k + \frac{1}{2}h_{ij}^\alpha(2\kappa^i \tilde{X}^j - \tilde{X}^{ij}) - \frac{1}{2}h_{ijk}^\alpha \kappa^{i,j}\tilde{X}^k\right\} + O_p(n^{-3/2}),\end{aligned}$$

where, and hereafter, the Einstein's summation convention is assumed. That is, if the same index is used twice both as a subscript and as a superscript then summation is automatically taken with respect to that index; e.g. $h_{ij}^\alpha(\tilde{X}^i \tilde{X}^j - \kappa^{i,j}) = \sum_{i=1}^d \sum_{j=1}^d h_{ij}^\alpha(\tilde{X}^i \tilde{X}^j - \kappa^{i,j})$.

In contrast, the stabilized version of the usual bias-adjusted estimator

$$\hat{\theta}_*^\alpha = \hat{\theta}^\alpha - \frac{1}{2n}h_{ij}^\alpha(\bar{\boldsymbol{X}})\hat{\kappa}^{i,j}$$

admits expansion

$$\tilde{\theta}_*^\alpha = \sqrt{n}(\hat{\theta}_*^\alpha - \theta^\alpha) = h_i^\alpha \tilde{X}^i + \frac{1}{2\sqrt{n}}h_{ij}^\alpha(\tilde{X}^i \tilde{X}^j - \kappa^{ij}) + O_p(n^{-1}). \tag{3.3}$$

From (3.3) and (3.3) we see that the jackknife bias-adjusted estimator and the usual bias-adjusted estimator enjoy the same stochastic expansion up to $O_p(n^{-1/2})$, from which we immediately have

THEOREM 3.3. *Edgeworth expansions of both the density functions and the cumulative distribution functions of $\tilde{\theta}_J$ and $\tilde{\theta}_*$ agree up to $O(1/\sqrt{n})$.*

3.2. Edgeworth expansions. To compute the asymptotic moments and cumulants of $\tilde{\theta}_J$, we first state the following lemmas and propositions.

LEMMA 3.4. *Rewrite (3.3) as*

$$\tilde{\theta}_J^\alpha = A_0^\alpha + \frac{1}{\sqrt{n}}A_1^\alpha + \frac{1}{n}A_2^\alpha + O_p(n^{-3/2}).$$

Then we have

$$E[A_0^\alpha(A_1^\beta + \frac{1}{\sqrt{n}}A_2^\beta)] = 0,$$

$$cum(\tilde{\theta}_J^\alpha, \tilde{\theta}_J^\beta) = cov(A_0^\alpha, A_0^\beta) + \frac{1}{n}cov(A_1^\alpha, A_1^\beta). \tag{3.4}$$

Define

$$\kappa^{\alpha,\beta} \equiv h_i^\alpha h_j^\beta \kappa^{i,j},$$
$$\kappa^{\alpha,\beta,\gamma} \equiv h_i^\alpha h_j^\beta h_k^\gamma \kappa^{i,j,k},$$
$$\kappa^{\alpha,\beta,\gamma,\delta} \equiv h_i^\alpha h_j^\beta h_k^\gamma h_l^\delta \kappa^{i,j,k,l}.$$

After some algebraic manipulations the first four moments of $\tilde{\theta}_J$ can be expanded by the following asymptotic series to the order $O(1/n)$.

$$E(\tilde{\theta}_J^\alpha) = O(n^{-3/2}), \tag{3.5}$$

$$E(\tilde{\theta}_J^\alpha\tilde{\theta}_J^\beta) = \kappa^{\alpha,\beta} + \frac{1}{2n}h_{ij}^\alpha h_{kl}^\beta \kappa^{i,k}\kappa^{j,l} + O(n^{-2}), \tag{3.6}$$

$$E(\tilde{\theta}_J^\alpha\tilde{\theta}_J^\beta\tilde{\theta}_J^\gamma) = \frac{1}{\sqrt{n}}\left(\kappa^{\alpha,\beta,\gamma} + h_i^\alpha h_j^\beta h_{kl}^\gamma \kappa^{i,k}\kappa^{j,l}[3]_{\alpha\beta\gamma)}\right) + O(n^{-3/2}), \tag{3.7}$$

$$\begin{aligned} E(\tilde{\theta}_J^\alpha\tilde{\theta}_J^\beta\tilde{\theta}_J^\gamma\tilde{\theta}_J^\delta) &= \kappa^{\alpha,\beta}\kappa^{\gamma,\delta}[3]_{(\alpha\beta\gamma\delta)} + \frac{1}{n}\Big\{\kappa^{\alpha,\beta,\gamma,\delta} \\ &+\frac{1}{2}h_i^\alpha h_j^\beta h_k^\gamma h_{lm}^\delta(6\kappa^{i,l}\kappa^{j,k,m} + \kappa^{l,m}\kappa^{i,j,k})[4]_{(\alpha\beta\gamma,\delta)} \\ &+h_i^\alpha h_j^\beta h_k^\gamma h_{lmn}^\delta \kappa^{i,l}\kappa^{j,m}\kappa^{k,n}[4]_{(\alpha,\beta,\gamma,\delta)} \\ &+\frac{1}{2}\kappa^{\alpha,\beta}h_{kl}^\gamma h_{mn}^\delta \kappa^{k,m}\kappa^{l,n}[6]_{(\alpha\beta\gamma\delta)}\Big\} + O(n^{-2}). \end{aligned} \tag{3.8}$$

PROPOSITION 3.5. *Let*

$$\kappa_n^\alpha \equiv cum(\tilde{\theta}_J^\alpha),$$
$$\kappa_n^{\alpha,\beta} \equiv cum(\tilde{\theta}_J^\alpha, \tilde{\theta}_J^\beta),$$
$$\kappa_n^{\alpha,\beta,\gamma} \equiv cum(\tilde{\theta}_J^\alpha, \tilde{\theta}_J^\beta, \tilde{\theta}_J^\gamma),$$
$$\kappa_n^{\alpha,\beta,\gamma,\delta} \equiv cum(\tilde{\theta}_J^\alpha, \tilde{\theta}_J^\beta, \tilde{\theta}_J^\gamma, \tilde{\theta}_J^\delta),$$

be the first four cumulants of $\tilde{\theta}_J$. *Then we have*

$$\kappa_n^\alpha = O(n^{-3/2}), \tag{3.9}$$

$$\kappa_n^{\alpha,\beta} = \kappa^{\alpha,\beta} + \frac{1}{2n} h_{ij}^\alpha h_{kl}^\beta \kappa^{i,k} \kappa^{j,l} + O(n^{-2}), \tag{3.10}$$

$$\kappa_n^{\alpha,\beta,\gamma} = \frac{1}{\sqrt{n}} \left(\kappa^{\alpha,\beta,\gamma} + h_i^\alpha h_j^\beta h_{kl}^\gamma \kappa^{i,k} \kappa^{j,l} [3]_{(\alpha\beta\gamma)} \right) + O(n^{-3/2}), \tag{3.11}$$

$$\begin{aligned} \kappa_n^{\alpha,\beta,\gamma,\delta} &= \frac{1}{n} \Big\{ \kappa^{\alpha,\beta,\gamma,\delta} + \frac{1}{2} h_i^\alpha h_j^\beta h_k^\gamma h_{lm}^\delta (6\kappa^{i,l}\kappa^{j,k,m} + \kappa^{l,m}\kappa^{i,j,k})[4]_{(\alpha\beta\gamma\delta)} \\ &\quad + h_i^\alpha h_j^\beta h_k^\gamma h_{lmn}^\delta \kappa^{i,l}\kappa^{j,m}\kappa^{k,n}[4]_{(\alpha,\beta,\gamma,\delta)} \Big\} + O(n^{-2}). \end{aligned} \tag{3.12}$$

Now we give the third order Edgeworth expansion for the density function of $\tilde{\theta}_J$. We introduce some notations first. Rewrite the r-th cumulant of $\tilde{\theta}_J$ as

$$\kappa_n^{\alpha_1\cdots\alpha_r} = n^{-\frac{r-2}{2}} (C_0^{\alpha_1\cdots\alpha_r} + \frac{1}{n} C_1^{\alpha_1\cdots\alpha_r} + \cdots) \quad (r \geq 1). \tag{3.13}$$

Define the covariant form $C_{i,\alpha_1\cdots\alpha_r}$ of $C_i^{\alpha_1\cdots\alpha_r}$ by

$$C_{i,\alpha_1\cdots\alpha_r} = C_i^{\beta_1\cdots\beta_r} \kappa_{\alpha_1,\beta_1} \cdots \kappa_{\alpha_r,\beta_r}, \tag{3.14}$$

where $\kappa_{\alpha,\beta}$ is the inverse of $\kappa^{\alpha,\beta} = h_i^\alpha h_j^\beta \kappa^{i,j}$.

Let $\phi(\boldsymbol{y}; \kappa^{\alpha,\beta})$ be the density function of the d-dimensional normal distribution with mean 0 and covariance matrix $(\kappa^{\alpha,\beta})$, i.e.

$$\phi(\boldsymbol{y}; \kappa^{\alpha,\beta}) = \| \kappa^{\alpha,\beta} \|^{-\frac{1}{2}} (2\pi)^{-\frac{k}{2}} \exp(-\frac{1}{2}\kappa_{\alpha,\beta} y^\alpha y^\beta)$$

where $\| A \|$ is the determinant of A and $(\kappa_{\alpha,\beta})$ denotes the inverse of $(\kappa^{\alpha,\beta})$. Let $D^\alpha = \kappa^{\alpha,\beta}(\partial/\partial y^\beta)$ and $D^{\alpha_1\cdots\alpha_r} = \mathcal{D}^{\alpha_1}\cdots\mathcal{D}^{\alpha_r}$ be the differential operators with respect to the covariance matrix $(\kappa^{\alpha,\beta})$. The Hermite polynomial $H^{\alpha_1\cdots\alpha_r}(\boldsymbol{y})$ of degree r with respect to $(\kappa^{\alpha,\beta})$ is defined by the following identity

$$\mathcal{D}^{\alpha_1\cdots\alpha_r}\phi(\boldsymbol{y}; \kappa^{\alpha,\beta}) = (-1)^r H^{\alpha_1\cdots\alpha_r}(\boldsymbol{y})\phi(\boldsymbol{y}; \kappa^{\alpha,\beta}).$$

THEOREM 3.6. *Under regularity conditions similar to those of [7], the density function of* $\tilde{\theta}_J$ *can be expanded as*

$$f(\boldsymbol{y}) = \phi(y; \kappa^{\alpha,\beta})\Big(1 + \frac{1}{\sqrt{n}} q_1(\boldsymbol{y}) + \frac{1}{n} q_2(\boldsymbol{y})\Big) + O(n^{-3/2}), \tag{3.15}$$

where

$$q_1(\boldsymbol{y}) = \frac{1}{3!} C_{0,\alpha\beta\gamma} H^{\alpha\beta\gamma}(\boldsymbol{y}),$$

$$q_2(\boldsymbol{y}) = \frac{1}{2!} C_{1,\alpha\beta} H^{\alpha\beta}(\boldsymbol{y}) + \frac{1}{4!} C_{0,\alpha\beta\gamma\delta} H^{\alpha\beta\gamma\delta}(\boldsymbol{y}) + \frac{1}{6!} C_{0,\alpha\beta\gamma} C_{0,\delta\epsilon\lambda} H^{\alpha\beta\gamma\delta\epsilon\lambda}(\boldsymbol{y})[10]_{(\alpha\beta\gamma\delta\epsilon\lambda)}.$$

and $C_{0,\alpha\beta\gamma}$, $C_{1,\alpha\beta}$, $C_{0,\alpha\beta\gamma\delta}$ *are defined by (3.14), which in turn are defined by (3.13).*

The Edgeworth expansion can be obtained from the corresponding Gram-Charlier expansion; see [1] for a detailed discussion of the relation between the Gram-Charlier expansion and the Edgeworth expansion.

4. The Jackknife-t. Now we turn to discuss the Jackknife-t method. The asymptotic theories become quite involved due to studentization.

4.1. Stochastic expansion. Similar to Lemma 3.1 we also have the following decompose concerning the third order sample cumulants. These results are refinements of the law of large numbers.

LEMMA 4.1. *Let* $X_p^{ijk} = X_p^i X_p^j X_p^k$, $\bar{X}^{ijk} = \sum_{p=1}^n X_p^{ijk}/n$, $\tilde{X}^{ijk} = \sqrt{n}(\bar{X}^{ijk} - \eta^{ijk})$ *and* $\hat{\kappa}^{i,j,k} = n^{-1}\sum_{p=1}^n (X_p^i - \bar{X}^i)(X_p^j - \bar{X}^j)(X_p^k - \bar{X}^k)$. *Then* $\tilde{\kappa}^{i,j,k} = \sqrt{n}(\hat{\kappa}^{i,j,k} - \kappa^{i,j,k})$ *can be decomposed as follows.*

$$\tilde{\kappa}^{i,j,k} = -(\eta^{ij} - 2\eta^i\eta^j)\tilde{X}^k[3]_{(ijk)} - \eta^i\tilde{X}^{jk}[3]_{(ijk)} + \tilde{X}^{ijk} + O_p(n^{-1/2}). \tag{4.1}$$

Using both Lemmas 3.1 and 4.1 we obtain the following expansion for the jackknife-t statistic to order $O_p(1/n)$. We shall omit the tedious derivation.

PROPOSITION 4.2. *Let* $g_i = h_i^\alpha/\sigma^\alpha$, $g_{ij} = h_{ij}^\alpha/\sigma^\alpha$, $g_{ijk} = h_{ijk}^\alpha/\sigma^\alpha$. *Under mild regularity conditions, the jackknife-t statistic can be expanded as follows.*

$$\begin{aligned}
T^\alpha = g_i^\alpha\tilde{X}^i &+ \frac{1}{\sqrt{n}}\Big\{\frac{1}{2}g_{ij}(\tilde{X}^i\tilde{X}^j - \kappa^{i,j}) - g_i g_{jk} g_l \kappa^{k,l}\tilde{X}^i\tilde{X}^j - \frac{1}{2}g_i g_j g_k(\tilde{X}^i\tilde{X}^{jk} - 2\eta^j\tilde{X}^i\tilde{X}^k)\Big\}\\
&+ \frac{1}{n}\Big\{-\frac{1}{2}g_{ij}g_{kl}h_m\kappa^{l,m}(\tilde{X}^i\tilde{X}^j\tilde{X}^k - \kappa^{i,j}\tilde{X}^k) - \frac{1}{4}h_{ij}h_k h_l(\tilde{X}^i\tilde{X}^j - \kappa^{i,j})(\tilde{X}^{kl} - 2\eta^k\tilde{X}^l)\\
&+ \frac{1}{6}g_{ijk}\tilde{X}^i\tilde{X}^j\tilde{X}^k + \frac{1}{2}g_{ij}(2\eta^i\tilde{X}^j - \tilde{X}^{ij}) - \frac{1}{2}g_{ijk}\kappa^{i,j}\tilde{X}^k\\
&+ \frac{3}{2}g_i g_{jl} g_{km} g_n g_n \kappa^{l,n}\kappa^{m,o}\tilde{X}^i\tilde{X}^j\tilde{X}^k + \frac{3}{2}g_i g_{jm} g_k g_l g_n \kappa^{m,n}(\tilde{X}^i\tilde{X}^j\tilde{X}^{kl} - 2\eta^k\tilde{X}^i\tilde{X}^j\tilde{X}^l)\\
&+ \frac{3}{8}g_i g_j g_k g_l g_m(\tilde{X}^i\tilde{X}^{jk}\tilde{X}^{lm} - 4\tilde{X}^i\tilde{X}^{jk}\tilde{X}^l\eta^m + 4\eta^i\eta^j\tilde{X}^k\tilde{X}^l\tilde{X}^m)\\
&- \frac{1}{2}g_i g_{jkl} g_m \kappa^{l,m}\tilde{X}^i\tilde{X}^j\tilde{X}^k - \frac{1}{2}g_i g_{jl} g_{km}\kappa^{l,m}\tilde{X}^i\tilde{X}^j\tilde{X}^k + \frac{1}{2}g_i g_j g_k(\tilde{X}^i\tilde{X}^j\tilde{X}^k - \kappa^{i,j}\tilde{X}^k)\\
&- g_i g_j g_{kl}(\tilde{X}^i\tilde{X}^{jk}\tilde{X}^l - \eta^j\tilde{X}^k\tilde{X}^i\tilde{X}^l[2]_{(jk)}) + \frac{1}{2}g_i g_j g_{kl}\kappa^{j,k,l}\tilde{X}^i\Big\} + O_p(n^{-3/2}).
\end{aligned}$$

4.2. Edgeworth expansions. In calculating the cumulants, we frequently encounter cumulants of the types $\kappa^{i,jk} = \text{cum}(X^i, X^{jk})$, $\kappa^{i,j,kl} = \text{cum}(X^i, X^j, X^{kl})$ and $\kappa^{ij,kl} = \text{cum}(X^{ij}, X^{kl}) = \text{cum}(X^iX^j, X^kX^l)$. The following lemmas can be obtained by using the relationships between moments and cumulants.

LEMMA 4.3. *Cumulants* $\kappa^{i,jk}$, $\kappa^{i,j,kl}$ *and* $\kappa^{kl,mn}$ *can be decomposed as*

$$\begin{aligned}
\kappa^{i,jk} &= \kappa^{i,j,k} + \kappa^j\kappa^{i,k}[2]_{(jk)},\\
\kappa^{i,j,kl} &= \kappa^{i,j,k,l} + \kappa^k\kappa^{l,i,j}[2]_{(kl)} + \kappa^{k,i}\kappa^{j,l}[2]_{(ij)},\\
\kappa^{ij,kl} &= \kappa^{i,j,k,l} + \kappa^i\kappa^{j,k,l}[4]_{(ijkl)} + \kappa^i\kappa^j\kappa^{k,l}[6]_{(ijkl)} + \kappa^{i,k}\kappa^{l,j}[2]_{(kl)} - \kappa^{i,j}\kappa^k\kappa^l - \kappa^i\kappa^j\kappa^{k,l}.
\end{aligned}$$

LEMMA 4.4. *Define the following generalized moments* $\eta^{i,j,k,lm} = E(\tilde{X}^i\tilde{X}^j\tilde{X}^k\tilde{X}^{lm})$, $\eta^{i,j,kl,mn} = E(\tilde{X}^i\tilde{X}^j\tilde{X}^{kl}\tilde{X}^{mn})$, $\eta^{i,j,k,l,mn} = E(\tilde{X}^i\tilde{X}^j\tilde{X}^k\tilde{X}^l\tilde{X}^{mn})$, $\eta^{i,j,k,l,m,no} =$

$E(\tilde{X}^i\tilde{X}^j\tilde{X}^k\tilde{X}^l\tilde{X}^m\tilde{X}^{no})$ and $\eta^{i,j,k,l,mn,op} = \mathcal{E}(\tilde{X}^i\tilde{X}^j\tilde{X}^k\tilde{X}^l\tilde{X}^{mn}\tilde{X}^{op})$. The following decompositions hold.

$$
\begin{aligned}
\eta^{i,j,k,lm} &= \kappa^{i,j}\kappa^{k,l,m}[3]_{(ijk)} + \kappa^{i,j}\kappa^{k,l}\kappa^{m}[3]_{(ijk)}[2]_{(lm)} + O(n^{-1}),\\
\eta^{i,j,kl,mn} &= \kappa^{i,j}\kappa^{k,l,m,n} + \kappa^{i,j}\kappa^{k}\kappa^{l,m,n}[4]_{(klmn)} + \kappa^{i,j}\kappa^{k}\kappa^{l}\kappa^{m,n}[6]_{(klmn)} + \kappa^{i,j}\kappa^{k,m}\kappa^{n,l}[2]_{(mn)}\\
&\quad -\kappa^{i,j}\kappa^{k,l}\kappa^{m}\kappa^{n} - \kappa^{i,j}\kappa^{k}\kappa^{l}\kappa^{m,n} + (\kappa^{i,k,l} + \kappa^{i,k}\kappa^{l}[2]_{(kl)})(\kappa^{j,m,n} + \kappa^{j,m}\kappa^{n}[2]_{(mn)})\\
&\quad +(\kappa^{i,m,n} + \kappa^{(i,m)}\kappa^{n}[2]_{(mn)})(\kappa^{j,k,l} + \kappa^{j,k}\kappa^{l}[2]_{(kl)}) + O(n^{-1}).\\
\eta^{i,j,k,l,mn} &= \frac{1}{\sqrt{n}}\Big[\kappa^{i,k}(\kappa^{k,l,m,n} + 2\kappa^{k,l,m}\kappa^{n} + [2]_{(mn)}\kappa^{m,k}\kappa^{l,n})[6]_{(ijkl)}\\
&\quad +\kappa^{i,j,k}(\kappa^{l,m,n} + 2\kappa^{l,m}\kappa^{n})[4]_{(ijkl)}\Big] + O(n^{-3/2}),\\
\eta^{i,j,k,l,m,no} &= \kappa^{i,j}\kappa^{k,l}(\kappa^{m,n,o} + 2\kappa^{m,n}\kappa^{o})[15]_{(ijklm)} + O(n^{-1}),\\
\eta^{i,j,k,l,mn,op} &= \kappa^{i,j}\kappa^{k,l}[3]_{(ijkl)}(\kappa^{m,n,o,p} + \kappa^{m}\kappa^{n,o,p}[4]_{(mnop)} + \kappa^{m}\kappa^{n}\kappa^{o,p}[6]_{(mnop)} + \kappa^{m,o}\kappa^{p,n}[2]_{(op)}\\
&\quad -\kappa^{m,n}\kappa^{o}\kappa^{p}\kappa^{m}\kappa^{n}\kappa^{o,p}) + (\kappa^{k,m,n} + 2\kappa^{k,m}\kappa^{n})(\kappa^{l,o,p}\kappa^{i,j} + 2\kappa^{l,o}\kappa^{p})[12]_{(ijkl)} + O(n^{-1}).
\end{aligned}
$$

To obtain the asymptotic formulae for the cumulants we first state the results for the first four moments up to order $O(n^{-1})$.

PROPOSITION 4.5. *The first moment of T is given by*

$$
E[T^\alpha] = -\frac{1}{\sqrt{n}}\frac{1}{(\sigma^\alpha)^3}(h_i^\alpha h_{jk}^\alpha h_l^\alpha \kappa^{k,l}\kappa^{i,j} + \frac{1}{2}\kappa_A^{\alpha,\alpha,\alpha}) + O(n^{-3/2}). \tag{4.2}
$$

PROPOSITION 4.6. *The second moment of T, $E[T^\alpha T^\beta]$ is given by the following formula.*

$$
\begin{aligned}
&\frac{1}{\sigma^\alpha\sigma^\beta}\kappa_A^{\alpha,\beta} + \frac{1}{n}\overset{[2]}{\underset{(\alpha,\beta)}{}}\Big\{\frac{1}{2\sigma^\alpha(\sigma^\beta)^2}h_i^\alpha h_{jk}^\beta\kappa^{i,j,k} - \frac{1}{2\sigma^\alpha(\sigma^\beta)^3}\kappa_A^{\alpha,\beta,\beta,\beta}\\
&-\frac{1}{\sigma^\alpha(\sigma^\beta)^3}h_i^\alpha h_j^\beta h_k^\beta h_{lm}^\beta(2\kappa^{k,m}\kappa^{i,j,l} + \kappa^{i,m}\kappa^{j,k,l} + \frac{1}{2}\kappa^{i,j}\kappa^{k,l,m})\\
&-\frac{1}{2\sigma^\alpha(\sigma^\beta)^3}h_i^\alpha h_{jk}^\beta h_{lm}^\beta h_n^\beta(3\kappa^{i,j}\kappa^{k,l}\kappa^{m,n} + \kappa^{k,m}\kappa^{i,n}\kappa^{j,l}) - \frac{1}{2\sigma^\alpha(\sigma^\beta)^3}h_i^\alpha h_{jk}^\beta h_l^\beta h_m^\beta\kappa^{i,j}\kappa^{k,l,m}\\
&-\frac{1}{2\sigma^\alpha\sigma^\beta}h_i^\alpha h_{jk}^\beta\kappa^{i,j,k} + \frac{3}{2\sigma^\alpha(\sigma^\beta)^5}h_i^\alpha h_j^\beta h_{km}^\beta h_{ln}^\beta h_o^\beta h_p^\beta\kappa^{m,o}\kappa^{n,p}[3]\kappa^{(i,j}\kappa^{k,l)}\\
&+\frac{3}{2\sigma^\alpha(\sigma^\beta)^5}h_i^\alpha h_j^\beta h_{kn}^\beta h_l^\beta h_m^\beta h_o^\beta\kappa^{n,o}[3]\kappa^{(i,j}\kappa^{k),l,m} + \frac{3}{8\sigma^\alpha(\sigma^\beta)^5}\kappa_A^{\alpha,\beta}\kappa_A^{\beta,\beta,\beta,\beta}\\
&+\frac{3}{4\sigma^\alpha\sigma^\beta}\kappa_A^{\alpha,\beta} + \frac{3}{4\sigma^\alpha(\sigma^\beta)^5}\kappa_A^{\alpha,\beta,\beta}\kappa_A^{\beta,\beta,\beta} - \frac{1}{2\sigma^\alpha(\sigma^\beta)^3}h_i^\alpha h_j^\beta h_{k,l,m}^\beta h_n^\beta\kappa^{m,n}[3]\kappa^{(i,j}\kappa^{k,l)}\Big\}\\
&+\frac{1}{n}\Big\{\frac{1}{2(\sigma^\alpha\sigma^\beta)^2}h_{ij}^\alpha h_{i'j'}^\beta\kappa^{i,i'}\kappa^{j,j'} - \frac{\overset{[2]}{\underset{(\alpha\beta)}{}}}{(\sigma^\alpha)^2(\sigma^\beta)^3}h_{ij}^\alpha h_{i'}^\beta h_{j'k'}^\beta h_{l'}^\beta\kappa^{i,i'}\kappa^{j,j'}\kappa^{k',l'}\\
&-\frac{\overset{[2]}{\underset{(\alpha\beta)}{}}}{2(\sigma^\alpha)^2(\sigma^\beta)^3}h_{ij}^\alpha h_{i'}^\beta h_{j'}^\beta h_{k'}^\beta\kappa^{i,i'}\kappa^{j,j',k'} + \frac{1}{(\sigma^\alpha\sigma^\beta)^3}h_i^\alpha h_{jk}^\alpha h_l^\alpha h_{i'}^\beta h_{j'k'}^\beta h_{l'}^\beta\kappa^{k,l}\kappa^{k',l'}[3]\kappa^{(i,j}\kappa^{i',j')}\\
&+\frac{\overset{[2]}{\underset{(\alpha\beta)}{}}}{2(\sigma^\alpha\sigma^\beta)^3}h_i^\alpha h_{jk}^\alpha h_l^\alpha h_{i'}^\beta h_{j'}^\beta h_{k'}^\beta\kappa^{k,l}[3]\kappa^{(i,j}\kappa^{i'),j',k'}\\
&+\frac{1}{4(\sigma^\alpha\sigma^\beta)^3}(\kappa_A^{\alpha,\beta}\kappa_A^{\alpha,\alpha,\beta,\beta} + 2(\kappa_A^{\alpha,\beta})^3 + 2\kappa_A^{\alpha,\alpha,\alpha}\kappa_A^{\beta,\beta,\beta})\Big\} + O(n^{-2}).
\end{aligned}
$$

PROPOSITION 4.7. *Up to order $O(1/n)$ the third moment of T is given by*

$$E[T^\alpha T^\beta T^\gamma] = \frac{1}{\sqrt{n}}\Big\{\frac{1}{\sigma^\alpha\sigma^\beta\sigma^\gamma}\kappa_A^{\alpha,\beta,\gamma} + \frac{1}{\sigma^\alpha\sigma^\beta}[3]h_i^\alpha h_j^\beta\Big[\frac{1}{(\sigma^\gamma)^2}h_{kl}^\gamma\kappa^{i,k}\kappa^{j,l}$$
$$-\frac{1}{(\sigma^\gamma)^3}h_k^\gamma h_{lm}^\gamma h_n^\gamma\kappa^{m,n}[3]\kappa^{(i,j}\kappa^{k,l)} - \frac{1}{2(\sigma^\gamma)^3}h_k^\gamma h_l^\gamma h_m^\gamma[3]\kappa^{(i,j}\kappa^{k),l,m}\Big]\Big\} + O(n^{-3/2}).$$

PROPOSITION 4.8. *To order $O(1/n)$, the fourth moment of T, $E[T^\alpha T^\beta T^\gamma T^\delta]$, can be written as follows. by the*

$$\frac{[3]}{\sigma^\alpha\sigma^\beta\sigma^\gamma\sigma^\delta}\kappa_A^{(\alpha,\beta}\kappa_A^{\gamma,\delta)} + \frac{1}{n}\Big\{\frac{1}{\sigma^\alpha\sigma^\beta\sigma^\gamma\sigma^\delta}\kappa_A^{\alpha,\beta,\gamma,\delta} + \frac{1}{\sigma^\alpha\sigma^\beta\sigma^\gamma}\underset{(\alpha,\beta,\gamma,\delta)}{[4]}\; h_i^\alpha h_j^\beta h_k^\gamma\Big[$$
$$\frac{1}{2(\sigma^\delta)^2}h_{lm}^\delta([10]\kappa^{(i,j}\kappa^{k,l,m)} - \kappa^{l,m}\kappa^{i,j,k}) - \frac{1}{(\sigma^\delta)^3}h_l^\delta h_{mn}^\delta h_o^\delta\kappa^{n,o}([10]\kappa^{(i,j}\kappa^{k,l,m)} - \frac{[3]}{4}\kappa^{(i,j}\kappa^{k),l,o}\kappa^{m,n})$$
$$-\frac{1}{2(\sigma^\delta)^3}h_l^\delta h_m^\delta h_n^\delta([6]\kappa^{(i,j}(\kappa^{\dot{k},l,m,n} + 2\kappa^{m,(\dot{k}}\kappa^{\dot{l})),n}) + [4]\kappa^{(i,j,k}\kappa^{l),m,n})$$
$$-\frac{1}{2(\sigma^\delta)^3}h_{lm}^\delta h_{no}^\delta h_p^\delta\kappa^{o,p}([15]\kappa^{(i,j}\kappa^{k,l}\kappa^{m,n)} - [3]\kappa^{l,m}\kappa^{(i,j}\kappa^{k,n)}) - \frac{[15]}{4(\sigma^\delta)^3}h_{lm}^\delta h_n^\delta h_o^\delta\kappa^{(i,j}\kappa^{k,l}\kappa^{m),n,o}$$
$$+\frac{1}{\sigma^\delta}h_{lmn}^\delta\kappa^{i,l}\kappa^{j,m}\kappa^{k,n} - \frac{[3]}{2\sigma^\delta}h_{lm}^\delta\kappa^{(i,j}\kappa^{k),l,m} + \frac{3}{2(\sigma^\delta)^5}h_l^\delta h_{mp}^\delta h_n^\delta h_o^\delta h_q^\delta\kappa^{p,q}[15]\kappa^{(i,j}\kappa^{k,l}\kappa^{m,)n,o}$$
$$+\frac{3}{2(\sigma^\delta)^5}h_{i'}^\delta h_{j'l'}^\delta h_{k'm'}^\delta h_{n'}^\delta h_{o'}^\delta\kappa^{l',n'}\kappa^{m',o'}[15]\kappa^{(i,j}\kappa^{k,i'}\kappa^{j',k')}$$
$$+\frac{3}{8(\sigma^\delta)^5}h_l^\delta h_m^\delta h_n^\delta h_o^\delta h_p^\delta(3\kappa^{i,j}\kappa^{k,l}\kappa^{m,n,o,p} + 2[3]\kappa^{(i,j}\kappa^{k,l)}\kappa^{m,o}\kappa^{p,n} + [12]\kappa^{(i,j}\kappa^{\dot{k},m,n}\kappa^{\dot{l},o,p)})$$
$$-\frac{1}{2(\sigma^\delta)^3}h_{i'}^\delta h_{j'k'l'}^\delta h_{m'}^\delta\kappa^{l',m'}[15]\kappa^{(i,j}\kappa^{k,i'}\kappa^{j',k')} - \frac{1}{2(\sigma^\delta)^3}h_{i'}^\delta h_{j'l'}^\delta h_{k'm'}^\delta\kappa^{l',m'}[15]\kappa^{(i,j}\kappa^{k,i'}\kappa^{j',k')}$$
$$+\frac{1}{2(\sigma^\delta)^3}h_{i'}^\delta h_{j'}^\delta h_{k'}^\delta([15]\kappa^{(i,j}\kappa^{k,i'}\kappa^{j',k')} - \kappa^{i',j'}[3]\kappa^{(i,j}\kappa^{k,k')})$$
$$-\frac{1}{(\sigma^\delta)^3}h_l^\delta h_m^\delta h_{no}^\delta([15]\kappa^{(i,j}\kappa^{k,l}\kappa^{o),m,n} - \frac{[3]}{2}\kappa^{(i,j}\kappa^{k,l)}\kappa^{m,n,o})\Big]$$
$$+\frac{\underset{(\alpha,\beta,\gamma,\delta)}{[6]}}{\sigma^\alpha\sigma^\beta}h_i^\alpha h_j^\beta\Big[\frac{1}{2(\sigma^\gamma\sigma^\delta)^2}h_{kl}^\gamma h_{mn}^\gamma(\kappa^{i,j}\kappa^{k,m}\kappa^{l,n} + 2\kappa^{i,k}\kappa^{j,m}\kappa^{l,n} + 2\kappa^{i,m}\kappa^{j,k}\kappa^{l,n})$$
$$-\frac{\underset{(\gamma,\delta)}{[2]}}{2(\sigma^\gamma)^2(\sigma^\delta)^3}h_{kl}^\gamma h_m^\delta h_{no}^\delta h_p^\delta\kappa^{o,p}([15]\kappa^{(i,j}\kappa^{k,l}\kappa^{m,n)} - [3]\kappa^{(i,j}\kappa^{m,n)}\kappa^{k,l})$$
$$-\frac{\underset{(\gamma,\delta)}{[2]}}{4(\sigma^\gamma)^2(\sigma^\delta)^3}h_{kl}^\gamma h_m^\delta h_n^\delta h_o^\delta([15]\kappa^{(i,j}\kappa^{k,l}\kappa^{m),n,o} - [3]\kappa^{k,l}\kappa^{(i,j}\kappa^{m),n,o})$$
$$+\frac{1}{(\sigma^\delta\sigma^\delta)^3}h_k^\gamma h_{lm}^\gamma h_n^\gamma h_{k'}^\delta h_{l'm'}^\delta h_{n'}^\delta\kappa^{m,n}\kappa^{m',n'}[15]\kappa^{(i,j}\kappa^{k,l}\kappa^{k',l')}$$
$$+\frac{\underset{(\gamma,\delta)}{[2]}}{2(\sigma^\delta\sigma^\delta)^3}h_k^\gamma h_{lm}^\gamma h_n^\gamma h_o^\delta h_p^\delta h_q^\delta\kappa^{m,n}[15]\kappa^{(i,j}\kappa^{k,l}\kappa^{o),p,q}$$
$$+\frac{1}{4(\sigma^\delta\sigma^\delta)^3}h_k^\gamma h_l^\gamma h_m^\gamma h_{k'}^\delta h_{l'}^\delta h_{m'}^\delta([3]\kappa^{(i,j}\kappa^{k,n)}\kappa^{l,m,o,p}$$
$$+2[3]\kappa^{(i,j}\kappa^{k,n)}\kappa^{l,o}\kappa^{p,m} + [12]\kappa^{(i,j}\kappa^{\dot{k},l,m}\kappa^{\dot{n},o,p)})\Big]\Big\} + O(n^{-2}).$$

Since cumulants of odd order can be expressed as asymptotic series in power of $n^{-(2j-1)/2}$ for $j = 1, 2, \cdots$. Third order asymptotic theories therefore only require us to evaluate the first and the third cumulants to order $O(n^{-1/2})$. In contrast evaluations of the even cumulants require more algebraic manipulations.

THEOREM 4.9. *With remainder term of order $n^{-3/2}$, the first and the third cumulants can be expressed in asymptotic series as follows.*

$$\kappa_T^{\alpha} = -\frac{1}{\sqrt{n}}\frac{1}{(\sigma^\alpha)^3}(h_i^\alpha h_{jk}^\alpha h_l^\alpha \kappa^{k,l}\kappa^{i,j} + \frac{1}{2}\kappa^{\alpha,\alpha,\alpha}) + O(n^{-3/2}),$$

$$\begin{aligned}\kappa_T^{\alpha,\beta,\gamma} = \frac{1}{\sqrt{n}}\Big[&\frac{1}{\sigma^\alpha\sigma^\beta\sigma^\gamma}\kappa^{\alpha,\beta,\gamma} + \frac{1}{\sigma^\alpha\sigma^\beta}h_i^\alpha h_j^\beta\big(\frac{1}{(\sigma^\gamma)^2}h_{kl}^\gamma\kappa^{i,k}\kappa^{j,l}\\ &-\frac{1}{(\sigma^\gamma)^3}h_k^\gamma h_{lm}^\gamma h_n^\gamma\kappa^{m,n}(\kappa^{i,k}\kappa^{j,l}+\kappa^{i,l}\kappa^{j,k})\\ &-\frac{1}{2(\sigma^\gamma)^3}h_k^\gamma h_l^\gamma h_m^\gamma(\kappa^{i,k}\kappa^{j,l,m}+\kappa^{j,k}\kappa^{i,l,m})\big)\Big][3]_{(\alpha\beta\gamma)} + O(n^{-3/2}).\end{aligned}$$

THEOREM 4.10. *The second cumulant of T, $\kappa_T^{\alpha,\beta}$ can be expressed in asymptotic series to order $O(n^{-1/n})$ as follows.*

$$\begin{aligned}&\frac{1}{\sigma^\alpha\sigma^\beta}\kappa^{\alpha,\beta} + \frac{1}{n}\Big\{\frac{1}{2\sigma^\alpha\sigma^\beta}h_i^\alpha h_{jk}^\beta\kappa^{i,j,k} - \frac{1}{2\sigma^\alpha(\sigma^\beta)^3}\kappa^{\alpha,\beta,\beta,\beta}\\ &-\frac{1}{\sigma^\alpha(\sigma^\beta)^3}h_i^\alpha h_j^\beta h_k^\beta h_{lm}^\beta(2\kappa^{k,m}\kappa^{i,j,l}+\kappa^{i,m}\kappa^{j,k,l}+\frac{1}{2}\kappa^{i,j}\kappa^{k,l,m})\\ &-\frac{1}{2\sigma^\alpha(\sigma^\beta)^3}h_i^\alpha h_{jk}^\beta h_{lm}^\beta h_n^\beta(3\kappa^{i,j}\kappa^{k,l}\kappa^{m,n}+\kappa^{k,m}\kappa^{i,n}\kappa^{j,l})\\ &-\frac{1}{2\sigma^\alpha(\sigma^\beta)^3}h_i^\alpha h_{jk}^\beta h_l^\beta h_m^\beta\kappa^{i,j}\kappa^{k,l,m} - \frac{1}{2\sigma^\alpha\sigma^\beta}h_i^\alpha h_{jk}^\beta\kappa^{i,j,k}\\ &+\frac{3}{2\sigma^\alpha(\sigma^\beta)^5}h_i^\alpha h_j^\beta h_{km}^\beta h_{ln}^\beta h_o^\beta h_p^\beta\kappa^{m,o}\kappa^{n,p}\kappa^{i,j}\kappa^{k,l}[3]_{(ijkl)}\\ &+\frac{3}{2\sigma^\alpha(\sigma^\beta)^5}h_i^\alpha h_j^\beta h_{kn}^\beta h_l^\beta h_m^\beta h_o^\beta\kappa^{n,o}\kappa^{i,j}\kappa^{k,l,m}[3]_{(ijk)}\\ &+\frac{3}{8\sigma^\alpha(\sigma^\beta)^5}\kappa^{\alpha,\beta}\kappa^{\beta,\beta,\beta,\beta} + \frac{3}{4\sigma^\alpha\sigma^\beta}\kappa^{\alpha,\beta} + \frac{3}{4\sigma^\alpha(\sigma^\beta)^5}\kappa^{\alpha,\beta,\beta}\kappa^{\beta,\beta,\beta}\\ &-\frac{1}{2\sigma^\alpha(\sigma^\beta)^3}h_i^\alpha h_j^\beta h_{k,l,m}^\beta h_n^\beta\kappa^{m,n}\kappa^{i,j}\kappa^{k,l}[3]_{(ijkl)}\Big\}[2]_{(\alpha\beta)}\\ &+\frac{1}{n}\Big\{\frac{1}{2\sigma^\alpha\sigma^\beta}h_{ij}^\alpha h_{i'j'}^\beta\kappa^{i,i'}\kappa^{j,j'} - \frac{1}{2\sigma^\alpha(\sigma^\beta)^3}h_{ij}^\alpha h_{i'}^\beta h_{j'}^\beta h_{k'}^\beta\kappa^{i,i'}\kappa^{j,j',k'}[2]_{(\alpha\beta)}\\ &-\frac{1}{\sigma^\alpha(\sigma^\beta)^3}h_{ij}^\alpha h_k^\beta h_{lm}^\beta h_n^\beta\kappa^{i,k}\kappa^{j,l}\kappa^{m,n}[2]_{(\alpha\beta)}\\ &+\frac{1}{(\sigma^\alpha\sigma^\beta)^3}h_i^\alpha h_{jk}^\alpha h_l^\alpha h_{i'}^\beta h_{j'k'}^\beta h_{l'}^\beta\kappa^{k,l}\kappa^{k',l'}(\kappa^{i,i'}\kappa^{j,j'}[2]_{(ij)})\\ &+\frac{1}{2(\sigma^\alpha\sigma^\beta)^3}h_i^\alpha h_{jk}^\alpha h_l^\alpha h_{i'}^\beta h_{j'}^\beta h_{k'}^\beta\kappa^{k,l}[2]_{(\alpha\beta)}(\kappa^{i,i'}\kappa^{j,j',k'}[2]_{(ij)})\\ &+\frac{1}{4(\sigma^\alpha\sigma^\beta)^3}(\kappa^{\alpha,\beta}\kappa^{\alpha,\alpha,\beta,\beta}+2(\kappa^{\alpha,\beta})^3+\kappa^{\alpha,\alpha,\alpha}\kappa_A^{\beta,\beta,\beta})\Big\} + O(n^{-2}).\end{aligned}$$

Finally we compute the fourth cumulant, $\kappa_T^{\alpha,\beta,\gamma,\delta}$. Note that the fourth cumulant can be expressed in terms of moments as follows.

$$\begin{aligned}\kappa_T^{\alpha,\beta,\gamma,\delta} &= \mu_T^{\alpha,\beta,\gamma,\delta} - [4]\mu_T^{(\alpha}\mu_T^{\beta,\gamma,\delta)} - [3]\mu_T^{(\alpha,\beta}\mu_T^{\gamma,\delta)} + 2[6]\mu_T^{(\alpha}\mu_T^{\beta}\mu_T^{\gamma,\delta)} - 6\mu_T^{\alpha}\mu_T^{\beta}\mu_T^{\gamma}\mu_T^{\delta} \\ &= \mu_T^{\alpha,\beta,\gamma,\delta} - [4]\mu_T^{(\alpha}\mu_T^{\beta,\gamma,\delta)} - [3]\mu_T^{(\alpha,\beta}\mu_T^{\gamma,\delta)} + 2[6]\mu_T^{(\alpha}\mu_T^{\beta}\mu_T^{\gamma,\delta)} + O(n^{-2})\end{aligned} \tag{4.3}$$

where $\mu_T^\alpha = E[T^\alpha]$, $\mu_T^{\alpha,\beta} = E[T^\alpha T^\beta]$, $\mu_T^{\alpha,\beta,\gamma} = E[T^\alpha T^\beta T^\gamma]$ and $\mu_T^{\alpha,\beta,\gamma,\delta} = E[T^\alpha T^\beta T^\gamma T^\delta]$. To compute $\kappa_T^{\alpha,\beta,\gamma,\delta}$ it suffices therefore to evaluate the appropriate moments appearing at the right hand side of (4.3). Combining all the results we have the following expansion for $\kappa_T^{\alpha,\beta,\gamma,\delta}$. Since the derivation is tedious we shall omit the proof.

THEOREM 4.11. *The fourth cumulant of jackknife T can be expressed as asymptotic series to order $O(n^{-1/n})$ as follows.*

$$\begin{aligned}
n\kappa_T^{\alpha,\beta,\gamma,\delta} = \Big\{&(\sigma^\alpha\sigma^\beta\sigma^\gamma\sigma^\delta)^{-1} + \sum_{\alpha,\beta,\gamma,\delta}^{[4]} (\sigma^\alpha\sigma^\beta\sigma^\gamma)^{-1} h_i^\alpha h_j^\beta h_k^\gamma \Big[\\
&\frac{1}{2}(\sigma^\delta)^{-1} h_{lm}^\delta ([10]\kappa^{(i,j}\kappa^{k,l,m)} - \kappa^{i,j,k}\kappa^{l,m}) \\
&- (\sigma^\delta)^{-3} h_l^\delta h_{mn}^\delta h_o^\delta (\kappa^{no}[10]\kappa^{(i,j}\kappa^{k,l,m)} - \frac{1}{4}[3]\kappa^{(i,j}\kappa^{k),l,o}\kappa^{mn}) \\
&- \frac{1}{2}(\sigma^\delta)^{-3} h_l^\delta h_m^\delta h_n^\delta ([6]\kappa^{(i,j}\kappa^{k,l),m,n} + 2[6]\kappa^{i,j}\kappa^{m,k}\kappa^{n,l} + [4]\kappa^{i,j,k}\kappa^{l,m,n}) \\
&- \frac{1}{2}(\sigma^\delta)^{-3} h_{lm}^\delta h_{no}^\delta h_p^\delta \kappa^{o,p} ([15]\kappa^{(i,j}\kappa^{k,l}\kappa^{m,n)} - [3]\kappa^{(i,j,k}\kappa^{l),m,n}) \\
&- \frac{1}{4}(\sigma^\delta)^{-3} h_{lm}^\delta h_n^\delta h_o^\delta [15]\kappa^{(i,j}\kappa^{k,l}\kappa^{m),n,o} \\
&+ (\sigma^\delta)^{-1} h_{lmn}^\delta \kappa^{i,l}\kappa^{j,m}\kappa^{k,n} - \frac{1}{2}(\sigma^\delta)^{-1} h_{lm}^\delta [3]\kappa^{(i,j}\kappa^{k),l,m} \\
&+ \frac{3}{2}(\sigma^\delta)^{-5} h_l^\delta h_{mn}^\delta h_{op}^\delta h_q^\delta h_r^\delta \kappa^{n,q}\kappa^{p,r}[15]\kappa^{(i,j}\kappa^{k,l}\kappa^{m,o)} \\
&+ \frac{3}{2}(\sigma^\delta)^{-5} h_l^\delta h_{mp}^\delta h_n^\delta h_o^\delta h_q^\delta \kappa^{p,q}[15]\kappa^{(i,j}\kappa^{k,l}\kappa^{m),n,o)} \\
&+ \frac{9}{8}(\sigma^\delta)^{-5} h_l^\delta \kappa^{i,j}\kappa^{k,l}\kappa^{\delta,\delta,\delta,\delta} + \frac{3}{4}(\sigma^\delta)^{-1} h_l^\delta [3]\kappa^{(i,j}\kappa^{k,l)} \\
&+ \frac{3}{4}(\sigma^\delta)^{-5} h_l^\delta h_m^\delta h_n^\delta h_o^\delta h_p^\delta [6]\kappa^{i,j}\kappa^{k,m,n}\kappa^{l,o,p)} \\
&- \frac{1}{2}(\sigma^\delta)^{-3} h_l^\delta h_{mno}^\delta h_p^\delta \kappa^{o,p}[15]\kappa^{(i,j}\kappa^{k,l}\kappa^{m,n)} \\
&- \frac{1}{2}(\sigma^\delta)^{-3} h_l^\delta h_{mn}^\delta h_{op}^\delta \kappa^{n,p}[15]\kappa^{(i,j}\kappa^{k,l}\kappa^{m,o)} \\
&+ \frac{1}{2}(\sigma^\delta)^{-3} h_l^\delta h_m^\delta h_n^\delta ([15]\kappa^{(i,j}\kappa^{k,l}\kappa^{m,o)} - \kappa^{l,m}[3]\kappa^{(i,j}\kappa^{k,n)}) \\
&- \frac{1}{2}(\sigma^\delta)^{-3} h_l^\delta h_m^\delta h_{no}^\delta ([15]\kappa^{(i,j}\kappa^{k,l}\kappa^{o),m,n} - \frac{1}{2}[3]\kappa^{(i,j}[3]\kappa^{k,l)}\kappa^{m,n,o)})\Big] \\
&+ \sum_{\alpha,\beta,\gamma,\delta}^{[6]} (\sigma^\alpha\sigma^\beta)^{-1} h_i^\alpha h_j^\beta \Big[\\
&+ \frac{1}{2}(\sigma^\gamma\sigma^delta)^{-1} h_{kl}^\gamma h_{mn}^\gamma (\kappa^{i,j}\kappa^{k,m}\kappa^{l,n} + 2\kappa^{i,k}\kappa^{j,m}\kappa^{l,n} + 2\kappa^{i,m}\kappa^{j,k}\kappa^{l,n}) \\
&- \frac{1}{2}\sum_{(\gamma,\delta)}^{[2]} (\sigma^\gamma)^{-1}(\sigma^\delta)^{-3} h_{kl}^\gamma h_m^\delta h_{no}^\delta h_p^\delta \kappa^{o,p}([15]\kappa^{(i,j}\kappa^{k,l}\kappa^{m,n)} - [3]\kappa^{(i,j}\kappa^{m,n)}\kappa^{k,l}) \\
&- \frac{1}{4}\sum_{(\gamma,\delta)}^{[2]} (\sigma^\gamma)^{-1}(\sigma^\delta)^{-3} h_{kl}^\gamma h_m^\delta h_n^\delta h_o^\delta ([15]\kappa^{(i,j}\kappa^{k,l}\kappa^{m),n,o)} - [3]\kappa^{k,l}\kappa^{(i,j}\kappa^{m),n,o}) \\
&+ (\sigma^\gamma\sigma^\delta)^{-3} h_k^\gamma h_{lm}^\gamma h_n^\gamma h_o^\delta h_{pq}^\delta h_r^\delta \kappa^{m,n}\kappa^{q,r}[15]\kappa^{(i,j}\kappa^{k,l}\kappa^{o,p)} \\
&+ \frac{1}{2}\sum_{(\gamma,\delta)}^{[2]} (\sigma^\gamma\sigma^\delta)^{-3} h_k^\gamma h_{lm}^\gamma h_n^\gamma h_o^\delta h_p^\delta h_q^\delta \kappa^{m,n}[15]\kappa^{(i,j}\kappa^{k,l}\kappa^{o),p,q}
\end{aligned}$$

$$
\begin{aligned}
&+ \frac{1}{4}(\sigma^\gamma\sigma^\delta)^{-3} h_k^\gamma h_l^\gamma h_m^\gamma h_n^\delta h_o^\delta h_p^\delta ([3]\kappa^{(i,j}\kappa^{k,n)}\kappa^{l,m,o,p} \\
&+ 2[3]\kappa^{(i,j}\kappa^{k,n)}\kappa^{l,o}\kappa^{p,m} + [12]\kappa^{i,j}\kappa^{k,l,m}\kappa^{n,o,p})]\Big\} \\
&+ \frac{1}{n} \sum^{[4]}_{(\alpha,\beta,\gamma,\delta)} (\sigma^\alpha)^{-3}\Big\{(\sigma^\beta\sigma^\gamma\sigma^\delta)^{-1} h_i^\alpha h_{jk}^\alpha h_l^\alpha \kappa^{i,j}\kappa^{k,l}\kappa^{\beta,\gamma\delta} \\
&+ h_i^\alpha h_{jk}^\alpha h_l^\alpha \kappa^{i,j}\kappa^{k,l} \sum^{[3]}_{(\beta,\gamma,\delta)} (\sigma^\beta\sigma^\gamma\sigma^\delta)^{-1} h_m^\beta h_n^\gamma h_{op}^\delta \kappa^{m,o}\kappa^{n,p} \\
&- h_i^\alpha h_{jk}^\alpha h_l^\alpha \kappa^{i,j}\kappa^{k,l} \sum^{[3]}_{(\beta,\gamma,\delta)} (\sigma^\beta\sigma^\gamma)^{-1}(\sigma^\delta)^{-3} h_m^\beta h_n^\gamma h_o^\delta h_o^\delta h_{pq}^\delta \kappa^{q,r}[3]\kappa^{(m,n}\kappa^{o,p)} \\
&- \frac{1}{2} h_i^\alpha h_{jk}^\alpha h_l^\alpha h_m^\beta h_n^\gamma h_o^\delta h_p^\delta h_q^\delta \kappa^{i,j}\kappa^{k,l} \sum^{[3]}_{(\beta,\gamma,\delta)} (\sigma^\beta\sigma^\gamma)^{-1}(\sigma^\delta)^{-3}[3]\kappa^{(m,n}\kappa^{o),p,q} \\
&+ \frac{1}{2}(\sigma^\alpha)^{-3}(\sigma^\beta\sigma^\gamma\sigma^\delta)^{-1}\kappa^{\alpha,\alpha,\alpha}\kappa^{\beta,\gamma,\delta} \\
&+ \frac{1}{2}\kappa^{\alpha,\alpha,\alpha} \sum^{[3]}_{(\beta,\gamma,\delta)} (\sigma^\beta\sigma^\gamma\sigma^\delta)^{-1} h_m^\beta h_n^\gamma h_{op}^\delta \kappa^{m,o}\kappa^{n,p} \\
&- \frac{1}{2}\kappa^{\alpha,\alpha,\alpha} \sum^{[3]}_{(\beta,\gamma,\delta)} (\sigma^\beta\sigma^\gamma)^{-1}(\sigma^\delta)^{-3} h_m^\beta h_n^\gamma h_o^\delta h_{pq}^\delta h_r^\delta [3]\kappa^{(m,n}\kappa^{o,p)} \\
&- \frac{1}{4}\kappa^{\alpha,\alpha,\alpha} \sum^{[3]}_{(\beta,\gamma,\delta)} (\sigma^\beta\sigma^\gamma)^{-1}(\sigma^\delta)^{-3} h_m^\beta h_n^\gamma h_o^\delta h_p^\delta h_q^\delta [3]\kappa^{(m,n}\kappa^{o),p,q} \\
&- \frac{1}{n} \sum^{[6]}_{(\alpha,\beta,\gamma,\delta)} (\sigma^\alpha\sigma^\beta)^{-1}\kappa^{\alpha,\beta}\Big\{ \sum^{[2]}_{(\gamma,\delta)} \Big[\\
&- (\sigma^\gamma)^{-1}(\sigma^\delta)^{-3} h_i^\gamma h_j^\delta h_k^\delta h_{lm}^\delta (2\kappa^{i,j,l}\kappa^{k,m} + \frac{3}{2}\kappa^{i,m}\kappa^{j,k,l} + \frac{1}{2}\kappa^{i,j}\kappa^{k,l,m} \\
&- \frac{1}{2}(\sigma^\gamma)^{-1}(\sigma^\delta)^{-3}\kappa^{\gamma,\delta,\delta,\delta} \\
&- \frac{1}{2}(\sigma^\gamma)^{-1}(\sigma^\delta)^{-3} h_i^\gamma h_{jk}^\delta h_{lm}^\delta h_n^\delta (3\kappa^{i,j}\kappa^{k,l}\kappa^{m,n} + \kappa^{i,l}\kappa^{j,n}\kappa^{k,m} + \kappa^{k,m}\kappa^{i,n}\kappa^{j,l} \\
&- \frac{3}{2}(\sigma^\gamma)^{-1}(\sigma^\delta)^{-5} h_i^\gamma h_j^\delta h_{km}^\delta h_{ln}^\delta h_o^\delta h_p^\delta \kappa^{m,o}\kappa^{n,p}[3]\kappa^{(i,j}\kappa^{k,l)} \\
&- \frac{3}{2}(\sigma^\gamma)^{-1}(\sigma^\delta)^{-5} h_i^\gamma h_j^\delta h_{kn}^\delta h_l^\delta h_m^\delta h_o^\delta \kappa^{n,o}[3]\kappa^{(i,j}\kappa^{k),l,m} \\
&- \frac{3}{8}(\sigma^\gamma)^{-1}(\sigma^\delta)^{-5}\kappa^{\gamma,\delta}\kappa^{\delta,\delta,\delta,\delta} + \frac{3}{4}(\sigma^\gamma\sigma^\delta)^{-1}\kappa^{\gamma,\delta} + \frac{3}{4}(\sigma^\gamma)^{-1}(\sigma^\delta)^{-5}\kappa^{\gamma,\delta,\delta}\kappa^{\delta,\delta,\delta} \\
&- \frac{1}{2}(\sigma^\gamma)^{-1}(\sigma^\delta)^{-3} h_i^\gamma h_j^\delta h_{klm}^\delta h_n^\delta \kappa^{m,n}[3]\kappa^{(i,j}\kappa^{k,l)}\Big] \\
&+ \frac{1}{2}(\sigma^\gamma\sigma^\delta)^{-1} h_{ij}^\gamma h_{kl}^\delta \kappa^{i,k}\kappa^{j,l} \\
&- \sum^{[2]}_{(\gamma,\delta)} (\sigma^\gamma)^{-1}(\sigma^\delta)^{-3} h_{ij}^\gamma h_k^\delta h_{lm}^\delta h_n^\delta \kappa^{i,k}\kappa^{j,l}\kappa^{m,n} \\
&- \frac{1}{2} \sum^{[2]}_{(\gamma,\delta)} (\sigma^\gamma)^{-1}(\sigma^\delta)^{-3} h_{ij}^\gamma h_k^\delta h_l^\delta h_m^\delta \kappa^{i,k}\kappa^{j,l,m} \\
&+ (\sigma^\gamma\sigma^\delta)^{-3} h_i^\gamma h_{jk}^\gamma h_l^\gamma h_m^\delta h_{no}^\delta h_p^\delta \kappa^{k,l}\kappa^{o,p}[3]\kappa^{(i,j}\kappa^{m,n)} \\
&+ \frac{1}{2} \sum^{[2]}_{(\gamma,\delta)} (\sigma^\gamma\sigma^\delta)^{-3} h_i^\gamma h_{jk}^\gamma h_l^\gamma h_m^\delta h_n^\delta h_o^\delta \kappa^{k,l}[3]\kappa^{(i,j}\kappa^{m),n,o} \\
&+ \frac{1}{4}(\sigma^\gamma\sigma^\delta)^{-3}(\kappa^{\gamma,\delta}\kappa^{\gamma,\gamma,\delta,\delta} + 2(\kappa^{\gamma,\delta})^3)\Big\} \\
&+ \frac{1}{n} \sum^{[6]}_{(\alpha,\beta,\gamma,\delta)} (\sigma^\alpha\sigma^\beta)^{-3}(\sigma^\gamma\sigma^\delta)^{-1}\kappa^{\gamma,\delta}\Big[\\
&\quad 2h_i^\alpha h_{jk}^\alpha h_l^\alpha h_m^\beta h_{no}^\beta h_p^\beta \kappa^{i,j}\kappa^{k,l}\kappa^{m,n}\kappa^{o,p} \\
&+ h_i^\alpha h_{jk}^\alpha h_l^\alpha \kappa^{i,j}\kappa^{k,l}\kappa^{\beta,\beta,\beta} + h_i^\beta h_{jk}^\beta h_l^\beta \kappa^{i,j}\kappa^{k,l}\kappa^{\alpha,\alpha,\alpha} + O(n^{-2})
\end{aligned}
$$

Now we are in a position to present the third order Edgeworth expansions for the density function of T. Let $g^{\alpha,\beta} = (\sigma^\alpha\sigma^\beta)^{-1}\kappa^{\alpha,\beta}$. Let $\phi(\boldsymbol{y}; g^{\alpha,\beta})$ be the density function of the d-dimensional normal distribution with mean 0 and covariance matrix $(g^{\alpha,\beta})$. Let $H^{\alpha_1\cdots\alpha_r}(\boldsymbol{y})$

be the Hermite polynomial $H^{\alpha_1\cdots\alpha_r}(\boldsymbol{y})$ of degree r with respect to $(g^{\alpha,\beta})$. Similar to the unstudentized case that the cumulants of T can be written in the following form:

$$\kappa_T^{\alpha_1,\cdots,\alpha_r} = n^{-\frac{r-2}{2}}(C_0^{\alpha_1,\cdots,\alpha_r} + \frac{1}{n}C_1^{\alpha_1,\cdots,\alpha_r} + \frac{1}{n^2}C_2^{\alpha_1,\cdots,\alpha_r} + \cdots),$$

where $\kappa_n^{\alpha,\beta}$ and $C_0^{\alpha\beta} = g^{\alpha,\beta}$. The covariant form $C_{i;\alpha_1\cdots\alpha_r}$ of $C_i^{\alpha_1,\cdots,\alpha_r}$ with respect to $(g^{\alpha,\beta})$ are defined similarly by the following relation

$$C_i^{\alpha_1\cdots\alpha_r} = C_{i;\beta_1\cdots\beta_r} g^{\alpha_1,\beta_1}\cdots g^{\alpha_r,\beta_r}.$$

THEOREM 4.12. *Under regularity conditions similar to those in Theorem 3.6, the density function $f(\boldsymbol{t})$ of T can be expanded as*

$$f(\boldsymbol{t}) = \phi(\boldsymbol{y}; g^{\alpha,\beta})\Big(1 + \frac{1}{\sqrt{n}}q_1(\boldsymbol{t}) + \frac{1}{n}q_2(\boldsymbol{t})\Big) + O(n^{-3/2}), \tag{4.4}$$

where

$$q_1(\boldsymbol{t}) = C_{1,\alpha}H^{\alpha}(\boldsymbol{t}) + \frac{1}{3!}C_{0,\alpha\beta\gamma}H^{\alpha\beta\gamma}(\boldsymbol{t}),$$

$$q_2(\boldsymbol{t}) = \frac{1}{2!}(C_{1,\alpha}C_{1,\beta} + C_{1,\alpha\beta})H^{\alpha\beta}(\boldsymbol{t}) + \frac{1}{4!}(C_{0,\alpha\beta\gamma\delta} + C_{1,\alpha}C_{0,\beta\gamma\delta}[4]_{(\alpha\beta\gamma\delta)})H^{\alpha\beta\gamma\delta}(\boldsymbol{t})$$
$$+\frac{1}{6!}C_{0,\alpha\beta\gamma}C_{0,\delta\epsilon\lambda}[10]_{(\alpha\beta\gamma\delta\epsilon\lambda)}H^{\alpha\beta\gamma\delta\epsilon\lambda}(\boldsymbol{t}).$$

REFERENCES

[1] S.-I. AMARI, *Differential-Geometrical Methods in Statistics*, Lecture Notes in Statistics, vol.28, Springer, New York, 1985.

[2] A. C. DAVISON AND D. V. HINKLEY, *Bootstrap Methods and Their Applications*, Cambridge U.P., Cambridge, 1997.

[3] H. DOSS AND J. SETHURAMAN, *The proce of bias reduction when there is no unbiased estimate*, Ann. Statist., 17 (1989), pp. 440–442.

[4] B. EFRON, *Bootstrap methods: another look at the jackknife*, Ann. Statist., 7 (1979), pp. 1–26.

[5] ———, *The Jackknide, the Bootstrap and Other Resampling Plans*, SIAM, Philadephia, 1982.

[6] B. EFRON AND R. TIBSHIRANI, *An Introduction to the Bootstrap*, Chapman & Hall, New York, 1993.

[7] P. HALL, *The Bootstrap and Edgeworth Expansion*, Springer, New York, 1992.

[8] D. V. HINKLEY, *Improving the jackknife with special reference to the correlation coefficient*, Biometrika, 65 (1978), pp. 13–21.

[9] M. QUENOUILLE, *Approximate tests of correlation in time series*, J. Roy. Statist. Soc. Ser. B, 11 (1949), pp. 18–84.

[10] J. TUKEY, *Bias and confidence in not quite large samples, abstract*, Ann. Math. Statist., 29 (1958), pp. 614.

[11] J. WANG AND M. TAGURI, *Jackknifing: higher order accurate confidence intervals*, J. Jap. Statist. Soc., 26 (1996), pp. 69–82.

In: Focus on Computational Neurobiology
Editor: Lei Li, pp. 49-64

ISBN 1-59033-915-0

CONVERGENCE ANALYSIS OF ADAPTIVE FINITE DIFFERENCE METHODS USING STRETCHING FUNCTIONS FOR BOUNDARY VALUE PROBLEMS WITH SINGULAR SOLUTIONS

QING FANG*, YUKIHIRO SHOGENJI†, AND TETSURO YAMAMOTO‡

Abstract. In this paper, we consider adaptive finite difference methods using polynomial and exponential stretching functions for Dirichlet boundary value problems in a domain Ω, whose solutions have singular derivatives near a part or the whole of the boundary of Ω. In the case where Ω is the unit square, it is shown that the methods are convergent and the convergence can be accelerated by varying parameters in the stretching functions. Numerical examples are given to illustrate how the effect of stretching functions depends on the choice of parameters.

Key words. mesh refinement, adaptive finite difference methods, Dirichlet problems, stretching functions, accelerated convergence

AMS subject classifications. 65M06, 65M12

1. Introduction. The finite difference methods (FDM) for solving boundary value problem usually use the uniform mesh size h to partition the domain. If the solution of the problem is sufficiently smooth, then, by J. H. Bramble-B. E. Hubbard's result [1], the Shortley-Weller formula gives $O(h^2)$ accuracy even if there are grid points near the boundary such as the local truncation errors $O(h)$. But if the problem has singular solutions, the methods often lead to inconsistent schemes, that is, the truncation errors diverge and the methods may lose their validity or yield low accuracy. Therefore, the study of mesh refinement has recently been a major theme in FD analysis.

In 1974, J. F. Thompson, J. F. Thames and C. W. Mastin [17] proposed a technique of generating nonuniform finite difference grid points by body-fitted curvilinear coordinate system for two-dimensional problems. Further development of this technique can be found in J. F. Thompson, Z. U. A. Warsi and C. W. Mastin [18] in 1985. In 1994, W. Huang and D. M. Sloan [7] and W. Huang, Y. Ren and R. D. Russell [6] suggested some adaptive grid generation methods and executed many numerical experiments to check their validity. Later on, a lot of work has been devoted to the adaptive grid generation both for two-dimensional and one-dimensional problems as well as both for steady and time-dependent problems. For example, refer to L. S. Mulholland, Y. Qiu and D. M. Sloan [13] (1997), W. Cao, W. Huang and R. D. Russell [2] (1999), Y. Qiu and D. M. Sloan [14] (1999), Y. Qiu, D. M. Sloan and T. Tang [15] (2000), J. A. Mackenzie and M. L. Robertson [9] (2000), T. Tang, W. Xue and P. Zhang [16] (2001), etc. But it appears that there is little theoretical error analysis of adaptive finite difference methods except for [14], [15] done for one-dimensional problems. In 2000, T. Yamamoto [21] proved that even in inconsistent schemes, FDM with the equidistributed grid points converges to the true solution, and that the convergence can be accelerated by using polynomial stretching functions to generate the adaptive mesh sizes. Q. Fang, T. Matsubara, Y. Shogenji and T. Yamamoto [4] applied the

*Department of Mathematical Sciences, Ehime University, Matsuyama 790-8577, Japan (fang@math.sci.ehime-u.ac.jp); Corresponding author.

†Information Processing Center, Shimane University, Matsue 690-8504, Japan (shogenji@ipc.shimane-u.ac.jp).

‡Department of Mathematical Sciences, Ehime University, Matsuyama 790-8577, Japan (yamamoto@math.sci.ehime-u.ac.jp); Waseda University, Tokyo since April 2002.

acceleration technique to some problems whose solutions have singular derivatives on the boundary.

In this paper, we consider the adaptive finite difference methods using polynomial and exponential stretching functions which are applied to the Dirichlet boundary value problem

$$-\Delta u + c(x,y)u = f(x,y) \quad \text{in } \Omega, \tag{1.1}$$

$$u = g(x,y) \quad \text{on } \Gamma = \partial\Omega, \tag{1.2}$$

where $\Omega \subset \mathbb{R}^2$ is a bounded domain, f, g and c are given functions with $c \geq 0$. Throughout this paper, we assume that the problem (1.1)–(1.2) has a unique solution.

Let Ω_h be the set of the grid points $P_{i,j} = (x_i, y_j)$ in Ω which construct a net over $\overline{\Omega}$. Let Γ_h be the set of grid points on Γ and P any grid point of Ω_h. As is shown in Figures 1.1–1.2, let P_E, P_W, P_S, P_N be the four neighbor grid points of P and denote their distances to P by h_E, h_W, h_S, h_N. We denote by Ω_h^1 the set of grid points P for which at least one of four neighbor grid points belong to Γ_h, and $\Omega_h^c = \Omega_h \setminus \Omega_h^1$.

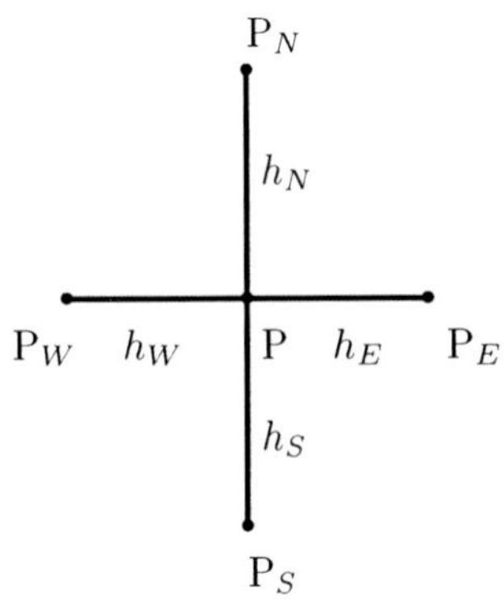

Figure 1.1

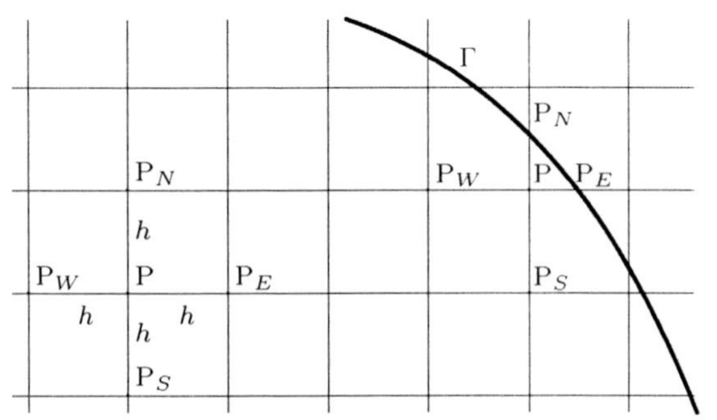

Figure 1.2

We discretize $-\Delta u$ at $P = P_{i,j} \in \Omega_h$ by the Shortley-Weller (S-W) formula

$$\begin{aligned} -\Delta_h U(P) \equiv & \left(\frac{2}{h_E h_W} + \frac{2}{h_S h_N}\right) U(P) - \frac{2}{h_E(h_E + h_W)} U(P_E) \\ & - \frac{2}{h_W(h_E + h_W)} U(P_W) - \frac{2}{h_S(h_S + h_N)} U(P_S) \\ & - \frac{2}{h_N(h_S + h_N)} U(P_N), \end{aligned} \tag{1.3}$$

where $U(P)$ denotes the approximation of the exact value $u(P)$ at $P \in \Omega_h$.

Let $\tau(P)$ be the local truncation error of the formula (1.3) at $P \in \Omega_h$ which is given by

$$\tau(P) = -\Delta_h u(P) - f(P). \tag{1.4}$$

Then it is well known from the fundamental convergence theorem due to Gerschgorin (cf. Gorenflo [5]) that

$$u(P) - U(P) = \mathrm{O}(\|\tau\|_\infty) \quad \text{as } h \to 0 \tag{1.5}$$

holds, where $\|\tau\|_\infty = \max_{P\in\Omega_h}|\tau(P)|$ and h denotes the maximal mesh size in x and y directions. As is easily verified, we have

$$\begin{aligned}\tau(P) &= \frac{1}{3}\left[(h_E - h_W)u_{xxx}(P) + (h_N - h_S)u_{yyy}(P)\right]\\ &\quad + \frac{1}{12}\left[\frac{h_E^3 u_{xxxx}(Q_E) + h_W^3 u_{xxxx}(Q_W)}{h_E + h_W}\right] + \frac{1}{12}\left[\frac{h_N^3 u_{yyyy}(Q_N) + h_S^3 u_{yyyy}(Q_S)}{h_S + h_N}\right]\\ &= \frac{1}{3}\left[(h_E - h_W)u_{xxx}(P) + (h_N - h_S)u_{yyy}(P)\right]\\ &\quad + \frac{1}{12}\left[\frac{h_E^3 + h_W^3}{h_E + h_W}u_{xxxx}(Q_x) + \frac{h_N^3 + h_S^3}{h_S + h_N}u_{yyyy}(Q_y)\right],\end{aligned}$$

where

$$Q_E \in \overline{PP_E},\quad Q_W \in \overline{PP_W},\quad Q_N \in \overline{PP_N},\quad Q_S \in \overline{PP_S},\quad Q_x \in \overline{P_W P_E},\quad Q_y \in \overline{P_S P_N}.$$

Hence $\tau(P) = O(h)$ if $(h_W, h_E, h_S, h_N) \neq (h, h, h, h)$.

When $u \in C^4(\overline{\Omega})$ and $h_W = h_E = h_S = h_N = h$ are taken for every $P \in \Omega_h^c$, J. H. Bramble and B. E. Hubbard [1] showed the following result:

$$u(P) - U(P) = O(h^2) \quad \text{as } h \to 0,$$

even if there exists any point $P \in \Omega_h^1$ such as $(h_E, h_W, h_S, h_N) \neq (h, h, h, h)$. As a refinement of this result, N. Matsunaga and T. Yamamoto [10] proved the following superconvergence property for the S-W approximate solution.

THEOREM 1.1 (N. Matsunaga and T. Yamamoto [10]). *Let Ω be a bounded convex domain with a piecewise $C^{2,\alpha}$ boundary, where $0 < \alpha < 1$. Suppose Ω is partitioned with the uniform mesh size h. Take a number $\gamma > 1$ and put $\mathcal{S}(h,\gamma) = \{P \in \Omega_h \mid \operatorname{dist}(P,\Gamma) \leq \gamma h\}$. Then, if $u \in C^{2,\alpha}(\overline{\Omega})$, the estimate*

$$|u(P) - U(P)| \leq \begin{cases} O(h^{1+\alpha}) & \text{if } P \in \mathcal{S}(h,\gamma), \\ O(h^\alpha) & \text{otherwise} \end{cases} \tag{1.6}$$

holds, even if there exists any $P \in \Omega_h^1$ with $(h_E, h_W, h_S, h_N) \neq (h, h, h, h)$. Moreover, if $u \in C^{3,1}(\overline{\Omega})$, then

$$|u(P) - U(P)| \leq \begin{cases} O(h^3) & \text{if } P \in \mathcal{S}(h,\gamma), \\ O(h^2) & \text{otherwise,} \end{cases} \tag{1.7}$$

holds.

T. Yamamoto, Q. Fang and X. Chen [22] considered some cases where $\Omega = (0,1)\times(0,1)$ and the exact solution of the problem (1.1)–(1.2) has singular derivatives on the boundary. The result is stated as follows:

THEOREM 1.2 (T. Yamamoto, Q. Fang, X. Chen [22]). *Let $\Omega = (0,1) \times (0,1)$ be partitioned uniformly by h. Assume that $u \in C(\overline{\Omega}) \cap C^4(\Omega)$ is the exact solution of problem (1.1)-(1.2), where $c(x,y) = 0$ and $f(x,y) = F(x) + G(y)$. If u satisfies*

$$\sup_{x\in(0,1)} \frac{x^i(1-x)^i}{x^p(1-x)^q}\left|\frac{\partial^i u}{\partial x^i}(x,y)\right| \leq K_1 < \infty, \quad i = 2, 4, \tag{1.8}$$

$$\sup_{y\in(0,1)} \frac{y^i(1-y)^i}{y^p(1-y)^q}\left|\frac{\partial^i u}{\partial y^i}(x,y)\right| \leq K_2 < \infty, \quad i = 2, 4, \tag{1.9}$$

for some positive constants K_1 *and* K_2, *where* $p, q \in (0, 2)$, *and if*

$$\omega(d) \equiv \sup_{\text{dist}(P,Q)\le d} |u(P) - u(Q)| \le C_0\, d^\sigma \text{ at } P, Q \text{ near } \Gamma \tag{1.10}$$

for some positive constant C_0, *where* $\sigma = \min\{p, q\}$, *then*

$$|u(P) - U(P)| \le \mathrm{O}(h^\sigma) \quad \forall P \in \Omega_h, \tag{1.11}$$

where $U(P)$ *is the S-W approximate value at* $P \in \Omega_h$.

The numerical results show that superconvergence property does not hold for the problem (1.1)–(1.2) whose solution is singular in the sense of (1.8)–(1.10). Note that in this case the truncation error $\|\tau\|_\infty \to \infty$ as $h \to 0$ so that the usual convergence theorem (1.5) does not guarantee the convergence of the S-W approximation.

Q. Fang, T. Matsubara, Y. Shogenji and T. Yamamoto [4] extended Theorem 1.2 to the case where the function $f(x, y)$ is of any form:

THEOREM 1.3 (Q. Fang, T. Matsubara, Y. Shogenji and T. Yamamoto [4]). *Let* $\Omega = (0, 1) \times (0, 1)$ *be uniformly partitioned by* h. *If* $u \in C(\overline{\Omega}) \cap C^4(\Omega)$ *is the exact solution of the problem* (1.1)–(1.2) *and satisfies* (1.8)–(1.10), *then we have*

$$|u(P) - U(P)| \le \mathrm{O}(h^\sigma) \quad \forall P \in \Omega_h, \tag{1.12}$$

where $U(P)$ *is the S-W approximate value at* $P \in \Omega_h$.

Recently, T. Yamamoto [21] developed an adaptive finite difference method to accelerate the convergence. Let $\varphi(t)$ be the stretching function

$$\varphi(t) = c_p \int_0^t \{s(1 - s)\}^p ds, \quad 0 \le t \le 1 \tag{1.13}$$

with

$$c_p = \left[\int_0^1 \{s(1 - s)\}^p ds\right]^{-1}.$$

The nonuniform grid points $P_{i,j}$, $i, j = 1, 2, \ldots, n$ are constructed by using the function $\varphi(t)$ as follows:

$$h = \frac{1}{n+1}, \quad t_i = ih, \ i = 0, 1, 2, \ldots, n + 1 \tag{1.14}$$

$$x_i = \varphi(t_i), \quad y_j = \varphi(t_j), \ i, j = 0, 1, 2, \ldots, n + 1. \tag{1.15}$$

Then the following result is known.

THEOREM 1.4 (T. Yamamoto [21]). *Let* $\Omega = (0, 1) \times (0, 1)$ *and the grid points* $P_{i,j} = (x_i, y_j)$ *be generated by* (1.14)–(1.15) *with* φ *defined by* (1.13). *If* $u \in C(\overline{\Omega}) \cap C^4(\Omega)$ *is the exact solution of problem* (1.1)–(1.2) *and satisfies*

$$\sup_{x\in(0,1)} \frac{x^i(1 - x)^i}{x^{\alpha_1}(1 - x)^{\alpha_2}} \left|\frac{\partial^i u}{\partial x^i}(x, y)\right| \le K_1 < \infty, \quad i = 2, 3, 4, \tag{1.16}$$

$$\sup_{y\in(0,1)} \frac{y^i(1 - y)^i}{y^{\beta_1}(1 - y)^{\beta_2}} \left|\frac{\partial^i u}{\partial y^i}(x, y)\right| \le K_2 < \infty, \quad i = 2, 3, 4, \tag{1.17}$$

$$\sup_{\text{dist}(P,Q)\le d} |u(P) - u(Q)| \le C_0\, d^\sigma \text{ at } P, Q \text{ near } \Gamma \tag{1.18}$$

for some positive constants K_1, K_2 *and* C_0, *where* $\alpha_i, \beta_i \in (0,2)$ $(i = 1,2)$ *and* $\sigma = \min_i\{\alpha_i, \beta_i\}$, *then the S-W approximate solution* $U(P)$ *satisfies*

$$|u(P) - U(P)| \leq \begin{cases} O(h^r) & \text{if } r < 2, \\ O(h^2 \log \frac{1}{h}) & \text{if } r = 2 \end{cases} \tag{1.19}$$

for any $P = P_{i,j}$, *where* $r = \sigma(p+1)$.

On the other hand, M. Ishiguro [8] and A. P. Costa Mouro [12] have reported that the grid generation by the exponential stretching function

$$\varphi(t) = \frac{e^{at} - 1}{e^a - 1}, \quad 0 \leq t \leq 1. \tag{1.20}$$

leads to satisfactory numerical results. However, it appears that there is no mathematical discussion about how accurate results will be obtained by such a function with the parameter a. Even the convergence proof of the approximate solution has not yet been known.

In this paper, for the problem (1.1)–(1.2), we study the effect of mesh refinement by stretching functions in the case where Ω is the unit square $(0,1) \times (0,1)$. First, in Section 2, we state a result concerning the effect of mesh refinement by the polynomial stretching function

$$\varphi(t) = t^{p+1}, \quad 0 \leq t \leq 1, \tag{1.21}$$

provided that the problem has singularity at the origin, that is, the derivatives of the exact solution may go to infinity near the origin. The result corresponds to Theorem 1.4 for the function (1.13).

In Section 3, we study the effect of the exponential stretching functions (1.20) for the problem (1.1)–(1.2), under the same assumptions as in Section 2. By employing the same argument as in [21], it is shown that the corresponding Shortley-Weller approximate solution also improves the convergence. Since the polynomial stretching function can be computed easier than the exponential stretching function, it is an interesting task to compare these two stretching functions.

In Section 4, numerical examples are given to illustrate the results in Sections 2–3. Especially, we vary the parameters in the exponential stretching functions and the polynomial stretching functions widely and carefully in order to see which stretching function should be chosen in different cases.

Our argument can also be applied to the Dirichlet problem in a disk or a sector domain. This will be shown in a forthcoming paper.

2. Effect of Polynomial Stretching Function. In this section, we consider the problem (1.1)–(1.2) in $\Omega = (0,1) \times (0,1)$, whose solution u belongs to $C(\overline{\Omega}) \cap C^4(\overline{\Omega} \backslash \{xy = 0\})$ and has singular derivatives near the part of the boundary $\Gamma_0 = \{(x,y) \in \Gamma \mid x = 0 \text{ or } y = 0\}$ such that

$$\sup_{x \in (0,1)} \frac{x^j \left| \dfrac{\partial^j u}{\partial x^j}(x,y) \right|}{x^\sigma} \leq K_1 < \infty, \tag{2.1}$$

$$\sup_{y \in (0,1)} \frac{y^j \left| \dfrac{\partial^j u}{\partial y^j}(x,y) \right|}{y^\sigma} \leq K_2 < \infty, \quad j = 2,3,4 \tag{2.2}$$

for some constants $\sigma \in (0,2)$, K_1, $K_2 > 0$ and

$$\omega(d) \equiv \sup_{\mathrm{dist}(P,Q)\le d} |u(P) - u(Q)| \le C_0\, d^\sigma \text{ at } P, Q \text{ near } \Gamma_0 \tag{2.3}$$

for some positive constant C_0. Let $\varphi(t)$ be the polynomial stretching function defined by (1.21). Observe that $\varphi(t) = t$ if $p = 0$. We then put

$$h = \frac{1}{n+1}, \quad t_i = ih, \ i = 0, 1, 2, \dots, n+1, \tag{2.4}$$

$$x_i = \varphi(t_i), \quad y_j = \varphi(t_j), \ i, j = 0, 1, 2, \dots, n+1 \tag{2.5}$$

and generate nonuniform grid points $P_{i,j} = (x_i, y_j)$. The set of the grid points is denoted by Ω_h. The set Γ_h is also defined as before. Then, at $P = P_{i,j}$, $1 \le i, j \le n$, we obtain from (1.21)

$$h_E = x_{i+1} - x_i = h\varphi'(t_i + \theta_i^+ h) < h\varphi'(t_{i+1}), \ 0 < \theta_i^+ < 1, \tag{2.6}$$

$$h_W = x_i - x_{i-1} = h\varphi'(t_i - \theta_i^- h) < h\varphi'(t_i), \quad 0 < \theta_i^- < 1, \tag{2.7}$$

$$h_N = y_{j+1} - y_j = h\varphi'(t_j + \theta_j^+ h) < h\varphi'(t_{j+1}), \ 0 < \theta_j^+ < 1, \tag{2.8}$$

$$h_S = y_j - y_{j-1} = h\varphi'(t_j - \theta_j^- h) < h\varphi'(t_j), \quad 0 < \theta_j^- < 1, \tag{2.9}$$

$$\begin{aligned} h_E - h_W &= x_{i+1} - 2x_i + x_{i-1} \\ &= h^2\varphi''(t_i + \theta_i^1 h), \quad -1 < \theta_i^1 < 1, \end{aligned} \tag{2.10}$$

$$\begin{aligned} h_N - h_S &= y_{j+1} - 2y_j + y_{j-1}, \\ &= h^2\varphi''(t_j + \theta_j^2 h), \quad -1 < \theta_j^2 < 1. \end{aligned} \tag{2.11}$$

We have the following result, which is essentially due to T. Yamamoto [21].

THEOREM 2.1. *Let $\Omega = (0,1) \times (0,1)$ and the grid points $P_{i,j} = (x_i, y_j)$ be generated by (2.4)–(2.5) with φ as in (1.21). Let $u \in C(\overline{\Omega}) \cap C^4(\overline{\Omega} \setminus \{xy = 0\})$ be the exact solution of the problem (1.1)–(1.2) whose solution satisfies the conditions (2.1)–(2.3). Denote by U the S-W approximate solution of the problem (1.1)–(1.2). Then, if $r = \sigma(p+1) < 2$, we have*

$$|u(P) - U(P)| \le K(p)h^r + L(p)h^2 \tag{2.12}$$

for any $P = P_{i,j}$, where

$$K(p) = C\{(p+1)2^p\}^3, \tag{2.13}$$

$$L(p) = \begin{cases} 4C'(p+1)^2 & \text{if } p - 1 \ge 0, \\ 2C'(\kappa^{p-1} + 1)(p+1)^2 & \text{if } p - 1 < 0 \end{cases} \tag{2.14}$$

for some positive constants C, C' and any small constant $\kappa > 0$. If $r = 2$, then the estimate (2.12) is replaced by

$$|u(P) - U(P)| \le K(p)h^2 \log\frac{1}{h} + L(p)h^2 \tag{2.15}$$

for any $P = P_{i,j}$.

The stretching function (1.21) is different from (1.13). However, Theorem 2.1 easily follows from the proof of Theorem 1.4.

3. Effect of Exponential Stretching Function. In this section, we consider the problem (1.1)–(1.2) in $\Omega = (0,1) \times (0,1)$, whose solution satisfies the same assumptions as in Section 2.

Let $\varphi(t)$ be the exponential stretching function defined by (1.20). We then put

$$h = \frac{1}{n+1}, \quad t_i = ih, \ i = 0, 1, 2, \ldots, n+1, \tag{3.1}$$

$$x_i = \varphi(t_i), \ y_j = \varphi(t_j), \quad i, j = 0, 1, 2, \ldots, n+1 \tag{3.2}$$

and generate nonuniform grid points $P_{i,j} = (x_i, y_j)$. The set of the grid points are again denoted by Ω_h. The set Γ_h is also defined as before. Then, at $P = P_{i,j}$, $1 \le i, j \le n$, we obtain from (1.20)

$$h_E = x_{i+1} - x_i = h\varphi'(t_i + \theta_i^+ h) < h\varphi'(t_{i+1}), \ 0 < \theta_i^+ < 1, \tag{3.3}$$

$$h_W = x_i - x_{i-1} = h\varphi'(t_i - \theta_i^- h) < h\varphi'(t_i), \quad 0 < \theta_i^- < 1, \tag{3.4}$$

$$h_N = y_{j+1} - y_j = h\varphi'(t_j + \theta_j^+ h) < h\varphi'(t_{j+1}), \ 0 < \theta_j^+ < 1, \tag{3.5}$$

$$h_S = y_j - y_{j-1} = h\varphi'(t_j - \theta_j^- h) < h\varphi'(t_j), \quad 0 < \theta_j^- < 1, \tag{3.6}$$

$$\begin{aligned} h_E - h_W &= x_{i+1} - 2x_i + x_{i-1} \\ &= h^2\varphi''(t_i + \theta_i^1 h) < h^2\varphi''(t_{i+1}), \quad -1 < \theta_i^1 < 1, \end{aligned} \tag{3.7}$$

$$\begin{aligned} h_N - h_S &= y_{j+1} - 2y_j + y_{j-1} \\ &= h^2\varphi''(t_j + \theta_j^2 h) < h^2\varphi''(t_{j+1}), \quad -1 < \theta_j^2 < 1. \end{aligned} \tag{3.8}$$

We prove the following result:

THEOREM 3.1. *Let $\Omega = (0,1) \times (0,1)$ and the grid points $P_{i,j} = (x_i, y_j)$ be generated by (3.1)–(3.2) with φ as in (1.20). Let $u \in C(\overline{\Omega}) \cap C^4(\overline{\Omega} \setminus \{xy = 0\})$ be the exact solution of the problem (1.1)–(1.2) whose solution satisfies (2.1)–(2.3). Denote by U the S-W approximate solution of (1.1)–(1.2). Then, for $a \ge \log 2$, we have*

$$|u(P) - U(P)| \le \lambda(a)h^\sigma + \mu(a)h^2 \tag{3.9}$$

for any $P = P_{i,j}$, where

$$\lambda(a) = Ca^\sigma e^{-\rho_1 a} + C' a^\sigma e^{-\rho_2 a}, \tag{3.10}$$

$$\mu(a) = \mathrm{O}(a^2) \quad \text{as } a \to \infty, \tag{3.11}$$

and ρ_1, ρ_2, C, C' are some positive constants.

Proof. We give here a proof along the same line as in [21]. Take a positive number $\kappa < \frac{1}{4}$ which is determined later and set $I = [\frac{\kappa}{h}]$. Define $\Omega_h^{(i)}$ inductively by

$$\Omega_h^{(1)} = \{P \in \Omega_h \mid \text{at least one of the neighbors of } P \text{ belongs to } \Gamma_h \cap \Gamma_0\}, \Omega_h^{(i)}$$

$$= \{P \in \Omega_h \setminus \bigcup_{j=1}^{i-1} \Omega_h^{(j)} \text{at least one ofthe neighbors of } P \text{ belongs to } \Omega_h^{(i-1)}\} \quad (i \ge 2),$$

$$\text{and put} \Omega_h^{(0)} = \Omega_h \setminus \bigcup_{i=1}^{I} \Omega_h^{(i)}.$$

The number of the elements of $\Omega_h^{(i)}$ is denoted by m_i $(i = 0, 1, 2, \ldots, I)$ so that $m_0 = n^2 - \sum_{i=1}^{I} m_i$. We arrange the grid points of Ω_h in the order of $\Omega_h^{(1)}, \Omega_h^{(2)}, \ldots, \Omega_h^{(I)}, \Omega_h^{(0)}$. (The elements of $\Omega_h^{(i)}$ may be arranged appropriately for each $i \geq 0$). Let $\boldsymbol{e}^{(i)}$, $i = 0, 1, \ldots, I$ be the m_i-dimensional column vectors whose elements are all unity, and put $\boldsymbol{e} = (\boldsymbol{e}^{(1)^t}, \boldsymbol{e}^{(2)^t}, \cdots, \boldsymbol{e}^{(I)^t}, \boldsymbol{e}^{(0)^t})^t$. We denote by A the finite difference matrix corresponding to the S-W approximation and above ordering. The matrix A is an irreducibly diagonally dominant L-matrix so that A is an M-matrix and $A^{-1} \geq O$. Then, the element of $A\boldsymbol{e}$ corresponding to $P = (x, y) \in \Omega_h$ is given by

$$(A\boldsymbol{e})_P = 0 \quad \text{if } P \notin \Omega_h^{(1)} \text{and} (A\boldsymbol{e})_P \quad \geq \begin{cases} \dfrac{2}{h_E h_W} - \dfrac{2}{h_E(h_E + h_W)} = \dfrac{2}{h_W(h_E + h_W)} & (P \in \Omega_h^{(1)},\ x = x_1), \\ \dfrac{2}{h_S h_N} - \dfrac{2}{h_N(h_S + h_N)} = \dfrac{2}{h_S(h_S + h_N)} & (P \in \Omega_h^{(1)},\ y = y_1). \end{cases}$$

Hence, putting $h_E^{(i)} = x_{i+1} - x_i$, $h_W^{(i)} = x_i - x_{i-1}$ and $d_i = \frac{2}{h_E^{(i)} + h_W^{(i)}}$, $i = 1, 2, \ldots, I$, we obtain

$$A\boldsymbol{e} \geq \frac{d_1}{h_W^{(1)}} \begin{pmatrix} \boldsymbol{e}^{(1)} \\ \boldsymbol{0} \\ \vdots \\ \boldsymbol{0} \end{pmatrix} \qquad \text{or} \qquad A^{-1} \begin{pmatrix} d_1 \boldsymbol{e}^{(1)} \\ \boldsymbol{0} \\ \vdots \\ \boldsymbol{0} \end{pmatrix} \leq h_W^{(1)} \boldsymbol{e}.$$

Similarly, we have for $i \geq 2$

$$A \begin{pmatrix} \boldsymbol{0} \\ \vdots \\ \boldsymbol{0} \\ \boldsymbol{e}^{(i)} \\ \boldsymbol{e}^{(i+1)} \\ \vdots \\ \boldsymbol{e}^{(0)} \end{pmatrix} \geq \begin{pmatrix} \boldsymbol{0} \\ \vdots \\ -d_{i-1}/h_E^{(i-1)} \boldsymbol{e}^{(i-1)} \\ d_i/h_W^{(i)} \boldsymbol{e}^{(i)} \\ \boldsymbol{0} \\ \vdots \\ \boldsymbol{0} \end{pmatrix}.$$

Since $h_E^{(i-1)} = h_W^{(i)}$, we obtain

$$A^{-1} \begin{pmatrix} \boldsymbol{0} \\ \vdots \\ \boldsymbol{0} \\ d_i \boldsymbol{e}^{(i)} \\ \boldsymbol{0} \\ \vdots \\ \boldsymbol{0} \end{pmatrix} \leq h_W^{(i)} \begin{pmatrix} \boldsymbol{0} \\ \vdots \\ \boldsymbol{0} \\ \boldsymbol{e}^{(i)} \\ \boldsymbol{e}^{(i+1)} \\ \vdots \\ \boldsymbol{e}^{(0)} \end{pmatrix} + A^{-1} \begin{pmatrix} \boldsymbol{0} \\ \vdots \\ d_{i-1} \boldsymbol{e}^{(i-1)} \\ \boldsymbol{0} \\ \boldsymbol{0} \\ \vdots \\ \boldsymbol{0} \end{pmatrix}$$

Using the above inequality for $i = 2, 3, \cdots, j$, and setting j as i again, we have

$$A^{-1}\begin{pmatrix} \mathbf{0} \\ \vdots \\ \mathbf{0} \\ d_i \mathbf{e}^{(i)} \\ \mathbf{0} \\ \vdots \\ \mathbf{0} \end{pmatrix} \le h_W^{(i)}\mathbf{e} + h_W^{(i-1)}\mathbf{e} + \cdots + h_W^{(2)}\mathbf{e} + h_W^{(1)}\mathbf{e} = \varphi(t_i)\mathbf{e}.$$

Next, we observe that

$$\begin{aligned}
\tau(P) &= -\Delta_h u(P) + \Delta u(P) \\
&= \frac{2h_W\{u(P) - u(P_E)\} + 2h_E\{u(P) - u(P_W)\}}{h_E h_W (h_E + h_W)} \\
&\quad + \frac{2h_S\{u(P) - u(P_N)\} + 2h_N\{u(P) - u(P_S)\}}{h_S h_N (h_S + h_N)} + u_{xx}(P) + u_{yy}(P) \\
&= \frac{2}{h_E h_W}\left[\alpha\{u(P) - u(P_E)\} + (1-\alpha)\{u(P) - u(P_W)\}\right] \\
&\quad + \frac{2}{h_S h_N}\left[\beta\{u(P) - u(P_N)\} + (1-\beta)\{u(P) - u(P_S)\}\right] + u_{xx}(P) + u_{yy}(P)
\end{aligned}$$

where

$$\alpha = \frac{h_W}{h_E + h_W}, \quad \beta = \frac{h_S}{h_S + h_N}. \tag{3.12}$$

Hence, if $P = (\varphi(t_k), \varphi(t_l)) \in \Omega_h^{(1)}$, then $\min\{k, l\} = 1$ and it follows from the conditions (2.1)–(2.3) that

$$\begin{aligned}
|\tau(P)| &\le \frac{4C_0 h_E^\sigma}{h_W^2} + \frac{4C_0 h_N^\sigma}{h_S^2} + K_1 x_k^{\sigma-2} + K_2 y_l^{\sigma-2} \\
&\le 4C_0\{h\varphi'(t_2)\}^\sigma \varphi(t_1)^{-2} + 4C_0\{h\varphi'(t_2)\}^\sigma \varphi(t_1)^{-2} \\
&\quad + K_1\varphi(t_1)^{\sigma-2} + K_2\varphi(t_1)^{\sigma-2} \\
&\le 8C_0\{h\varphi'(t_2)\}^\sigma \varphi(t_1)^{-2} + 2K_3\varphi(t_1)^{\sigma-2} \\
&\equiv \tau_\infty^{(1)} = \tau_1 + \tau_2,
\end{aligned} \tag{3.13}$$

where $K_3 = \max\{K_1, K_2\}$,

$$\tau_1 = 8C_0\left(\frac{ah\,e^{2ah}}{e^a - 1}\right)^\sigma \left(\frac{e^{ah} - 1}{e^a - 1}\right)^{-2} \tag{3.14}$$

and

$$\tau_2 = 2K_3\left(\frac{e^{ah} - 1}{e^a - 1}\right)^{\sigma-2}. \tag{3.15}$$

Furthermore, if $P = P_{k,l} = (\varphi(t_k), \varphi(t_l)) \in \Omega_h^{(i)}$ and $i \geq 2$, then it follows from (2.1)–(2.3) and (3.3)–(3.8) that

$$\begin{aligned}
|\tau(P)| &\leq \frac{1}{3}|h_E - h_W||u_{xxx}(P)| + \frac{1}{3}|h_N - h_S||u_{yyy}(P)| \\
&\quad + \frac{1}{12}\frac{h_E^3 + h_W^3}{h_E + h_W}|u_{xxxx}(Q_x)| + \frac{1}{12}\frac{h_S^3 + h_N^3}{h_S + h_N}|u_{yyyy}(Q_y)| \\
&\leq \frac{K_1}{3}\{h^2\varphi''(t_{k+1})\}\varphi(t_k)^{\sigma-3} + \frac{K_2}{3}\{h^2\varphi''(t_{l+1})\}\varphi(t_l)^{\sigma-3} \\
&\quad + \frac{K_1}{12}\{h\varphi'(t_{k+1})\}^2\varphi(t_{k-1})^{\sigma-4} + \frac{K_2}{12}\{h\varphi'(t_{l+1})\}^2\varphi(t_{l-1})^{\sigma-4} \\
&\leq \frac{K_1}{3}\left(h^2\frac{a^2e^{at_{k+1}}}{e^a - 1}\right)\left(\frac{e^{at_k} - 1}{e^a - 1}\right)^{\sigma-3} + \frac{K_2}{3}\left(h^2\frac{a^2e^{at_{l+1}}}{e^a - 1}\right)\left(\frac{e^{at_l} - 1}{e^a - 1}\right)^{\sigma-3} \\
&\quad + \frac{K_1}{12}\left(h\frac{ae^{at_{k+1}}}{e^a - 1}\right)^2\left(\frac{e^{at_{k-1}} - 1}{e^a - 1}\right)^{\sigma-4} + \frac{K_2}{12}\left(h\frac{ae^{at_{l+1}}}{e^a - 1}\right)^2\left(\frac{e^{at_{l-1}} - 1}{e^a - 1}\right)^{\sigma-4} \\
&\leq \frac{K_1}{3}\frac{a^2h^2e^{ah}}{(e^a - 1)^{\sigma-2}}\left(\frac{e^{at_k}}{(e^{at_k} - 1)^{3-\sigma}}\right) + \frac{K_2}{3}\frac{a^2h^2e^{ah}}{(e^a - 1)^{\sigma-2}}\left(\frac{e^{at_l}}{(e^{at_l} - 1)^{3-\sigma}}\right) \\
&\quad + \frac{K_1}{12}\frac{a^2h^2e^{4ah}}{(e^a - 1)^{\sigma-2}}\left(\frac{e^{at_{k-1}}}{(e^{at_{k-1}} - 1)^{4-\sigma}}\right) + \frac{K_2}{12}\frac{a^2h^2e^{4ah}}{(e^a - 1)^{\sigma-2}}\left(\frac{e^{at_{l-1}}}{(e^{at_{l-1}} - 1)^{4-\sigma}}\right),
\end{aligned} \tag{3.16}$$

where we have used the fact that at $P = P_{k,l} \in \Omega_h^{(i)}$

$$0 < h_E - h_W < h^2\varphi''(t_{k+1}), \quad |u_{xxx}(P)| \leq \varphi(t_k)^{\sigma-3}, \text{ etc.}$$

Since $e^{at}/(e^{at} - 1)$ is monotonically decreasing, (3.16) is monotonically decreasing with respect to t. Therefore, by $\min\{k, l\} = i$,

$$\begin{aligned}
|\tau(P)| &\leq \frac{2K_3}{3}\frac{a^2h^2e^{ah}}{(e^a - 1)^{\sigma-2}}\left(\frac{e^{at_i}}{(e^{at_i} - 1)^{3-\sigma}}\right) + \frac{K_3}{6}\frac{a^2h^2e^{4ah}}{(e^a - 1)^{\sigma-2}}\left(\frac{e^{at_{i-1}}}{(e^{at_{i-1}} - 1)^{4-\sigma}}\right) \\
&\equiv \tau_\infty^{(i)} \qquad (i \geq 2).
\end{aligned} \tag{3.17}$$

On the other hand, if $P = (\varphi(t_k), \varphi(t_l)) \in \Omega_h^{(0)}$, then there exists a positive constant C_1 such that

$$\begin{aligned}
|\tau(P)| &\leq \frac{1}{3}|h_E - h_W||u_{xxx}(P)| + \frac{1}{3}|h_N - h_S||u_{yyy}(P)| \\
&\quad + \frac{1}{12}\frac{h_E^3 + h_W^3}{h_E + h_W}|u_{xxxx}(Q_x)| + \frac{1}{12}\frac{h_S^3 + h_N^3}{h_S + h_N}|u_{yyyy}(Q_y)| \\
&\leq C_1[h^2\varphi''(t_{k+1}) + h^2\varphi''(t_{l+1}) + \{h\varphi'(t_{k+1})\}^2 + \{h\varphi'(t_{l+1})\}^2] \\
&\leq C_1a^2h^2\left[\left(\frac{e^{at_{k+1}}}{e^a - 1}\right) + \left(\frac{e^{at_{l+1}}}{e^a - 1}\right) + \left(\frac{e^{at_{k+1}}}{e^a - 1}\right)^2 + \left(\frac{e^{at_{l+1}}}{e^a - 1}\right)^2\right] \\
&\leq 12C_1\,a^2h^2 \\
&\equiv \tau_\infty^{(0)} \quad \text{(say)},
\end{aligned} \tag{3.18}$$

where we have used the fact that

$$\frac{e^{at_{k+1}}}{e^a - 1} \le \frac{e^a}{e^a - 1} \le 2 \qquad \text{for } a \ge \log 2, \tag{3.19}$$

and

$$\sup_{P \in \Omega^{(0)}} |u_{xxx}(P)| < \infty, \text{ etc.},$$

with $\Omega^{(0)} = \{(x, y) \in \Omega \mid \kappa \le x, y \le 1\} = [\kappa, 1] \times [\kappa, 1]$. Hence

$$\|\boldsymbol{\tau}^{(i)}\|_\infty = \sup_{P \in \Omega_h^{(i)}} |\tau(P)| \le \tau_\infty^{(i)}, \quad 0 \le i \le I. \tag{3.20}$$

Consequently, we have

$$\begin{aligned}
|\boldsymbol{u} - \boldsymbol{U}| &\le \sum_{i=1}^{I} \|\boldsymbol{\tau}^{(i)}\|_\infty A^{-1} \begin{pmatrix} \mathbf{0} \\ \vdots \\ \mathbf{0} \\ \boldsymbol{e}^{(i)} \\ \mathbf{0} \\ \vdots \\ \mathbf{0} \end{pmatrix} + \|\boldsymbol{\tau}^{(0)}\|_\infty A^{-1} \begin{pmatrix} \mathbf{0} \\ \vdots \\ \mathbf{0} \\ \boldsymbol{e}^{(0)} \end{pmatrix} \\
&\le \sum_{i=1}^{I} \tau_\infty^{(i)} \frac{h_E^{(i)} + h_W^{(i)}}{2} A^{-1} \begin{pmatrix} \mathbf{0} \\ \vdots \\ \mathbf{0} \\ d_i \boldsymbol{e}^{(i)} \\ \mathbf{0} \\ \vdots \\ \mathbf{0} \end{pmatrix} + \tau_\infty^{(0)} A^{-1} \boldsymbol{e} \\
&\le \sum_{i=1}^{I} \tau_\infty^{(i)} \frac{\varphi(t_{i+1}) - \varphi(t_{i-1})}{2} \varphi(t_i) \boldsymbol{e} + \mathrm{O}(a^2) h^2 A^{-1} \boldsymbol{e} \\
&\le \sum_{i=1}^{I} \tau_\infty^{(i)} [h\varphi'(t_{i+1})] \varphi(t_i) \boldsymbol{e} + \mathrm{O}(a^2) h^2 A^{-1} \boldsymbol{e}.
\end{aligned} \tag{3.21}$$

We obtain from (3.14) and (3.19) that

$$\left(\frac{ah\, e^{2ah}}{e^a - 1}\right)^\sigma = \left(\frac{e^a}{e^a - 1}\right)^\sigma \left(\frac{ah\, e^{2ah}}{e^a}\right)^\sigma \le 2^\sigma (ah)^\sigma e^{2ah\sigma - a\sigma}$$

and

$$\tau_1 \{h\varphi'(t_2)\} \varphi(t_1) \le 8 \cdot 2^\sigma C_0\, a^\sigma h^\sigma e^{-a(\sigma - 2h - 2h\sigma)}.$$

We also obtain from (3.15) and (3.19)

$$\tau_2 \{h\varphi'(t_2)\} \varphi(t_1) \le 2 \cdot 2^\sigma K_3\, a^\sigma h^\sigma e^{-a(\sigma - 2h - h\sigma)},$$

where we have used the inequality

$$ah \le e^{ah} - 1 \le ah\, e^{ah}.$$

Then, it follows that

$$\tau_\infty^{(1)}\{h\varphi'(t_2)\}\varphi(t_1) \le C_2\, a^\sigma h^\sigma e^{-a(\sigma-2h-2h\sigma)}, \tag{3.22}$$

where $C_2 = 2\max\{8 \cdot 2^{\sigma+1}C_0, 2 \cdot 2^\sigma K_3\}$. Furthermore, for $i \ge 2$, by similar computations, we obtain from (3.17) and (3.19)

$$\begin{aligned}
&\tau_\infty^{(i)}\{h\varphi'(t_{i+1})\}\varphi(t_i) \\
&\le \left[\frac{2K_3}{3}\frac{a^2h^2e^{ah}}{(e^a-1)^{\sigma-2}}\left(\frac{e^{at_i}}{(e^{at_i}-1)^{3-\sigma}}\right) + \frac{K_3}{6}\frac{a^2h^2e^{4ah}}{(e^a-1)^{\sigma-2}}\left(\frac{e^{at_{i-1}}}{(e^{at_{i-1}}-1)^{4-\sigma}}\right)\right] \\
&\quad \cdot \left(h\frac{ae^{at_{i+1}}}{e^a-1}\right)\left(\frac{e^{at_i}-1}{e^a-1}\right) \\
&\le \frac{2K_3}{3}\frac{a^3h^3e^{2ah}}{(e^a-1)^\sigma}\left(\frac{e^{2at_i}}{(e^{at_i}-1)^{2-\sigma}}\right) + \frac{K_3}{6}\frac{a^3h^3e^{6ah}}{(e^a-1)^\sigma}\left(\frac{e^{3at_{i-1}}(e^{at_i}-1)}{(e^{at_{i-1}}-1)^{4-\sigma}}\right) \\
&\le \frac{2K_3}{3}\frac{a^3h^3e^{2ah}}{(e^a-1)^\sigma}\left(\frac{e^{2at_i}(e^{at_i}-1)}{(e^{at_i}-1)^{3-\sigma}}\right) + \frac{K_3}{6}\frac{a^3h^3e^{6ah}}{(e^a-1)^\sigma}\left(\frac{e^{3at_{i-1}}}{(e^{at_{i-1}}-1)^{3-\sigma}}\right)\left(\frac{e^{at_i}-1}{e^{at_{i-1}}-1}\right) \\
&\le \frac{2K_3}{3}\frac{a^3h^3e^{2ah}}{(e^a-1)^\sigma}\left(\frac{e^{3at_i}}{(e^{at_i}-1)^{3-\sigma}}\right) + \frac{K_3}{6}\frac{a^3h^3e^{6ah}}{(e^a-1)^\sigma}\left(\frac{e^{3at_{i-1}}}{(e^{at_{i-1}}-1)^{3-\sigma}}\right)\left(\frac{e^{2ah}-1}{e^{ah}-1}\right) \\
&\le \frac{2K_3}{3}\frac{a^3h^3e^{2ah}}{(\frac{1}{2}e^a)^\sigma}\left(\frac{e^{3at_i}}{(at_i)^{3-\sigma}}\right) + \frac{K_3}{6}\frac{a^3h^3e^{6ah}}{(\frac{1}{2}e^a)^\sigma}\left(\frac{e^{3at_{i-1}}}{(at_{i-1})^{3-\sigma}}\right)\left(\frac{2ahe^{2ah}}{ah}\right) \\
&\le \frac{2^{\sigma+1}K_3}{3}\frac{a^3h^3e^{2ah}}{e^{a\sigma}}\left(\frac{e^{3aih}}{(aih)^{3-\sigma}}\right) + \frac{2^\sigma K_3}{3}\frac{a^3h^3e^{8ah}}{e^{a\sigma}}\left(\frac{e^{3a(i-1)h}}{(a(i-1)h)^{3-\sigma}}\right) \\
&\le \frac{2^{\sigma+1}K_3}{3}a^\sigma h^\sigma e^{-a(\sigma-2h-3\kappa)}i^{\sigma-3} + \frac{2^\sigma K_3}{3}a^\sigma h^\sigma e^{-a(\sigma-8h-3\kappa)}(i-1)^{\sigma-3} \\
&\le C_3\, a^\sigma h^\sigma e^{-a(\sigma-8h-3\kappa)}(i-1)^{\sigma-3},
\end{aligned} \tag{3.23}$$

where $C_3 = 2\max\{\frac{2^{\sigma+1}K_3}{3}, \frac{2^\sigma K_3}{3}\} = \frac{2^{\sigma+2}K_3}{3}$. Putting $\rho_1 = \sigma - 2h - 2h\sigma$, $\rho_2 = \sigma - 8h - 3\kappa$, we know $\rho_1 > 0$ and $\rho_2 > 0$ by choosing a small $\kappa > 0$. Therefore,

$$|\boldsymbol{u} - \boldsymbol{U}| \le C_2 a^\sigma h^\sigma e^{-\rho_1 a}\boldsymbol{e} + C_3\left(\sum_{i=1}^{I} i^{\sigma-3}\right)a^\sigma h^\sigma e^{-\rho_2 a}\boldsymbol{e} + \mathrm{O}(a^2)h^2A^{-1}\boldsymbol{e}, \tag{3.24}$$

where

$$\sum_{i=1}^{I} i^{\sigma-3} \le \sum_{i=1}^{\infty} i^{\sigma-3} \le C_4 < \infty,$$

since $\sigma - 3 < -1$. Next, to prove the boundedness of the vector $A^{-1}\boldsymbol{e}$, it suffices to repeat the same argument as in the proof of Theorem 2.2 in [10]. That is, we consider a domain D such that $D \supset \Omega$ and the boundary ∂D is sufficiently smooth so that the Dirichlet problem

$$\begin{aligned} -\Delta v &= 1 \quad \text{in } D, \\ v &= 0 \quad \text{on } \partial D \end{aligned}$$

has a (unique) solution $v \in C^{2,\alpha}(\overline{D})$, where α is the Hölder index with $0 < \alpha < 1$. Then we can prove that

$$A^{-1}\boldsymbol{e} \leq 2\boldsymbol{v},$$

where $\boldsymbol{v}$ is the n^2-dimensional vector whose components are $v(P)$, $P \in \Omega_h$. We thus conclude that

$$|u(P) - U(P)| \leq \lambda(a)h^{\sigma} + \mu(a)h^2, \tag{3.25}$$

where

$$\lambda(a) = C_2 a^{\sigma} e^{-\rho_1 a} + C_5 a^{\sigma} e^{-\rho_2 a}, \tag{3.26}$$

$$\mu(a) = O(a^2) \quad \text{as } a \to \infty \tag{3.27}$$

with $C_5 = C_3 C_4$. This completes the proof of Theorem 3.1. □

4. Numerical Examples. In this section, we give numerical examples to illustrate the effects of mesh refinements by polynomial and exponential stretching functions. In the following, we denote $\max_{P \in \Omega_h} |u(P) - U(P)|$ by ε. EXAMPLE 4.1. Let $\Omega = \{(x, y) \in (0,1) \times (0,1)\}$. We consider the following example

$$-\Delta u = f(x, y) \quad \text{in } \Omega, \tag{4.1}$$

$$u = 0 \quad \text{on } \Gamma, \tag{4.2}$$

where $f(x, y)$ is chosen so that the exact solution is $u(x, y) = x^{\sigma} y^{\sigma}(1 - x)(1 - y)$ with $\sigma \in (0, 2)$. It is noted that u satisfies the conditions (2.1)–(2.3). In this example, we test the two stretching functions defined by (1.21) and (1.20). Given σ, we take p and a as parameters for polynomial and exponential stretching functions, respectively. The numerical results in the cases $\sigma = 0.2$, 0.8 and 1.6 are shown in Figure 4.1 with $h = 1/400$, $1/500$ and $1/600$. Of course, the maximum error ε decreases as h decreases so that the upmost branch corresponds to $h = 1/400$ and the lowest branch corresponds to $h = 1/600$ in the figure. For the polynomial stretching function, it follows from Theorem 2.1 that given h, $E(p) = K(p)h^r$ is monotonically decreasing with respect to $p > 0$ if

$$\frac{E'(p)}{E(p)} = \frac{3}{p+1} + 3\log 2 + \sigma \log h < 0,$$

and $L(p)h^2$ is monotonically increasing for $p > 0$. Hence ε decreases in $(0, p_{max})$, where $p_{max} = \frac{2}{\sigma} - 1$, or for each σ there exists an optimal value p^* such that ε decreases as p varies from 0 to p^* and increases as p increases from p^* to $p_{\max}$. As Figure 4.1 shows, p^* moves to the left when σ increases, that is, when the singularity of the exact solution becomes weak.

The same remark applies to the exponential stretching function and there exists an optimal value a^* such that ε decreases for $0 < a < a^*$ and increases for $a > a^*$.

EXAMPLE 4.2. (M. Ishiguro [8]) Let $\Omega = \{(x, y) \in (0,1) \times (0,1)\}$ and we consider the following example

$$-\Delta u = f(x, y) \quad \text{in } \Omega, \tag{4.3}$$

$$u = g(x, y) \quad \text{on } \Gamma, \tag{4.4}$$

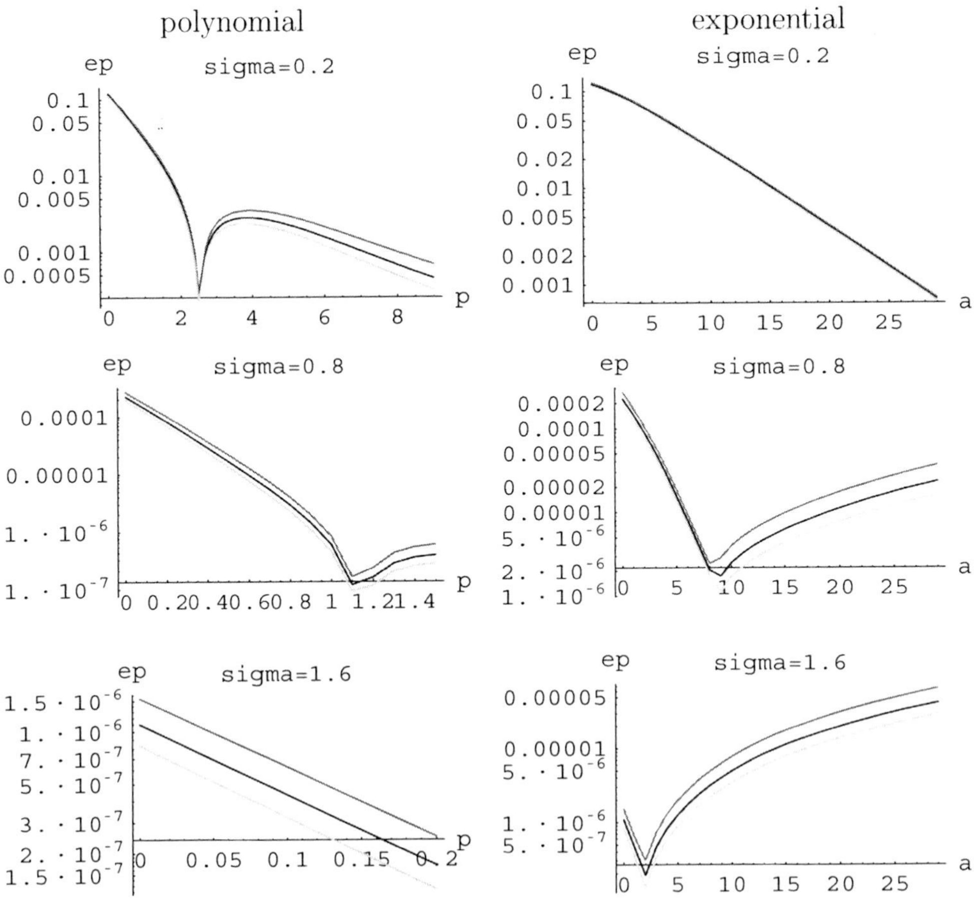

FIG. 4.1. *Effect of stretching functions for Example 4.1;* $\varepsilon = \max_{P\in\Omega_h} |u(P) - U(P)|$; $h = 1/400, 1/500, 1/600$.

where $f(x, y)$ and $g(x, y)$ are chosen so that the exact solution is $u(x, y) = \frac{1}{2}\log\{(x + \xi)^2 + (y + \eta)^2\}$. It is noted that if $\xi > 0$ and $\eta > 0$, then $u \in C^\infty(\overline{\Omega})$. However, the derivatives of the exact solution are nearly singular at the origin for sufficiently small $\xi > 0$ and $\eta > 0$. Therefore, we can also apply the adaptive finite difference techniques developed in Sections 2–3.

The results for the case $\xi = \eta = e^{-4}/\sqrt{2}$ are shown in Figure 4.2 with $h = 1/400, 1/500, 1/600$.

We note that the behaviors of the approximate solutions obtained by polynomial and exponential stretching functions in Example 4.2 are similar to those for Example 4.1.

REFERENCES

[1] J. H. BRAMBLE AND B. E. HUBBARD, *On the formulation of finite difference analogues of the Dirichlet problem for Poisson's equation*, Numer. Math., 4 (1962), pp. 313–327.

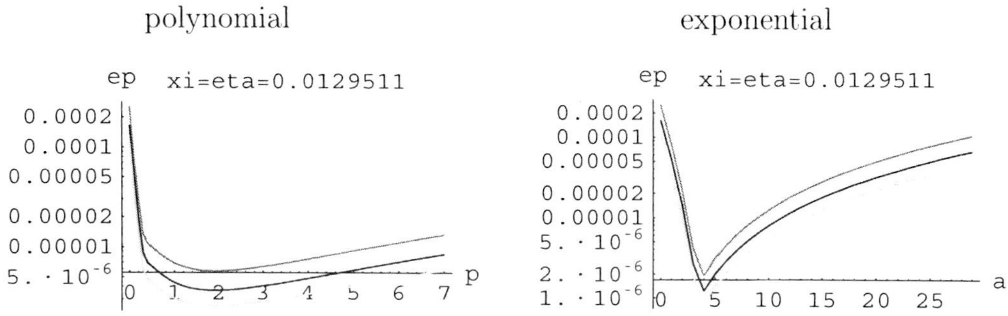

FIG. 4.2. *Effect of stretching functions for Example 4.2;*
$\varepsilon = \max_{P \in \Omega_h} |u(P) - U(P)|$*;* $h = 1/400, 1/500, 1/600$.

[2] W. CAO, W. HUANG AND R. D. RUSSELL, *A study of monitor functions for two dimensional adaptive mesh generation*, SIAM J. Sci. Comput., 20 (1999), pp. 1978–1994.

[3] X. CHEN, N. MATSUNAGA AND T. YAMAMOTO, *Smoothing Newton methods for nonsmooth Dirichlet problems*, in Reformulation—Nonsmooth, Piecewise Smooth, Semismooth and Smoothing Methods, M. Fukushima and L. Qi, Eds., Kluwer, Dordrecht 1998, pp. 56–79.

[4] Q. FANG, T. MATSUBARA, Y. SHOGENJI AND T. YAMAMOTO, *Convergence of inconsistent finite difference scheme for Dirichlet problem whose solution has singular derivatives at the boundary*, Information, 4 (2001), pp. 161–170.

[5] R. GORENFLO AND ÜBER S. GERSCHGORINS, *Methode der Fehlerabschatzung bei Differenzenzenverfahren*, Lecture Notes in Math., 333, Springer 1973, pp. 128–143.

[6] W. HUANG, Y. REN AND R. D. RUSSELL, *Moving mesh partial differential equations based on the equidistribution principle*, SIAM J. Numer. Anal., 31 (1994), pp. 709–730.

[7] W. HUANG AND D. M. SLOAN, *A simple adaptive grid method in two dimensions*, SIAM J. Sci. Comput., 15 (1994), pp. 776–797.

[8] M. ISHIGURO, *Numerical errors and condition number for two-dimensional Laplace's equation by stretching functions* (in Japanese), Abstract of JSIAM meeting 2000, pp. 470–471, September 2000.

[9] J. A. MACKENZIE AND M. L. ROBERTSON, *The numerical solution of one-dimensional phase change problems using an adaptive moving mesh method*, J. Comput. Phys., 161 (2000), pp. 537–557.

[10] N. MATSUNAGA AND T. YAMAMOTO, *Superconvergence of the Shortley-Weller approximation for Dirichlet problems*, J. Comp. Appl. Math., 116 (2000), pp. 263–273.

[11] N. MATSUNAGA AND T. YAMAMOTO, *Convergence of Swartztrauber-Sweet's approximation for the Poisson-type equation on a disk*, Numer. Funct. Anal. and Optimz., 20 (1999), pp. 917–928.

[12] A. P. COSTA MOURO, *On the use of nonuniform meshes in the numerical solution of singularly perturbed boundary value problems in two dimensions*, Abstract of ICCAM 2000, Leuven, July 2000.

[13] L. S. MULHOLLAND, Y. QIU AND D. M. SLOAN, *Solution of evolutionary partial differential equations using adaptive finite differences with pesudespectral post-processing*, J. Comp. Phys., 131 (1997), pp. 280–298.

[14] Y. QIU AND D. M. SLOAN, *Analysis of difference approximations to a singular perturbed two-point boundary value problem on an adaptively generated grid*, J. Comput. App. Math., 101 (1999), pp. 1–25.

[15] Y. QIU, D. M. SLOAN AND T. TANG, *Numerical solution of a singularly perturbed two-point boundary value problem using equidistribution: analysis of convergence*, J. Comput. Appl. Math., 116 (2000), pp. 121–143.

[16] T. TANG, W. XUE AND P. ZHANG, *Analysis of moving mesh methods based on geometrical variables*, J. Comput. Math., 19 (2001), pp. 41–54.

[17] J. F. THOMPSON, J. F. THAMES AND C. W. MASTIN, *Automatic numerical generation of body-fitted curvilinear coordinate system for field containing any number of arbitrary two-dimensonal bodies*, J. Comp. Phys., 15 (1974).

[18] J. F. THOMPSON, Z. U. A. WARSI AND C. W. MASTIN, *Numerical Grid Generation*, North-Holland, New York-Amsterdam, 1985.

[19] K. TSUBOI, *Condition number of tridiagonal matrix in stretching coordinate system* (in Japanese), JSIAM, 10 (2000), pp. 133–144.

[20] R. S. VARGA, *Matrix Iterative Analysis*, Prentice-Hall, 1962.

[21] T. YAMAMOTO, *Convergence of consistent and inconsist finite difference schemes and an acceleration technique*, to appear in J. Comput. Appl. Math..

[22] T. YAMAMOTO, Q. FANG AND X. CHEN, *Superconvergence and nonsuperconvergence of the Shortley-Weller approximations for Dirichlet problems*, Numer. Funct. Anal. Optimiz., 22 (2001), pp. 161–170.

In: Focus on Computational Neurobiology
Editor: Lei Li, pp. 65-70

ISBN 1-59033-915-0

TRAVELING SALESMAN CRYPTOSYSTEM*

TSUTOMU ANSAI†, HIROAKI MATSUYAMA‡, AND KUNIKATSU KOBAYASHI§

Abstract. We propose a public key cryptosystem using the traveling salesman problem that is a NP-complete problem. First, we show the outline on the traveling salesman cryptosystem, then investigate sequences used as the secret key in the traveling salesman cryptosystem. Next, we consider the public key generation for the traveling salesman cryptosystem, further propose the new encryption using the mixed sum and product operations. Finally, we examine the security of this cryptosystem against the attack using Shamir algorithm and LLL algorithm.

Key words. traveling salesman cryptosystem, NP-complete problem, public key cryptosystem, Shamir algorithm, LLL algorithm

1. Introduction. Cryptographic technology is one of the information security technologies, and various cryptography and signature methods have actively been investigated. The knapsack cryptosystem [1] is known as one of the public key cryptosystems that the NP-complete problem is applied, and many of the knapsack cryptosystems of additional type have been broken by Shamir algorithm [2] that obtains a secret key from a public key, LLL algorithm [3] that obtains the plain text from the public key and cipher text, and the like. The knapsack cryptosystem packs an arbitrary number of elements from the public key into a knapsack to compose the cipher text, whereas traveling salesman cryptosystem [4], [5], and [6] that the traveling salesman problem [7] is applied to the cryptosystem constitutes a cipher text by packing n distances between cities forming Hamilton cycle from the public key. When the number and procedure of packing are restricted like this, public key cryptosystems with tolerance against Shamir algorithm and LLL algorithm can be constructed because methods of composing cipher texts with the public key as well as variety of secret keys that can uniquely decrypt cipher text increase in comparison with cases when arbitrarily packed.

In this paper, we first the show outline on the traveling salesman cryptosystem, then investigate sequences used as the secret key in the knapsack cryptosystem and traveling salesman cryptosystem. Next, we consider with respect to transformation method of generating the public key from the secret key, further studied on encryption to make cipher text by means of the public key, and propose a multiplicative type encryption and a encryption using the mixed addition-multiplication against the attack using Shamir algorithm and LLL algorithm, and consider on cryptosystems with a high security.

2. Traveling Salesman Cryptosystem. In the traveling salesman problem, one of the NP-complete problems, the traveling salesman cryptosystem stands for what is applied to the public key cryptosystem by letting path (route) that a salesman traces correspond to a plain text while its path length to a cipher text.

2.1. Key generation. First, number of cities n is set and a sequence up to the $n(n-1)/2$-th term is determined as shown in Section 3, and this is given as the sequence of the secret key. Next, transformation shown in Section 4 is conducted on the sequence of the

*This research has been supported by the Kayamori Foundation of Informational Science Advancement and the Telecommunications Advancement Foundation.

†Ibaraki National College of Technology, Hitachinaka-shi, Japan (ansai@ee.ibaraki-ct.ac.jp)
‡Yamagata University, Yonezawa-shi, Japan (hiro@ee5.yz.yamagata-u.ac.jp)
§Yamagata University, Yonezawa-shi, Japan (kobayash@yz.yamagata-u.ac.jp)

secret key and obtains the sequence of the public key. The public key stands for the elements of the transformed sequence given as distances between each cities with an appropriate rule (corresponding to map) and values of modulo when the public key was obtained. In contrast to this, the secret key is the rule that allots sequence and its elements determined in the beginning as distances between each cities and parameters corresponding to the generating method of the public key.

2.2. Encryption. First, $(n-1)!/2$ different traveling paths are let to correspond to plain texts from No.1 to No.$(n-1)!/2$, and a traveling path is selected in dependence on the value of the plain text. And a path length C is obtained by packing distances between each city contained in the selected path and this is sent to a receiver as the cipher text. Description on this packing is given in Section 5.

2.3. Decryption. In decryption, an operation corresponding to an inverse operation to that performed when a public key is first made with respect to the cipher text by means of secret keys. Namely, multiplicative inverse of multiples for modulo comes to multiply when modular multiplication was used for generating the public key. Then factoring and division are conducted on the obtained values using elements of the secret key, and packed elements are found from remained values and inequality relation of the secret key in case of the mixed addition-multiplication type, to decrypt the path.

3. The Sequence Used as a Secret Key. The sequence employed as the secret key $\boldsymbol{A} = (a_1, a_2, \cdots, a_n)$ in a knapsack cryptosystem of multiplication type are mutually different prime sequence. In the traveling salesman cryptosystem of the mixed addition-multiplication type or the knapsack cryptosystem of addition type, in contrast, the cipher texts can efficiently be decrypted by means of the following several sequences as the secret key:

3.1. The Super-Increasing Sequence.

$$\begin{aligned} a_1 &> 0 \\ a_i &> \sum_{j=1}^{i-1} a_j \quad (i \geq 2). \end{aligned} \tag{3.1}$$

When this super-increasing sequence is used, the plain and cipher texts correspond 1 : 1 even though arbitrary number of elements are packed into a knapsack and cipher text can uniquely be decrypted. Density of this sequence is not higher than 1.

3.2. City sequence. When the number of cities is n, n initial values of the city sequence are determined so as to satisfy

$$\begin{aligned} a_2 &> a_1 > 0 \\ a_i &\geq \sum_{j=1}^{i-1} a_j \quad (j = 3, \cdots, n) \end{aligned} \tag{3.2}$$

and its general term is obtained with

$$a_{i+n} = \sum_{j=i}^{i+n-1} a_j \quad (i \geq 1). \tag{3.3}$$

When using this city sequence, plain and cipher texts correspond $1:1$ even if distances between n cities are arbitrarily packed into a knapsack. Decryption is conducted by using the backtracking procedure. Density of this sequence becomes higher than that of the super-increasing sequence.

3.3. The Fibonacci Sequence. Two initial values are determined so as to satisfy

$$a_2 > a_1 > 0 \tag{3.4}$$

and its general term is obtained with

$$a_i = a_{i-1} + a_{i-2} \quad (i \geq 3). \tag{3.5}$$

When using this Fibonacci sequence, the plain and cipher texts correspond $1:1$ even if the distances between n cities among those alloted under a certain rule are arbitrarily packed for the number of cities being $n \leq 13$. However, it is uncertain if the plain and cipher texts correspond $1:1$ even for $n \geq 14$. The density of this sequence becomes higher than that of the city sequence.

4. Transformation from the secret key to public key.

4.1. In case of mixed addition-multiplication type.

4.1.1. Modular multiplication. Using modulo p and multiplier w that are mutually prime, the secret key a_i is linear transformed as

$$b_i \equiv wa_i \pmod{p} \tag{4.1}$$

to get the public key b_i. Application of the Shamir algorithm to these public key b_i gives a highly probability of getting the secret key a_i. When applying the Shamir algorithm to public keys b_i obtained with modular multiplication, however, secret keys a_i are not always high in probability of obtaining them regardless of property of the sequence. When a_i are the super-increasing sequence or city sequence, probability to obtain those a_i is high, whereas when the combination of the super-increasing sequence and prime sequence having no relation with super-increasing property is used as the secret key, complexity of computing to find the secret key with the Shamir algorithm becomes close to that of the brute force attack.

4.1.2. Power transformation. Let $N = pq$, where p and q are prime numbers, and N is the modulo. The public key b_i is obtained by nonlinear transformation of the secret key a_i as

$$b_i \equiv a_i^p \pmod{N}. \tag{4.2}$$

It is difficult to obtain the secret key a_i even though those public key b_i are attacked with Shamir algorithm. Thus, power transformation is secure against Shamir algorithm. In this case, however, the modulo N must be hardly prime-factorized.

4.2. In case of multiplication type. The public key in the knapsack cryptosystem of multiplication type is obtained by power transformation of the secret key a_i as

$$b_i \equiv a_i^s \pmod{p} \tag{4.3}$$

by letting a prime number p as the modulo and using an appropriate integer s that is mutually prime with p. Secret keys a_i are hardly obtained even though these public keys b_i are applied with Shamir algorithm.

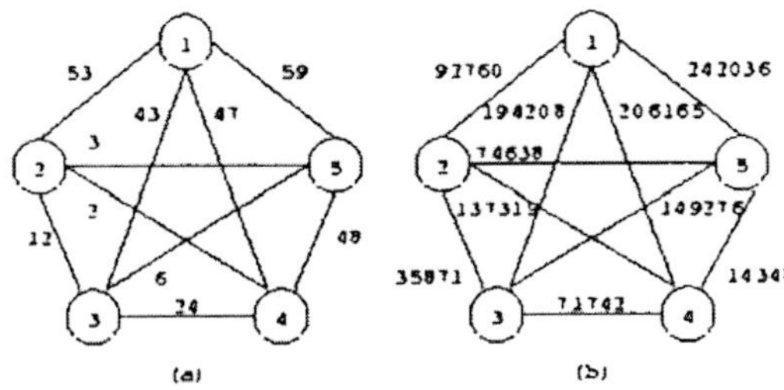

FIG. 5.1. *An example for addition-multiplication type Traveling Salesman Cryptosystem*

5. Method of encryption.

5.1. Multiplication type. This is a cryptosystem that the cipher text is given as the product of arbitrary elements of the public key obtained by power transformation under modulo p, and it is difficult to break this multiplication type cryptosystem with LLL algorithm.

5.2. Mixed addition-multiplication type. The knapsack cryptosystem packs arbitrary number of public keys into a knapsack, whereas the traveling salesman cryptosystem packs a fixed number of cities n into the knapsack. In the traveling salesman cryptosystem, accordingly, the cipher text may be obtained by the operation such as adding some of n public keys packed and multiplying the rest, thus, it is enabled to have a constitution of a new cryptosystem.

1. When a cipher text is determined by the mixed addition-multiplication operation by means of the public key obtained by power transformation of the secret key, this cryptosystem is hardly broken with Shamir algorithm or the LLL algorithm.

2. When a cipher text is determined by the mixed addition-multiplication operation by means of the public key obtained by modular transformation of the secret key, this cryptosystem is hardly broken with the LLL algorithm. The security against the Shamir algorithm depends on what kind of sequence used in the secret key is, and the secret key can be obtained from the public key when using the super-increasing sequence, whereas attack with the Shamir algorithm becomes difficult from view point of complexity of computing when using Fibonacci sequence or a combination of the super-increasing sequence and the prime sequence as the secret key. Shown below is an example of a simple traveling salesman cryptosystem consisting of 5 cities.

Example: Distance between each city is determined as shown in FIG. 5.1(a) by means of

$$A = (2, 3, 6, 12, 24, 48, 43, 47, 53, 59) \tag{5.1}$$

that is a combination of the super-increasing sequence and the prime sequence. When using a prime number $p = 262681$ larger than the longest path length $59 \times 53 \times (48+24+12)$ is used as the modulo p and setting a multiplier $w = 200000$ to conduct a modular transformation, the public key becomes

$$B = (137319, 74638, 149276, 35871, 71742, 143484, 194208, 206165, 92760, 242036) \tag{5.2}$$

to make FIG.5.1(b) public. When taking paths 1–2–3–4–5–1 as a plain text, the cipher text C becomes

$$\begin{aligned} C &= 242036 \times 92760 \times (143484 + 71742 + 35871) \pmod{262681} \\ &\equiv 193141. \end{aligned}$$

For decryption,

$$\begin{aligned} D(C) &= (w^{-1})^3 C \pmod{p} \\ &\equiv 262668 \end{aligned} \tag{5.3}$$

in obtained by using multiplicative inverse of $w : w^{-1} = 200004$ and this $D(C)$ is first divided with four prime numbers 43,47,53 and 59 to find two prime numbers that can exactly divide. Then by finding the remaining paths from inequality relations between values of obtained quotients and elements of super-increasing sequence, 1–2–3–4–5–1 is decrypted.
Plain text can not be obtained even though the LLL algorithm is applied to a matrix determined by the public key of (5.2) and the cipher text of (5.3). When the Shamir algorithm is applied to the public key of (5.2), on the other hand, sequence A of (5.1) can be found but complexity of computing required for this becomes close to the brute force attack. In short, when the secret key is determined with the combination of the super-increasing sequence and prime sequence, it becomes substantially difficult to obtain the secret key from the public key with the Shamir algorithm as the number of cities n increases.

6. Security evaluation. With respect to a cryptosystem combined the following three conditions:

1. Kind of the secret key(Trick for decryption),
2. Transformation method from the secret key into the public key (The method to make the trick incomprehensible), and
3. Relation between the public key and the cipher text(The method to make crypt-analysis difficult),

security against Shamir algorithm and LLL algorithm is discussed.

1. The Multiplicative type cryptosystem using the public key that the appropriate secret key (e.g. the prime sequences different from each other) was power transformed:
Cryptosystems of this type represented by the multiplicative type knapsack cryptosystem is secure against Shamir and the LLL algorithms.

2. The mixed addition-multiplication type cryptosystem by means of a public key that an appropriate secret key (e.g. a sequence consisting of a super-increasing sequence and a prime sequence) was power transformed:
Even though Shamir algorithm is applied to public keys determined with power transformation, secret keys are hardly obtained. Even though the LLL algorithm is applied to cipher texts determined by the mixed addition-multiplication operation of public keys, too, plain text are hardly obtained. In short, cryptosystems of this type is also secure against the Shamir and the LLL algorithms.

3. The mixed addition-multiplication type cryptosystem by means of the public key that the secret key comprising the super-increasing sequence and the prime sequence was modular transformed:
What was shown in the example is a cryptosystem of this type, and security against the Shamir algorithm becomes a problem because the public key has been determined by the modular transformation of the secret key. When density of the secret key vector is over 1 and yet some of specified prime numbers are included, however, it becomes difficult to obtain decodable keys with the Shamir algorithm as the number of cities n increases. Even though the LLL algorithm is applied to the cryptosystems of this type, too, the plain texts are hardly obtained.

7. Conclusion. We proposed algorithms of the traveling salesman cryptosystem and examined the security of this cryptosystem against the Shamir and LLL algorithms. The Shamir algorithm is a method to efficiently obtain the secret key from the public key, but what this method becomes effective is for the public key determined by the modular transformation of the secret key with density under 1 like a super-increasing vector, and not efficient for the public key that the secret key containing several specified prime numbers was modular-transformed. As the number of the secret key containing such a high density as this goes increased, complexity of computing necessary for getting the decodable key (the secret key itself) from the public key using the Shamir algorithm becomes almost equal to the brute force attack for keys, making it substantially difficult to solve the secret key. On the other hand, the LLL algorithm has widely been used for breaking linear cryptosystems and the like, and the addition type cryptosystems can be almost broken, but an attack becomes difficult when a nonlinear operation was used for encryption. In short, the traveling salesman cryptosystem and knapsack cryptosystem with security against the Shamir and LLL algorithms can be constituted by combining variations of the secret key, transformation methods from the secret key into the public key and encrypting methods.

The traveling salesman cryptosystem can be regarded as a conditional knapsack cryptosystem with such conditions that the number of packing into a knapsack is constant to the number of cities n and forms Hamilton cycle. By attaching these conditions, cipher texts can be composed by the mixed addition-multiplication operations of the public key, which is hardly realized with the knapsack cryptosystem, and security of the cryptosystem can be raised. Namely, NP-complete problems are considered to contain those fit for cryptosystems having security against attacking algorithms, and it is expected that the range of realizing cryptosystems with high securiry by applying these to the cryptosystems.

REFERENCES

[1] R. C. Merkle and M. E. Hellman, *Hiding information and signatures in trapdoor knapsacks*, IEEE Trans. Information Theory, 24, pp. 525–530(1978).

[2] A. Shamir,*A polynomial time algorithm for breaking the basic Merkle-Hellman cryptosystem*, Crypto 82Cpp. 279–288 (1983).

[3] A. M. Odlyzko,*Cryptanalytic attacks on the multiplicative knapsack cryptosystem and on Shamir's fast signature scheme*, IEEE Trans. Information Theory, 30, pp. 594–601(1984).

[4] T. Ansai, H. Matsuyama, T .Hayata, and K. Kobayashi, *An Application of the Traveling Salesman Problem to Public Key Cryptosystem*, Technical Report of IEICE,ISEC2000-91,pp. 89–96 (2000).

[5] H. Matsuyama, T. Ansai, T. Hayata, and K. Kobayashi ,*Public Key Cryptosystem Using the Traveling Salesman Problem*, SCIS2001,pp. 821–826 (2001).

[6] T. Ansai, H. Matsuyama, and K. Kobayashi, *Traveling Salesman Cryptosystem*, Technical Report of IEICE,ISEC2001-26,pp. 53–58 (2001).

[7] Edited by E. L. Lawler et al., *The Traveling Salesman Problem*, Jhon Wiley & Sons(1995).

In: Focus on Computational Neurobiology
Editor: Lei Li, pp. 71-83
ISBN 1-59033-915-0

EIGENMODE ANALYSIS OF OPTICAL WAVEGUIDES BY THE IMAGINARY-DISTANCE FULL-VECTORIAL BEAM-PROPAGATION METHOD BASED ON YEE'S MESH

JUNJI YAMAUCHI*, NAOFUMI MOROHASHI , AND HISAMATSU NAKANO

Abstract. Techniques for improving the imaginary-distance full-vectorial beam-propagation method based on Yee's mesh are presented for the eigenmode analysis of optical waveguides. Fourth- and sixth-order accuracies are achieved for the analysis of a graded-index waveguide. For a step-index waveguide, the conventional scheme is used together with a permittivity-averaging technique. Numerical results demonstrate a second-order accuracy even in the analysis of a rib waveguide. The effective index and the field profiles of major and minor components are presented and discussed.

Key words. Optical waveguides, eigenmode, Yee's mesh, beam-propagation method

1. Introduction. The knowledge of the eigenmodes in an optical waveguide is of fundamental importance in the design of photonic integrated circuits. To date many methods have been proposed for this important issue [1]. Finite-difference mode solvers are often preferred for their greater simplicity. Recently, Lee [2] has proposed the full-vectorial finite-difference beam-propagation method (FD-BPM) based on Yee's mesh [3]. Using the imaginary-distance procedure [4]-[6], he succeeded in developing an eigenmode solver. The use of Yee's mesh has the advantage that all electric- and magnetic-field components are simultaneously evaluated, and that the obtained eigenmode field is directly utilized for the time-domain Yee's algorithm, the so-called FD-TD method. It should be noted, however, that Lee employed the conventional second-order accurate scheme. In addition, he did not fully describe the treatment of the interface condition for a step-index waveguide.

In this paper, we discuss techniques for improving the accuracy of Lee's method. Higher-order accurate schemes are applied to the analysis of a graded-index waveguide, and the increased accuracy is demonstrated. The effective index is evaluated using a technique in which the reference index is renewed as the field propagates. For the analysis of a step-index waveguide, the higher-order schemes cannot be blindly used, since the interface condition predominates the accuracy. After confirming the second-order accuracy in a two-dimensional step-index waveguide, we analyze a rib waveguide using a permittivity-averaging technique. The calculated effective-index is compared with that obtained from the modal transverse resonance method [1, 7]. Calculation shows that the minor-field component has the same convergence rate as that of the major-field component, in spite of the existence of singularities at the corner [8]-[10]. The field profiles of major and minor components are presented and discussed.

2. Numerical method. We first summarize the formulation of the Yee's mesh FD-BPM, following Lee's procedure [2]. Consider a linear lossless medium with the permittivity ϵ and the permeability μ. The formulation begins with Maxwell's time-dependent equations:

$$\nabla \times \boldsymbol{\mathcal{E}} = -\mu \frac{\partial \boldsymbol{\mathcal{H}}}{\partial t} \tag{2.1}$$

$$\nabla \times \boldsymbol{\mathcal{H}} = \epsilon \frac{\partial \boldsymbol{\mathcal{E}}}{\partial t} \tag{2.2}$$

*Faculty of Engineering, Hosei University, 3-7-2 Kajino-cho Koganei, Tokyo 184-8584 Japan (j.yma@k.hosei.ac.jp).

where $\mathcal{E}$ and $\mathcal{H}$ are the electric and magnetic field vectors, respectively. The $\mathcal{E}$ and $\mathcal{H}$ are normalized so that their magnitudes may be of the same order, i.e., $\mathcal{E} = \sqrt{\mu_0}\,\boldsymbol{e}$ and $\mathcal{H} = \sqrt{\epsilon_0}\,\boldsymbol{h}$. Substituting the set of normalized fields into the original Maxwell's equations, we get

$$\nabla \times \boldsymbol{e} = -\mu_r \frac{\partial \boldsymbol{h}}{\partial \tau} \tag{2.3}$$

$$\nabla \times \boldsymbol{h} = \epsilon_r \frac{\partial \boldsymbol{e}}{\partial \tau} \tag{2.4}$$

where $\tau = ct$ ($c = 1/\sqrt{\epsilon_0\mu_0}$ is the velocity of light in free space), and $\epsilon_r(= n^2)$ and μ_r are the relative permittivity and permeability, respectively.

Let

$$\boldsymbol{e}(x, y, z, \tau) = \boldsymbol{E}(x, y, z)\exp[jk_0(\tau - n_0 z)] \tag{2.5}$$

$$\boldsymbol{h}(x, y, z, \tau) = \boldsymbol{H}(x, y, z)\exp[jk_0(\tau - n_0 z)] \tag{2.6}$$

where $\boldsymbol{E}$ and $\boldsymbol{H}$ are the slowly varying envelope functions of z, k_0 is the free-space wavenumber, and n_0 is the reference index. After substituting (2.5) and (2.6) into (2.3) and (2.4) and using the notation $(x, y, z) = (i\Delta x, m\Delta y, k\Delta z) = (i, m, k)$, we obtain the following difference equations based on Yee's mesh shown in Fig. 2.1.

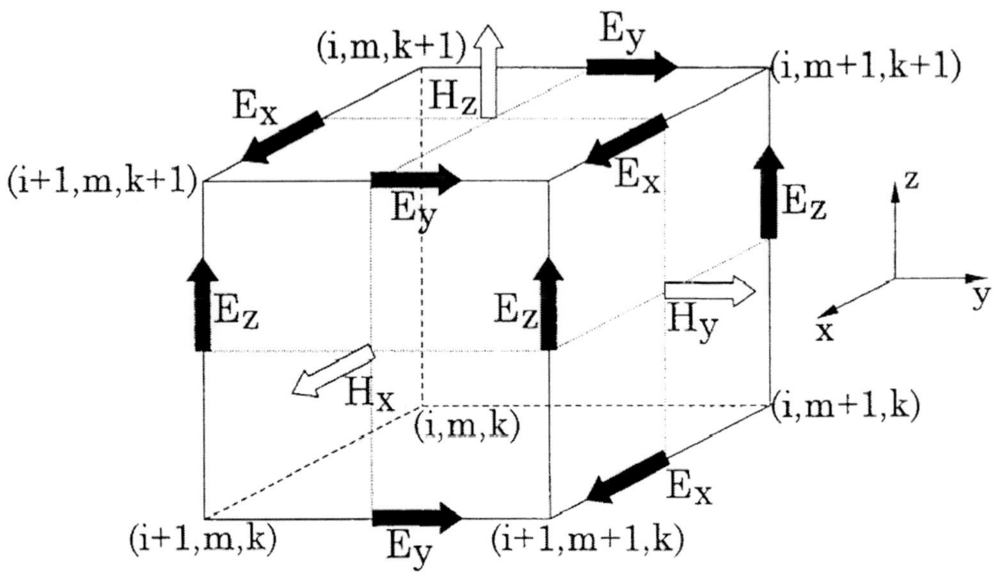

FIG. 2.1. *Yee's mesh*

$$\begin{aligned} E_x(i+1/2, m, k+1) = \frac{1}{1 - j\beta_0\Delta z/2}[&(1 + j\beta_0\Delta z/2)E_x(i+1/2, m, k) \\ &+\Delta z\delta_x E_z(i+1/2, m, k+1/2) \\ &-jk_0\Delta z H_y(i+1/2, m, k+1/2)] \end{aligned} \tag{2.7}$$

$$\begin{aligned} E_y(i,m+1/2,k+1) = \frac{1}{1-j\beta_0\Delta z/2}[(1+j\beta_0\Delta z/2)E_y(i,m+1/2,k) \\ +\Delta z\delta_y E_z(i,m+1/2,k+1/2) \\ +jk_0\Delta z H_x(i,m+1/2,k+1/2)] \end{aligned} \tag{2.8}$$

$$\begin{aligned} H_x(i,m+1/2,k+1/2) = \frac{1}{1-j\beta_0\Delta z/2}[(1+j\beta_0\Delta z/2)H_x(i,m+1/2,k-1/2) \\ +\Delta z\delta_x H_z(i,m+1/2,k) \\ +jk_0\Delta z n^2(i,m+1/2,k)E_y(i,m+1/2,k)] \end{aligned} \tag{2.9}$$

$$\begin{aligned} H_y(i+1/2,m,k+1/2) = \frac{1}{1-j\beta_0\Delta z/2}[(1+j\beta_0\Delta z/2)H_y(i+1/2,m,k-1/2) \\ +\Delta z\delta_y H_z(i+1/2,m,k) \\ -jk_0\Delta z n^2(i+1/2,m,k)E_x(i+1/2,m,k)] \end{aligned} \tag{2.10}$$

$$\begin{aligned} E_z(i,m,k+1/2) = \frac{1}{(1-j\beta_0\Delta z/2)n^2(i,m,k+1/2)} \\ \times[(1+j\beta_0\Delta z/2)n^2(i,m,k-1/2)E_z(i,m,k-1/2) \\ -\Delta z\delta_x\{n^2(i,m,k)E_x(i,m,k)\} \\ -\Delta z\delta_y\{n^2(i,m,k)E_y(i,m,k)\}] \end{aligned} \tag{2.11}$$

$$\begin{aligned} H_z(i+1/2,m+1/2,k+1) = \frac{1}{(1-j\beta_0\Delta z/2)} \\ \times[(1+j\beta_0\Delta z/2)H_z(i+1/2,m+1/2,k) \\ -\Delta z\delta_x H_x(i+1/2,m+1/2,k+1/2) \\ -\Delta z\delta_y H_y(i+1/2,m+1/2,k+1/2)] \end{aligned} \tag{2.12}$$

where $\delta_\alpha\{\alpha = x \text{ or } y\}$ is a difference operator, $\beta_0 = n_0k_0$, and μ_r is omitted due to its assumed unit value. It should be noted that the E_z and H_z components are determined using the relations of $\nabla \cdot n^2\boldsymbol{e} = 0$ and $\nabla \cdot \boldsymbol{h} = 0$. As found in Ref. [2], the use of divergence relations contributes to a reduction in round-off errors with subsequent stability of the numerical results.

In deriving (2.7) to (2.12), we use the conventional second-order central difference formula for the longitudinal direction. To evaluate the first derivatives δ_x and δ_y in the transverse directions, we can use higher-order formulas in addition to the second-order formula. For example, the finite-difference formulas with respect to x are summarized as

$$\delta_x\phi(i,m,k) = \frac{1}{\Delta x}\{\phi(i+1/2,m,k) - \phi(i-1/2,m,k)\} + O(\Delta x^2) \tag{2.13}$$

$$\begin{aligned} \delta_x\phi(i,m,k) = \frac{1}{\Delta x}[\frac{9}{8}\{\phi(i+1/2,m,k) - \phi(i-1/2,m,k)\} \\ -\frac{1}{24}\{\phi(i+3/2,m,k) - \phi(i-3/2,m,k)\}] + O(\Delta x^4) \end{aligned} \tag{2.14}$$

$$\begin{aligned}\delta_x\phi(i,m,k) = \frac{1}{\Delta x}[& -\frac{75}{64}\{\phi(i+1/2,m,k)-\phi(i-1/2,m,k)\} \\ & +\frac{25}{384}\{\phi(i+3/2,m,k)-\phi(i-3/2,m,k)\} \\ & -\frac{3}{640}\{\phi(i+5/2,m,k)-\phi(i-5/2,m,k)\}]+O(\Delta x^6)\end{aligned} \tag{2.15}$$

Higher-order formulas [11] are derived using a polynomial fitting technique (see Appendix).

At the edge of the computational window, a transparent boundary condition (TBC) is often used. In the imaginary-distance procedure, however, the TBC is not necessarily needed, as indicated in Ref. [2]. Therefore, we set the boundary terms to zero in this analysis.

Once the mode profile is obtained, we can evaluate the effective index by [2, 5]

$$\beta = n_0k_0 + j\frac{\int\int[\ln\{\phi(x,y,z+\Delta z)\} - \ln\{\phi(x,y,z)\}] \mid \phi(x,y,z) \mid^2 dxdy}{\Delta z \int\int \mid \phi(x,y,z) \mid^2 dxdy} \tag{2.16}$$

where $\phi(x,y,z)$ is the envelope function of any field component. Lee claimed that the choice of reference index n_0 is insensitive to accuracy, since the formulation is based on Maxwell's equation, as opposed to the Fresnel equation. This is true for the case when we use the second-order formula. Our calculation, however, shows that the choice of n_0 is crucial when we employ the higher-order formulas. It should be noted that the exact value of n_0 is unknown in practice. Therefore, we employ a new technique in which the reference index is renewed iteratively as the field propagates [12, 13]. This ensures a faster convergence rate as will be shown in Fig. 3.2.

3. Graded-index waveguide. We first consider the two-dimensional waveguide with a graded-index distribution expressed as $n^2(x) = n_s^2 + 2n_s\Delta n/\cosh^2(2x/w)$, where $n_s = 2.1455, \Delta n = 0.003$ and $w = 5\ \mu$m. In this case the accuracy is determined by the finite-difference formula to be used.

Figure 3.1 shows the overlap-integral error between the numerical and exact fields of TE_0 mode as a function of transverse mesh width Δx. The wavelength of $\lambda = 1.3\ \mu$m is used. The relation of $\Delta z/\Delta x = 1/2$ is fixed [2], and the computational window dimension is taken to be $2L_x = 120\ \mu$m. A unit amplitude field (1 for $-2.5 \le x \le 2.5\ \mu$m, but zero otherwise) is used as a starting field. It is found that the use of (2.14) and (2.15) achieves the higher-order accuracy, while the conventional formula (2.13) exhibits the second-order accuracy. It is interesting to note that the results obtained from the fourth-order scheme are close to the data obtained using the FD-BPM based on the generalized Douglas (GD) scheme [14].

Figure 3.2 shows the effective-index error in which the effective index is evaluated using an iteratively renewed index with an initial value of n_s. For comparison, the results in which n_0 is fixed to be n_s are also presented. Figure 3.2 clearly demonstrates that the renewing technique leads to higher-order accuracy, while the fixed index results in the second-order accuracy even if the higher-order formulas are used.

4. Step-index waveguide. So far, a graded-index waveguide has been discussed. Now we treat a step-index waveguide. At the interface with a large step-index discontinuity, the higher-order formulas cannot be blindly used, since the higher derivatives are no longer continuous. At present the modified finite-difference formula which takes into account the index discontinuity has not been derived in Yee's mesh. Consequently, for the step-index

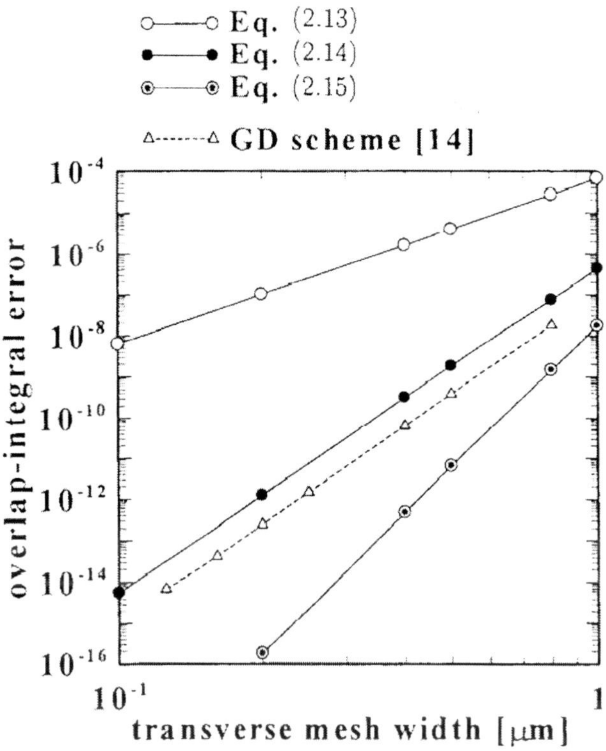

FIG. 3.1. *Overlap-integral error between the numerical and exact fields of TE_0 mode in a graded-index waveguide as a function of transverse mesh width.*

waveguide we use the conventional second-order formula, paying attention to the choice of the refractive index at the interface.

We treat the two-dimensional waveguide whose refractive indices of the core and cladding are $n_{co} = 3.512$ and $n_{cl} = 3.17$, respectively. The core width is taken to be $2d \simeq 0.316$ μm, and the wavelength is chosen to be $\lambda = 1.0$ μm, so that the normalized frequency is $V = 1.5$. The mesh width is taken to be $\Delta z/\Delta x = 1/2$. The computational window dimension is fixed to be $2L_x \simeq 4.5$ μm. The starting field is unity in the core and zero in the cladding.

Consideration is first given to the TE mode, in which E_y, H_x and H_z are treated. Figure 4.1 shows the effective-index error of the fundamental mode as a function of transverse mesh width. Two cases are shown. One is the case in which the interface is placed on the E_y component and the relative permittivity n^2 is averaged at the interface. The other is the case in which the interface is placed on the H_z component (no permittivity averaging is used). It is seen that the results using the former technique are slightly better than those in the latter, indicating the second-order accuracy.

The corresponding results for the TM mode, in which H_y, E_x and E_z are treated, are also presented in Fig. 4.1, where the two curves correspond to the cases in which the interface is placed on the E_z component, with or without using the averaging technique. The averaging technique again leads to the second-order accuracy, while the case without averaging results in the first-order accuracy. As a result, the averaging technique maintains the second-order accuracy for both the TE and TM modes.

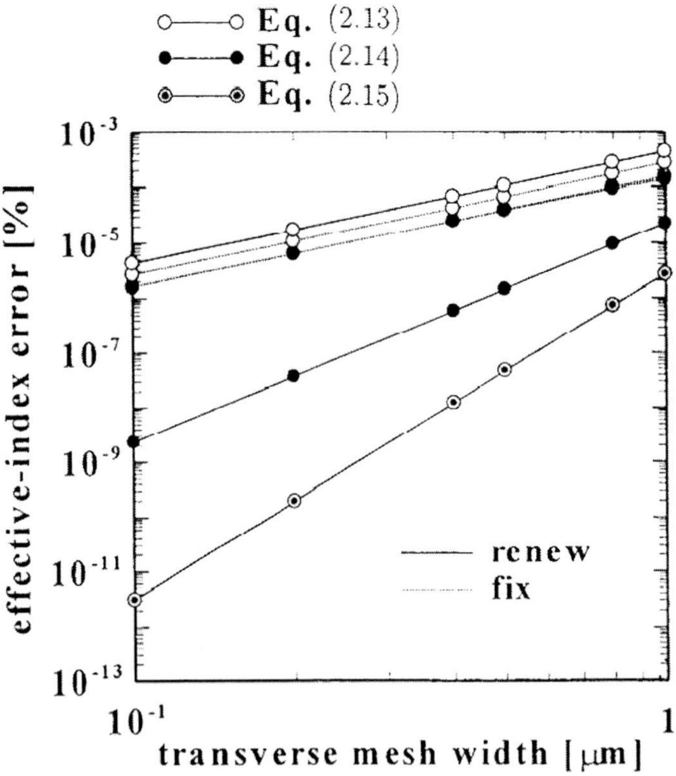

FIG. 3.2. *Effective-index error of TE_0 mode in a graded-index waveguide as a function of transverse mesh width.*

Since the validity of the averaging technique has been confirmed, we now analyze the dominant TE and TM modes of a rib waveguide as a classical benchmark. Detailed description of the geometry has been given in Ref. [1]. The configuration parameters are $n_s = 3.40$, $n_{gl} = 3.44$, rib width $= 3.0\ \mu m$, central rib height $= 1.0\ \mu m$, and lateral height $= 0.5\ \mu m$. The computational domain parameters are $Y_a = 0.5\ \mu m$ above the top of rib, $Y_s = 3.0\ \mu m$ below the guiding layer, $X_s = 2.5\ \mu m$ aside from the rib lateral side. A wavelength of $\lambda = 1.15\ \mu m$ is used.

Note that the E_z component should be located in the corner of the waveguide. This automatically satisfies the tangential continuity of E_z component across material interfaces, and avoids evaluation of divergent field components E_x and E_y at the corner due to a staggered mesh. In the corner, the relative permittivity is set to be an averaged value between the adjacent nodes. This technique is consistent with the fact derived from Ampere's circuital law, whose detailed discussion is found in Ref. [10].

As the starting field, we choose a step function as

$$\phi(x, y, 0) = \begin{cases} 1 & \text{for } 0 \le x \le 1.5\ \mu\text{m and } 0 \le y \le 1.0\ \mu\text{m} \\ 0 & \text{otherwise} \end{cases}$$

for the major component and zero for the minor component. Figure 4.2 shows the convergence behavior of the normalized effective index B as a function of propagation distance. The normalized propagation constant is defined by $B = (n_{\text{eff}}^2 - n_s^2)/(n_{gl}^2 - n_s^2)$ in which

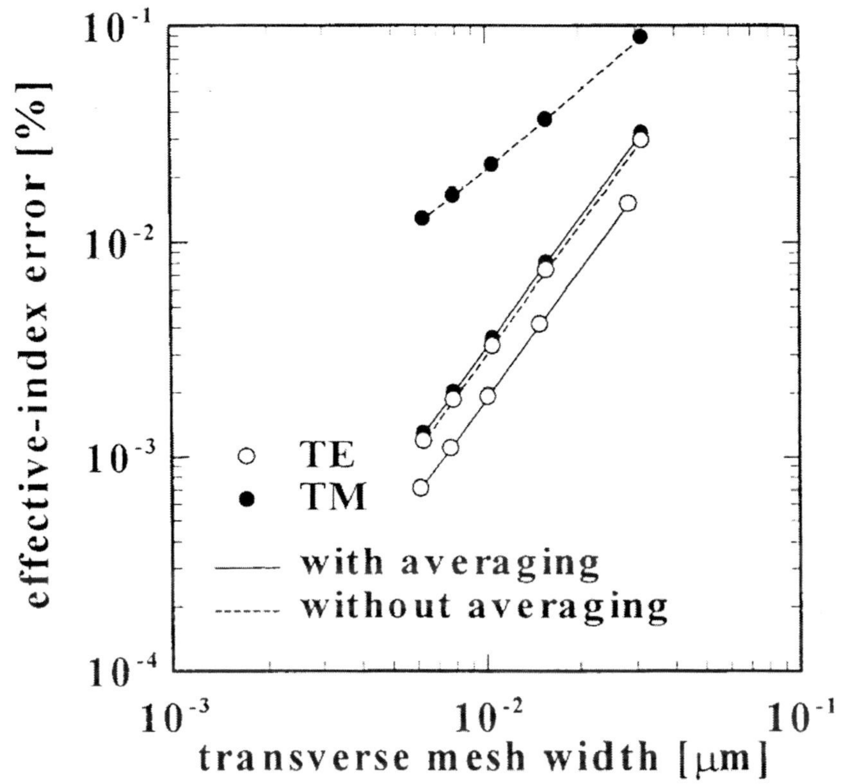

FIG. 4.1. *Effective-index error of TE_0 and TM_0 modes in a step-index waveguide as a function of transverse mesh width.*

$n_{\text{eff}} = \beta/k_0$. In this calculation, $\Delta(= \Delta x = \Delta y)$ is taken to be 0.025 μm. The relation of $\Delta z/\Delta = 1/2$ is maintained throughout. We can find rapid convergence for both the quasi-TE and quasi-TM modes.

The convergence behavior of the normalized effective-index B as the function of the mesh width Δ is shown in Fig. 4.3. For comparison, the results obtained from the modal transverse resonance method (MTRM) [1, 7] are also shown. It is seen that our results B_{YEE}'s converge to values close to the B_{MTRM}'s as the mesh width is decreased.

We determine a more precise effective index using an extrapolation technique. Assuming that $n_e(\Delta) = n_e(\Delta = 0) + \alpha\Delta^2$, we can readily determine $n_e(\Delta = 0)$ and α from data at two different Δ's. Figure 4.4 shows the effective-index error in which the extrapolated value is assumed to be exact: $[n_e(\Delta = 0) - n_e(\Delta)]/n_e(\Delta = 0) \times 100[\%]$. We can confirm the second-order accuracy for both the modes. In Fig. 4.4, the data is generated by the major-field component. Further calculation shows that each component produces the same curve within the thickness of line. In other words, the present method ensures the second-order accuracy in the minor-field component as well as the major-field component.

The extrapolation technique readily gives the B_{YEE} at $\Delta = 0$, from which the deviations from the MTRM, $(B_{\text{YEE}} - B_{\text{MTRM}}) \times 10^4$, is calculated. Calculation shows that the deviations for $\Delta = 0$ are -3 for the quasi-TE mode and +1 for the quasi-TM mode, while those for $\Delta = 0.02$ μm are -5 and +2, respectively.

Figures 4.5 and 4.6 illustrate the field profiles of major (E_x and H_y) and minor (E_y

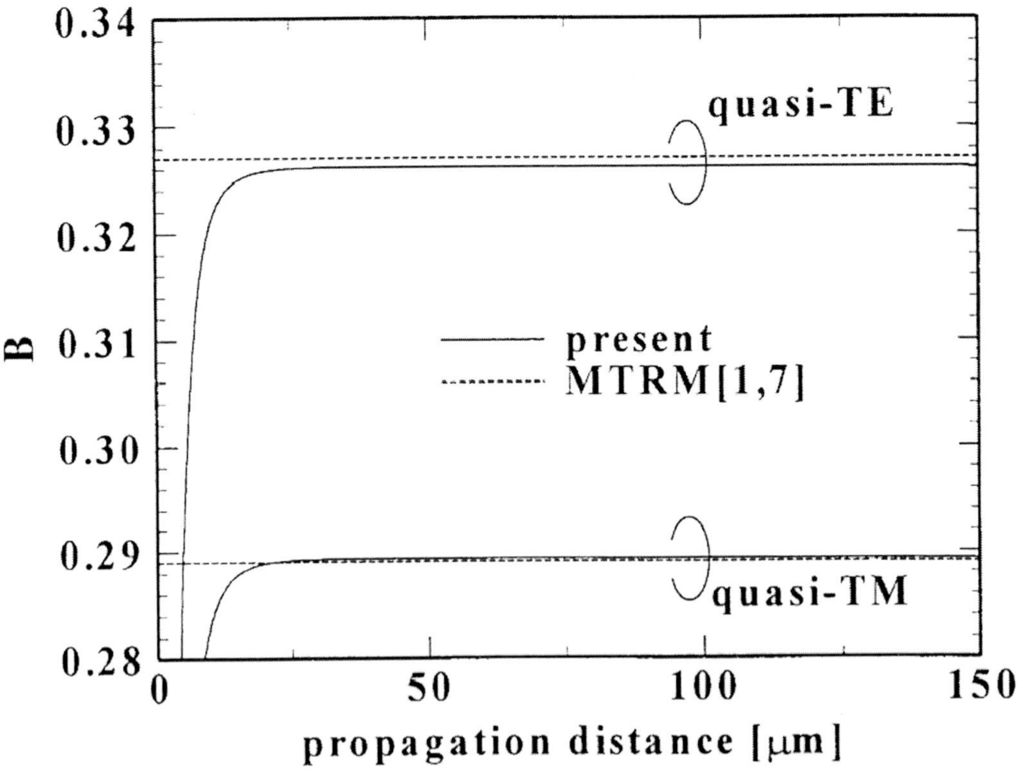

FIG. 4.2. *Convergence behavior of the normalized effective-index in a rib waveguide as a function of propagation distance.*

and H_x) components for the quasi-TE mode. The longitudinal components (E_z and H_z) are also presented for reference. As expected, the normal components of the E fields are discontinuous at the interface between different media. It is worth mentioning that the field singularity at the corner is clearly observed in the minor component. The singularity is more pronounced at the lower corner than at the upper one. Each figure also illustrates the field profile on the lines making the lower corner, i.e., $x = 0.5$ μm and $y = 1.5$ μm. Note that the transverse components are not necessarily plotted on the lines at $x = 0.5$ μm and $y = 1.5$ μm due to the use of a staggered mesh. Figures 4.5(a) and 4.6(b) demonstrate the difference in the peak behavior of the E and H fields.

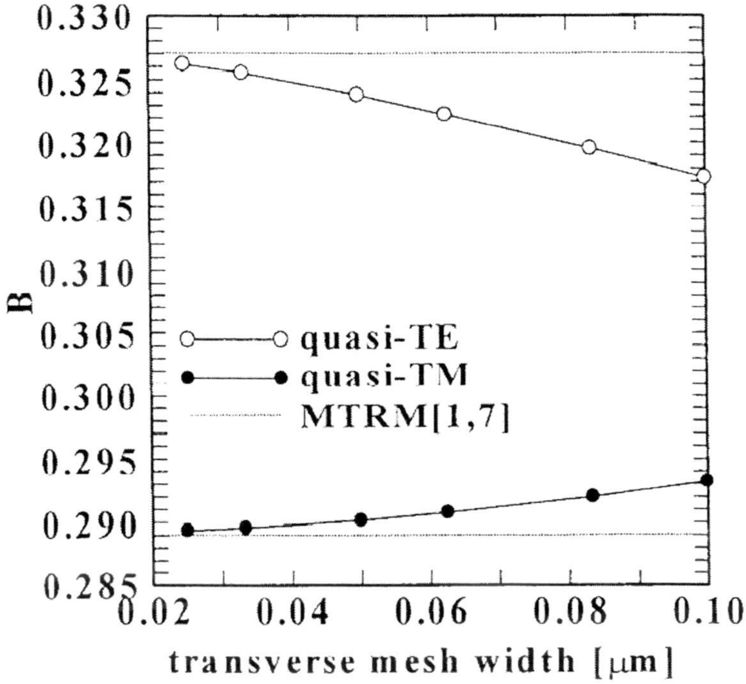

FIG. 4.3. *Convergence behavior of the normalized effective-index in a rib waveguide as a function of transverse mesh width.*

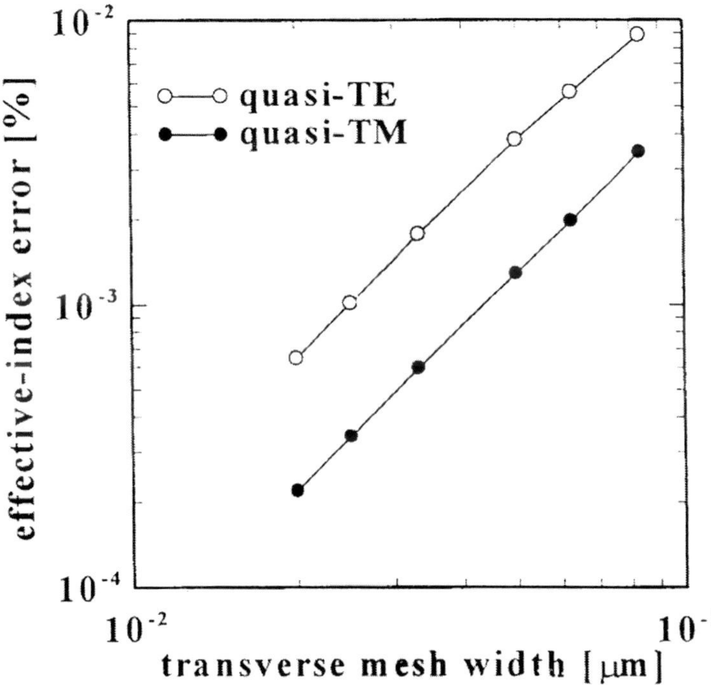

FIG. 4.4. *Effective-index error in a rib waveguide as a function of transverse mesh width.*

5. Conclusions. The imaginary-distance full-vectorial FD-BPM based on Yee's mesh has been improved. For the two-dimensional graded-index waveguide, the effective index is evaluated using the technique in which the reference index is renewed as the field propagates. The increased accuracy is achieved by higher-order schemes. The results obtained from the fourth-order scheme are close to those obtained from the generalized Douglas scheme. For the step-index waveguide, a permittivity-averaging technique maintains the second-order accuracy even in a three-dimensional waveguide with corners. All the components of E and H are calculated, showing the same convergence rate of each component. The present method clearly displays the field profiles with discontinuities in not only the major component but also the minor component.

Appendix: Derivation of higher-order formulas. We assume that the field at various x locations in the neighborhood of point i can be determined from

$$\phi(x) = \sum_{n=0}^{k} a_n x^n + O(\Delta x^{k+1}) \tag{5.1}$$

where $k(= 2, 4, 6, ...)$ is the order of accuracy to be desired. For convenience, we let $x = 0$ at point i, and $\Delta x =$ constant. In this case, the first derivative corresponds to the coefficient a_1:

$$\frac{\partial}{\partial x}\phi(x)\bigg|_i = a_1 \tag{5.2}$$

Here, we choose points from $i - k/2$ to $i + k/2$ and obtain

$$\phi(i \pm m/2) = a_0 + \sum_{n=1}^{k} (\pm m/2)^n a_n \Delta x^n, \quad m = 0, 2, 4, ..., k \tag{5.3}$$

Solving this simultaneous equations, we can determine the coefficient a_1.

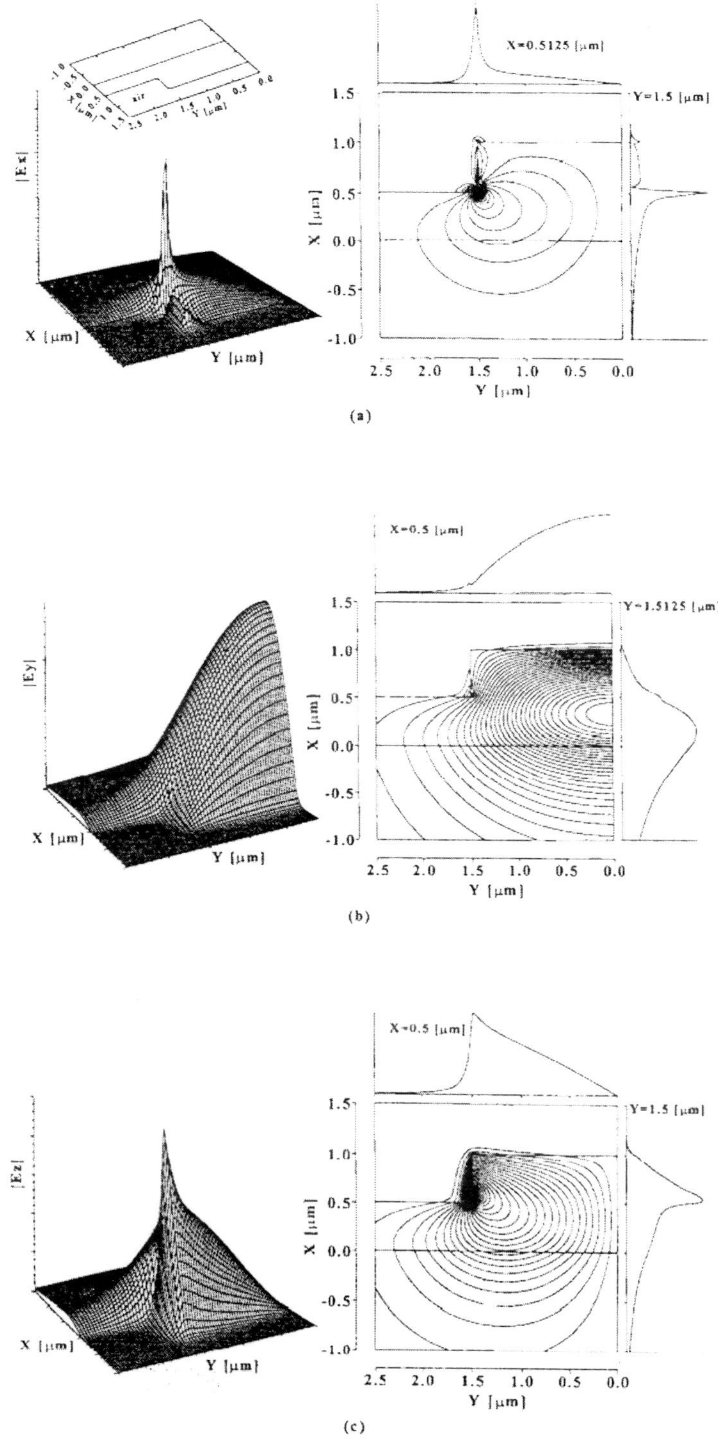

FIG. 4.5. *Electric field profiles of (a) E_x, (b) E_y, and (c) E_z components in a rib waveguide for the quasi-TE mode.*

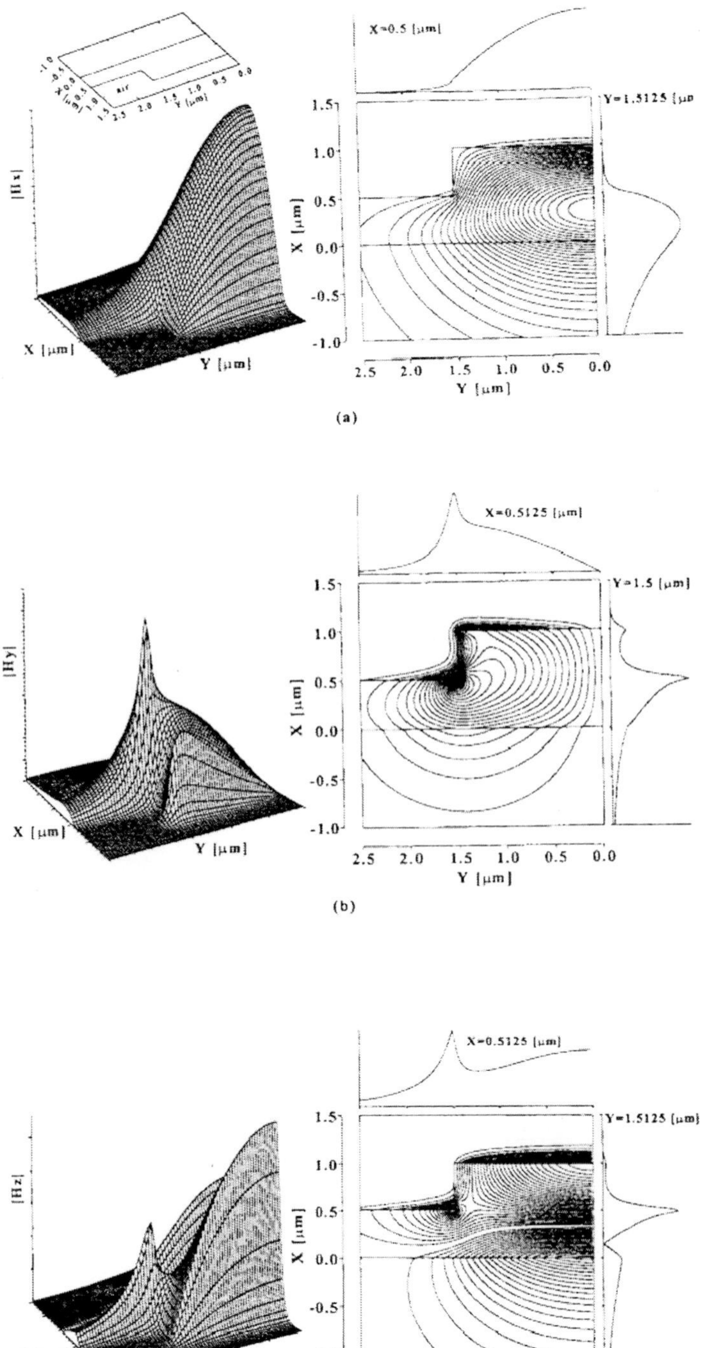

FIG. 4.6. *Magnetic field profiles of (a)* H_x*, (b)* H_y*, and (c)* H_z *components in a rib waveguide for the quasi-TE mode.*

REFERENCES

[1] C. Vassallo, *1993-1995 Optical mode solvers*, Optical and Quantum Electron., 29 (1997), pp. 95–114.

[2] S. M. Lee, *Finite-difference vectorial-beam-propagation method using Yee's discretization scheme for modal fields*, J. Opt. Soc. Am. A 13 (1996), pp. 1369–1377.

[3] K. S. Yee, *Numerical solution of initial boundary problems involving Maxwell's equations in isotropic media*, IEEE Trans. Antennas Propag., AP-14 (1966), pp. 302–307.

[4] D. Yevick and B. Hermansson, *New formulations of the matrix beam propagation method: application to rib waveguides*, IEEE J. Quantum Electron., 25 (1989), pp. 221–229.

[5] C. L. Xu, W. P. Huang and S. K. Chaudhuri, *Efficient and accurate vector mode calculations by beam propagation method*, J. Lightwave Technol., 11 (1993), pp. 1209–1215.

[6] S. Jüngling and J. C. Chen, *A study and optimization of eigenmode calculations using the imaginary-distance beam-propagation method*, IEEE J. Quantum Electron., 30 (1994), pp. 2098–2105.

[7] A. S. Sudbø, *Film mode matching: a versatile numerical method for vector mode field calculations in dielectric waveguides*, J. Europ. Opt. Soc. A, Pure Appl. Opt., 2 (1993), pp. 211–233.

[8] A. S. Sudbø, *Why are accurate computations of mode fields in rectangular dielectric waveguides difficult?*, J. Lightwave Technol., 10 (1992), pp. 418–419.

[9] W. W. Lui, C. L. Xu, W. P. Huang and K. Yokoyama, *Field singularities in full-vectorial optical waveguide analysis*, Integrated Photonics Research, Victoria, pp. 68-70, 1998.

[10] J. Yamauchi, N. Morohashi and H. Nakano, *Rib waveguide analysis by the imaginary-distance vectorial beam-propagation method based on Yee's mesh*, Optical and Quantum Electron., 30 (1998), pp. 397–401.

[11] A. Taflove, *Computational Electrodynamics*, Artech House, Chap.5, p. 102, 1995.

[12] J. Shibayama, M. Sekiguchi, J. Yamauchi and H. Nakano, *Eigenmode analysis of optical waveguides by an improved finite-difference imaginary-distance beam propagation method*, IEICE Trans., J81-C-1 (1998), pp. 9–16.

[13] J. Yamauchi, G. Takahashi and H. Nakano, *Modified finite-difference formula for semivectorial H-field solutions of optical waveguides*, IEEE Photon. Technol. Lett., 10, (1998), pp. 1127–1129.

[14] J. Yamauchi, J. Shibayama, M. Sekiguchi and H. Nakano, *Finite-difference beam propagation method based on the generalized Douglas scheme for a nonuniform grid*, IEEE Photon. Technol. Lett., 9 (1997), pp. 67–69.

In: Focus on Computational Neurobiology
Editor: Lei Li, pp. 85-96

ISBN 1-59033-915-0

NEW ADVANCES ON MULTI-LINGUAL MULTI-FUNCTION MULTI-MEDIA INTELLIGENT SYSTEM

FUJI REN* AND SHINGO KUROIWA†

Abstract. A large variety of information processing applications deal with natural language texts. Many such applications require extracting and processing the meanings of the natural language texts, in addition to processing their syntactic forms. In order to extract meanings from texts and manipulate them, a natural language processing system must have a significant amount of knowledge about the world and the domain of discourse. However, different kinds of knowledge are required for different languages, for different functions, and for different media. In this paper, we design a new general ontology based natural language processing system referred to as Multi-lingual Multi-function Multi-media Intelligent System (MMM-IS). MMM-IS is a big project, it is a complex system with multiple functions that can deal with multiple languages and multiple media. The general ontology consists of a static layer and a dynamic layer, and it provides a real world knowledge model for the natural language processing system. This paper presents the concept of MMM-IS and how to build MMM-IS for real applications, and describes some new advances on the project.

Key words. Multi-Lingual Multi-Function Multi-Media Intelligent System, Naturanl Language, Machine Translation, Automatic Abstracting, Super-Function, Speech Recognition

AMS subject classifications. 15A15, 15A09, 15A23

1. Introduction. As society has been becoming more and more information-oriented in recent years, there is a high demand for information systems. A large variety of information processing applications deal with natural language texts. Many such applications require extracting and processing the meanings of the natural language texts, in addition to processing their syntactic forms [17, 18, 30]. For example, applications such as machine translation, intelligent information retrieval, automatic document classification, and automatic derivation of programs from natural language specifications benefit greatly from understanding the underlying meaning of a text [19, 11, 22]. In order to extract meanings from texts and manipulate them, a natural language processing system must have a significant amount of knowledge about the world and the domain of discourse. However, different kinds of knowledge are required for different languages, for different functions, and for different media.

Ontologies provide many benefits for information system engineering [4]. They can be used at the design time for building knowledge based systems because they allow the knowledge engineers to use knowledge already acquired, conceptualized, and implemented in a formal language, reducing considerably the knowledge acquisition bottleneck and the conceptualization of the new system. They can also be used at the run-time by independent, heterogeneous, and cooperative systems that share knowledge and inferences. The use of ontologies for electronic commerce, enterprise integration, knowledge management, and access to information on the Web has become more and more popular in recent years. However, how to build and use an ontology in a real natural language processing application is still a research issue. In this paper, we design a new general ontology based natural language processing system referred to as Multi-lingual Multi-function Multi-media Intelligent System (MMM-IS). MMM-IS is a complex system with multiple functions that can

*FACULTY OF ENGINEERING, THE UNIVERSITY OF TOKUSHIMA, 2-1 MINAMIJOSAN-JIMA, TOKUSHIMA, 770-8506, JAPAN (REN@IS.TOKUSHIMA-U.AC.JP).
†FACULTY OF ENGINEERING, THE UNIVERSITY OF TOKUSHIMA, 2-1 MINAMIJOSAN-JIMA, TOKUSHIMA, 770-8506, JAPAN (KUORIWA@IS.TOKUSHIMA-U.AC.JP).

deal with multiple languages and multiple media. The general ontology consists of a static layer and a dynamic layer, and it provides a real world knowledge model for the natural language processing system [20]. This paper presents the concept of MMM-IS and how to build MMM-IS for real applications. Some new advances on the MMM-IS project are given.

2. Multi-Lingual Ontology. Ontologies support better communication between people and organization, better interoperability among software systems, systems engineering with better specification, reusability, and reliability in development of information systems [28]. In recent years, the use of ontologies for electronic commerce, enterprise integration, knowledge management, and access to information on the Web has become more and more popular. In this section, we first discuss the concept of ontology, and then present the design of a multi-lingual ontology for MMM-IS.

2.1. What is an Ontology?. From the perspective of artificial intelligence, Gruber defines an ontology as an explicit specification of a conceptualization [5]. Conceptualization refers to the concepts in some area of interest and their relations. A conceptualization is an abstract, simplified view of the world that we wish to represent for some purpose. To understand the concepts in an area and implement them on a computer, we must conceptualize the area. For instance, to develop a computer-aided program synthesizing system for a particular application area, we must conceptualize the application area and represent the concepts (nouns in the natural language specification) and their relations using symbols recognized by the computer. In the sentence "Compute the absolute value of a number," "compute" is a verb denoting an action, while "absolute value" is an object. The meaning of "the absolute value of a number" is the number itself when the number is nonnegative and the negative of the number when the number is negative. An ontology systematically specifies this kind of concepts.

From the perspective of knowledge-based systems, Mizoguchi defines an ontology as a theory of basic concepts and vocabulary used as building blocks of information processing systems [13]. Knowledge bases are necessary in construction of models for solving real world problems. In the context of problem solving, ontologies can be divided into two types: task ontology for the problem solving process and domain ontology for the domain where the tasks are performed. Although ontologies are different for different problems, an ontology can provide a common context for different people. For instance, in natural language processing, an ontology provides a common context for classification of concepts and description of inter-concept relations.

There is a wide spectrum of ontology research, ranging from account of existence in the world by philosophers to building models of concrete targets by computer scientists [13, 25, 7, 26]. Basic theories such as part-hood, integrity, identity, and dependence theories provide us with guidelines in building concrete top-level ontologies of interest and in investigating definitions and operations of basic semantic links. Sowa's ontology is based on the idea of the firstness which is defined without assuming any other things like man and house, the secondness which is defined depending on other things like son and husband, and thirdness which provides an environment or context where the secondness works like marriage and motherliness. He further introduces two important concepts, continuant and occurrent, in addition to the above three, and obtains 12 top-level categories by combining the primitive properties [25, 26]. Guarino's top-level ontology consists of two worlds: particulars such as things which exist in the world and universals which include concepts we need when we describe particulars [7].

Many machine-readable dictionaries have been developed in natural language processing

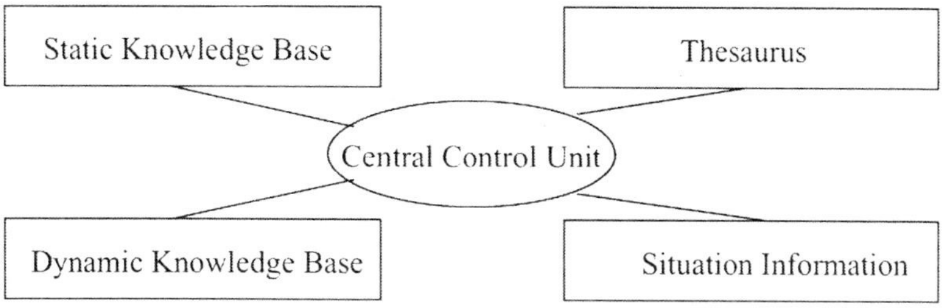

FIG. 2.1. *MLO Architecture*

community where ontology has been discussed as the upper level model of the word/concept structure. The well-known linguistic ontologies include WordNet [12], EDR [29], and Generalized Upper Model (GUM) [1]. WordNet is a general-purpose concept lexicon developed at Princeton University. It can be used both as an online dictionary or thesaurus for reference purposes, and as a taxonomic lexical database. EDR is a very large knowledge base of word knowledge built upon the generalized electronic dictionary that is an integrated collection of data and knowledge about the language to be used in natural language processing. It structures linguistic information along the description unit (superficial, conceptual, deep knowledge), the descriptive unit (word, sentence, text, and document), and the type of language unit (Japanese, Chinese, French, and English). GUM is a general task and domain-independent linguistic ontology developed at GMD/IPSI, Germany. It only includes the main linguistic concepts and how they are organized across languages, and omits details that differentiate languages for portability across different languages. It allows ontologies to be created about specific languages by entering the semantic distinctions of each language. The GUM ontology uses two hierarchies to model the domain: a conceptual taxonomy for concepts and a relational taxonomy for inter-concept relations. It provides detailed information about different kinds of relations, processes, objects, etc.

However, these ontology systems with different features do not fit well in MMM-IS. In this paper, we design a general ontology for MMM-IS.

2.2. A Multi-lingual Ontology. The multi-lingual ontology (MLO) we have developed is a real world knowledge model or a knowledge-based system that consists of a static knowledge base, a dynamic knowledge base, a thesaurus, and situation information operated through a central control unit, as shown in Fig. 2.1. While most of the ontologies developed so far are usually static, MLO is a dynamic knowledge system. MLO is based on the philosophy that all the things in the world, whether physical or spiritual, change in time and space. They usually change from one state to another, observable by the change of their attributes. In the static knowledge base, the basic components are concepts, objects, attributes, time, space, and events. The dynamic knowledge base is usually activated by the information of some external events. The basic components of the dynamic knowledge base are events, properties, attributes, history, and relations.

2.2.1. MLO Architecture. MLO is a complex system that contains both tree hierarchical and network structures. It groups the common parts of various natural languages into a common component. It separates the parts specific to each individual language from the common component. The specific component of each language is activated according to the situation information. This organization plays an important role in dealing with multiple languages.

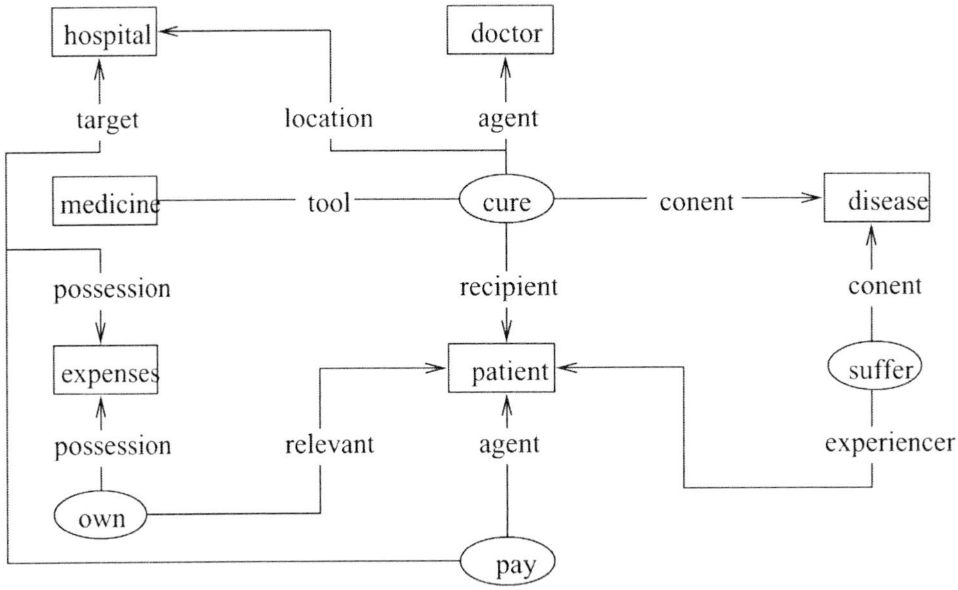

FIG. 2.2. *Network of Concepts Related to Hospital*

MLO represents both the general and the specific properties of each concept. Concepts form an interconnected network. For instance, in the concepts of "doctor" and "patient," their general property is "human being" which includes "walking on foot," "using language," etc. The concepts of "doctor" and "patient" have their own specific properties. The "doctor" is the agent of cure, while the "patient" is the experiencer of disease. Fig. 2.2 shows the network of concepts related to hospital. In order for the knowledge to be effectively used in MMM-IS, MLO attempts to represent the network of inter-concept relations and inter-attribute relations on the computer.

Since MLO attempts to handle multiple languages, MLO must represent both concepts common in different languages and concepts only existing in some languages. Theoretically, there is no difference between languages in deep level concepts. In practice, it is very difficult to only use deep level concepts to describe all the language phenomena. For instance, when we talk about the concept "sister" in English, we usually do not differentiate "younger sister" and "older sister." In Chinese, we always differentiate them and have two different words for them. Fig. 2.3 shows the common component of human relations. Based on this common component, the specific component of human relations in a particular language can be derived.

2.2.2. Concept classification. MLO uses a concept classification hierarchy to describe the attributes of concepts. It classifies concepts into five major classes: concrete objects, abstract objects, activities, time, and location. Fig. 2.4 shows a part of the classification of concrete objects.

2.2.3. Inter-Concept Relation Symbols. In natural language processing, we usually analyze the relationship among parts in a sentence. In the static knowledge base, we also need to specify the inter-concept relations. For instance, in the example of hospital,

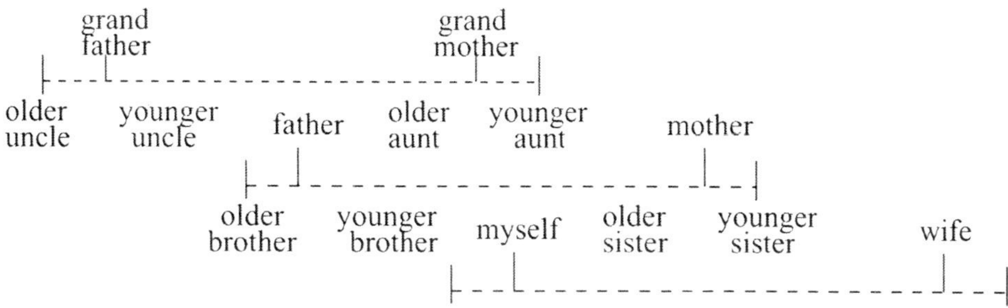

FIG. 2.3. *Common Component of Human Relations*

TABLE 2.1
Symbol Definition

Symbol	Meaning
agent	performer of action
recipient	recipient of action
object	attribute of object
tool	tool or means used in action
time	time event happens
time-from	time event starts
time-to	time event ends
location	location where event happens
location-from	location where event starts
location-to	location where event ends
cause	cause of event
purpose	purpose of event
material	material used in event
sequence	before-after relation of event
co-occurrence	co-occurrence of event

"doctor" is the agent of "cure," and "patient" is the recipient of "cure." Here, "agent" and "recipient" are called inter-concept relation symbols. The following table lists a few inter-concept relation symbols used in MLO. Using concepts and inter-concept relation symbols, MLO represents other relations such as depth relation (at different levels in the classification hierarchy), similarity relation (at same level in the same class), and opposite relation (with opposite meanings).

3. Super-Function Based Machine Translation. In MMM project, for constructing the MLO, a multilanguages automatic translation system is required. We proposed a new paradigm called Super-Function Based Machine Translation (SFBMT) to address the request. The SFBMT uses a bilingual dictionary and Super-Functions to produce a translation of a source text [21]. An input sentence, frist, is morphological analyzed, then matched with the source sentence and a SF. SFBMT produces sentence-by-sentence translation of the source text, falling back on phrase-by-phrase and word-by-word translation when no SF matches the input sentence.

The process of SFBMT consists of three major parts:

- concrete object
  - biological object
    - living object
      - human being
      - animal — lion, tiger
    - body part — hand, foot
    - plant
      - wild plant — pine tree, weed
      - crop — corn, rice
    - plant part — leaf, stalk
  - natural object
    - constituent — water, air
    - mineral — gold, copper
    - phenomenon — wind, light
    - ......
  - manufactured object
    - equipment
      - stationery — pen, paper
      - vehicle — car, airplane
      - ......
    - material — cement, sand
    - mechanical part — engine, brake
    - ......
  - ......

FIG. 2.4. *Classification of Concrete Objects*

1. Morphological analysis,
2. Super Function matching, and
3. Morphological tanslation.

3.1. Morphological Analysis. For Chinese and Japanese, morphological analysis process mainly do word segmentation. Much research has been done for morphological analysis, and the basic idea of our method is same as most morphological analysis systems do, but we have proposed a hybrid approach to Chinese text segmentation.

3.2. SF Matching. A SF is represented by a Node Table and an Edge Table. Matching a SF is simply matching each node of NTB and confirming the kind of each edge. The node sometimes has more than one value and sometimes can be specified.

3.3. Morphological Agreement. Morphological translation is done by tables describing correspondence between categories and sets of features and values in the source language and in the target language. Each category and each morphological feature of a word in the source language is mapped to a catagory and a set of features in the target language just likes GBMT.

3.4. Dispose of Unknown Words. Usually, we suggest an unknown word as noun to match a SF, and generate a target language translation using the string of nuknown source language word. However, for a specific language, we can make some rules to decide if an unknow word is a verb or a noun. For example, in Japanese, if an unknown word locates before a case particle, then the unknow word is considered as a noun; if an unknown word locates after the case particle "WO", then the unknown word is considered a verb.

4. Improved VSM for Information Retrieval. The Vector Space Model (VSM) [23] is a popular information retrieval model, which represents documents and queries by vectors in multidimensional space. The basic idea is to extract indexing terms from a document collection and to represent each document or query as a vector of weighted term frequencies. The similarity comparison among documents, and between documents and queries, is performed via the similarity between two vectors (e.g. cosine similarity). In VSM, the document vectors exhibit the following two properties:

1. Since the size of the indexing terms is typically large, the document vectors are high-dimensional.
2. Since the number of terms in one document is typically far less than the total number of indexing terms, the document vectors are very sparse.

High-dimensional and sparse vectors are susceptible to noise, and are difficult to capture the underlying semantic structure. Additionally, computing resources necessary for the storage and processing of such data is enormous. Dimensionality reduction is a way to overcome these problems. This is a method which maps vectors in high-dimensional space to vectors in a lower dimensional feature space. A variety of dimensionality reduction techniques have been studied extensively in statistical pattern recognition and matrix algebra, such as Singular Value Decomposition (SVD) or Karhunen-Loéve Transform. However, these standard techniques do not work adaptively and so are often much too slow for real-time applications.

In a context of information retrieval, Latent Semantic Indexing (LSI) [2] uses truncated SVD to reduce the dimensionality of the term-document space. LSI has demonstrated improved performance over conventional VSM for several document collections. Despite its effectiveness, however, SVD is computationally expensive for a large document collection. Researchers have tackled this problem using a variety of approximation techniques [14].

In the work described here, we use the Simple Principal Component Analysis (SPCA) [15], which is a data-oriented fast method for producing the principal components approximately, for dimensionality reduction of the vector space model. SPCA has been successfully used for high-dimensional handwritten characters data. In [10], we propose to use the SPCA for dimensionality reduction of vector space information retrieval model. Despite small amount of computation, SPCA-based method has achieved higher performance than conventional SVD-based method in the experiments. This advantage of SPCA can be attributed to its iterative procedure which is similar to clustering methods such as k-means clustering. We are now planning to apply some clustering techniques to the problem of dimensionality reduction.

5. Speech Recognition. The voice is the most natural interfaces in the communications between a person and a person. People also hope to be able to communicate with a machine only by the voice. To realize this hope on MMM-IS, we have been developing robust speech recognition techniques. By using these thechniques, you can ask anything to MMS-IS in the voice even from the cellular phone.

5.1. Endpoint Detection. Speech detection errors are the most serious ploblems in practical speech recognition systems. In order to solve these problems, we have proposed to utilize the log likelihood of partial sentence hypothesis rather than speech energy level[8]. Input speech to the systems is sometimes accompanied by various ambient noise and irrelevant sound such as speaker's coughing, lip noise and out-of-vocabulary utterances. Under such adverse environment, robust speech detection is a crucial issue in an design of practical systems. Conventional speech detection based on energy level gives rise to detection errors caused by low SNR, long pause between phrases, and irrelevant sounds prior to the task sentences. Therefore we developed an algorithm for speech detection and rejection of out-of-vocabulary utterances using log likelihood of partial sentence hypothesis. The partial sentence hypothesis means a sequence of recognized words that ends with a silence longer than a predetermined threshold. This algorithm consists of 1) Ending-point detection and 2) Beginning-point detection (detailed next subsection). The recognition process starts as soon as the last recognition process ends. Every partial sentence hypothesis, that is, a sequence of words with a /silence/ in the end, of the best score is examined with the following conditions.

1) The sequence can be accepted as a complete sentence by a given grammar.

2) The final word of the sequence is a /silence/ with a duration longer than D_{th}.

If the hypothesis satisfies the two conditions, the recognition process is terminated after output of the word sequence as a recognized result. This ending-point detection reduced over 90% of speech detection errors in a Voice Activated Telephone Exchange System compared to a conventional method by energy level.

5.2. Rejection of Unnecessary Sound. Though the ending-point detection automatically starts the next recognition process, irrelevant sounds or out-of-vocabulary utterances prior to the task sentence sometimes match words in error and degrade the recognition performance. The following beginning-point detection is performed by examining every utterance before a pause if it is a partial sentence or just an irrelevant sound to be rejected[8]. The system has two HMM networks for task grammar and for free connection of Japanese syllables without grammar constraints. An utterance before a short pause is examined by comparing the log likelihood of the task grammar network and the free syllable connection network, when the short pause satisfies the following two conditions.

1) A partial sentence hypothesis including a complete sentence hypothesis which terminates with a /silence/ has the maximum log likelihood in all active cells of the grammar network.
2) The duration of the stay at the /silence/ is longer than 100 ms.

The examination to determine if the utterance is a partial sentence hypothesis or an irrelevant sound consists of a test of the following two conditions.

$$\frac{(L(s,t) - L_p(t))}{D(s,t)} \geq L_{th} \tag{5.1}$$

$$0.6 \leq \frac{D(s,t)}{M(s)} \leq 2.0 \tag{5.2}$$

where, $L(s,t)$ is the likelihood of state s at time t, s is the state of the most likely path according to the grammar at time t, $L_p(t)$ is the maximum likelihood of the unconstrained phone network, L_{th} is the threshold value for a likelihood ratio test, $D(s,t)$ is a duration of a speech section that does not include a pause section, $M(s)$ is an expected duration that is the sum of "mean of the state-durations" of HMMs along the most likely path, and 0.6 and 2.0 are threshold values for minimum and maximum duration respectively, which were determined by a preliminary test.

The test of the first condition examines if the likelihood of the partial sentence hypothesis is not very small compared to that of the most likely sequence of syllables/phonemes. The test of the second condition examines if the duration of the partial sentence hypothesis is in a range of allowable duration. If the two conditions hold true, then the partial sentence hypothesis is accepted and the recognition process continues. Otherwise, the system rejects the hypothesis and restarts recognition from 50 ms earlier than time t. Recently, we also reported that a higher performance can be achieved by combining the proposed method and a garbege modelling technique[8].

5.3. Real-Time Cepstrum Mean Subtraction. It is known that a difference in frequency characteristics of the input system can cause an extreme deterioration in the recognition performance. In a microphone input system, however, this problem is solved by attaching a microphone to the product, or causing users to input training utterances for more than ten minutes. In the telephone input, however, it is impossible to make such preparations. Therefore, it is common to use Cepstrum Mean Subtraction (CMS) method which assumes a certain frequency characteristic based on the initial part of the input utterance.

To make this process more reliable, we have developed Real-Time Cepstrum Mean Subtraction based on the Most Likely Partial State Sequence which estimates candidates of recognition result and cepstrum mean at the same time[9]. Fig. 5.1 shows a block diagram of the Real-Time Cepstrum Mean Subtraction. Since the spectral difference of each state is compensated by the spectrum of the most likely candidate state, the estimated cepstrum mean is more stable and reliable compared to the conventional cepstrum mean subtraction and is applicable to relatively short speech inputs.

6. Speaker Verification. In speaker verification systems, a threshold for distinguishing a true speaker from an impostor is required and this threshold must be set a priori. However, determining the appropriate threshold is difficult because the likelihood of verification varies due to 1) differences of environments, 2) differences of speaking styles, and

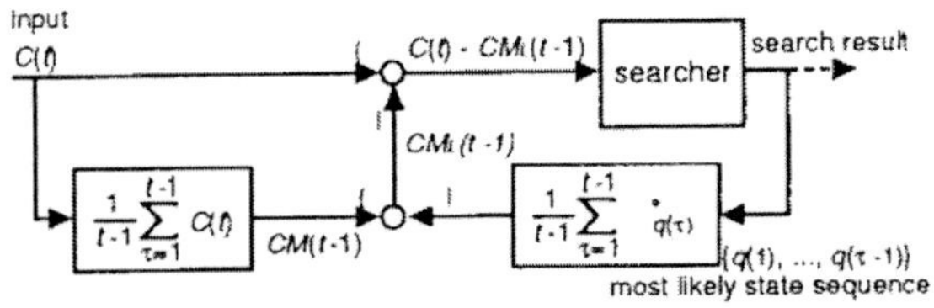

FIG. 5.1. *Block Diagram of Real-Time Cepstrum Mean Subtraction*

3) speaker variation. To tackle the first two problems, likelihood normalization techniques have been proposed and they are used in almost all speaker verification systems as the most effective method. On the other hand, the third problem due to the speaker variation has not solved completely yet. As challenges to solve this problem several methods have already proposed for setting threshold a priori for each speaker in HMM-based speaker verification. Most of them determine threshold based on the mean and standard deviation of intra-speaker and inter-speaker likelihood from training speech data. However, these methods require a huge speech database of various speakers and also require a large amount of computation to find a more appropriate threshold. Therefore we have proposed new methods to predict an appropriate threshold a priori for each true speaker using only cohort models and training data uttered by the true speaker[27].

In speaker verification using HMM, especially in text-prompted style one, creating speaker models by adaptive training from speaker-independent models has proven an effective method. In this training process, the degree of adaptation to a speaker is subject to change according to the speaker or training data. Consequently, the verification score varies over a wide range among speakers, making it difficult to set a stable threshold.

We have therefore propose new methods to determine a stable threshold a priori depending on the "adaptation degree" for each speaker. We use the gain in likelihood during the adaptation process from speaker-independent models as an index of the degree of adaptation to a speaker. We defined this gain as "speaker adaptation gain". As one reason to explain why setting stable thresholds is difficult, we showed that verification score after likelihood normalization still varies widely according to speaker adaptation gain. We also showed that there were some correlations between speaker adaptation gain and normalized likelihood. Therefore, we determine the threshold by the linear function of speaker adaptation gain. These methods use only the training data for the speaker models to estimate thresholds a priori and do not need a large amount of speech data or computations.

We have evaluated the proposed methods in text-prompted speaker verification experiments using connected digit speech. The results show that 1) thresholds set a priori by our proposed methods are stable and reliable regardless of the speakers, and 2) the estimated thresholds are relatively robust regardless of the amount of training data. Consequently, use of our new methods improves verification performance and reduces the error rate by 30 percent compared to conventional methods. Additionally, the proposed methods are practical for reducing training data at the registration stage, because input speech data uttered in the verification stage can be used for retraining speaker models and re-estimating thresholds properly.

7. Conclusion. MMM-IS aims to build a system with multiple functions that can deal with multiple languages and multiple media. It supports multiple natural languages such as English, Chinese, and Japanese. The system has a variety of natural language related functions such as language-oriented information retrieval and information extraction, corpus-based language modeling, machine translation and translation aids, natural language interfaces and dialogue systems, message and narrative understanding, and automatic or semi-automatic derivation of programs from natural language descriptions. The system accepts and manipulates various forms of information such as text, sound, and image. Over the past decade, there have been many experiments in MT, IR, Automatic Summarization, and so on. However, the research on natural language processing has not been incorporated into those systems. If one wants to have two or more functions, he or she needs two or more independent systems. Furthermore, it is difficult to solve problems in such independent systems without a real world knowledge model. MMM-IS attempts to integrate natural language processing functions into these systems.

This paper described a general ontology and a multi-lingual multi-function multi-media intelligent system based on it. Some new advances on the projest have been given. The future work is to construct a prototype MMM-IS system and do some experiments on it.

Acknowledgments. This project has been partially supported by the Education Ministry of Japan under Grant-in-Aid for Scientific Research.

REFERENCES

[1] J. Bateman, B. Magnini, and G. Fabris. The generalized upper model knowledge base: Organization and use. In N. Mars, editor, *Towards Very Large Knowledge Bases*, pages 60–72. IOS Press, Amsterdam, 1995.

[2] M. W. Berry, S. T. Dumais, and G. W. O'Brien. Using linear algebra for intelligent information retrieval. *SIAM Review*, 37(4):573–595, 1995.

[3] D. Farwell, L. Guthrie, and Y. Wilks. Automatically creating lexical entries for ultra, a multilingual MT system. *Machine Translation*, 8(3):127–146, 1993.

[4] A. Gomez-Perez. Knowledge sharing and reuse. In J. Liebowitz, editor, *The Handbook of Applied Expert Systems*, chapter 10. CRC Press, Boca Raton, FL, 1998.

[5] T. R. Gruber. A translation approach to portable ontologies. *Knowledge Acquisition*, 5(2):199–220, 1993.

[6] H. P. Luhn, The automatic creation of literature abstrats. *IBM journal of Research and Development*, 2(2):159–165, 1958.

[7] N. Guarino. Some organizing principles for a unified top-level ontology. In *Working Notes of AAAI Spring Symposium on Ontological Engineering*, Stanford, CA, March 1997.

[8] S. Kuroiwa, M. Naito, S. Yamamoto, and N. Higuchi. Robust speech detection method for telephone speech recognition system. *Speech Communication*, 27(2):135–148, Mar. 1999.

[9] S. Kuroiwa, T. Kato, and N. Higuchi. Real-time cepstrum mean subtraction using most likely path. *Transactions of IEICE D-II*, J82-D-II(3):332–339, Mar. 1999. (in Japanese).

[10] S. Kuroiwa, S. Tsuge, H. Tani, T. Xiaoying, M. Shishibori, and K. Kita. Dimensionality reduction of vector space model based on simple PCA. *Proc. Knowledge-Based Intelligent Information Engineering Systems and Allied Technologies (KES)*, pages 362–366, Sep. 2001.

[11] S. Li, F. Ren. Making a Local Map of Indoor Environments by Swiveling a Camera and a Sonar. *INFORMATION*, 4(2):223–232, 2001.

[12] G. Miller, et al. Five papers on WordNet. Technical report, Cognitive Science Laboratory, Princeton University, 1993.

[13] R. Mizoguchi. Knowledge acquisition and ontology. In *Proceedings of KB & KS'93*, pages 121–128, Tokyo, Japan, 1993.

[14] C. H. Papadimitriou, P. Raghavan, H. Tamaki, and S. Vempala. Latent semantic indexing: A probabilistic analysis. *Proceedings of the 17th ACM-SIGACT-SIGMOD-SIGART Symposium on Principles of Database Systems*, pages 159–168, 1998.

[15] M. Partridge and R. Calvo. Fast dimensionality reduction and simple PCA. *IDA*, 2(3):292–298, 1997.

[16] F. Ren. Super-function based machine translation. *Communications of COLIPS*, 9(1):83–100, 1999.

[17] F. Ren. On Rule Extraction from Translation Examples in Japanese-Chinese Machine Translation. *Communications of COLIPS*, 9(1):19–39, 1999.

[18] F. Ren, J. Nie. Chinese information retrieval: Using characters or words?. *Information Processing and Management*, 35(2):443–462, 1999.

[19] F. Ren, S. Li. Dialogue Machine Translation based upon Parallel Translation Engines and Face Image Processing. *INFORMATION*, 3(4):521–531, 2000.

[20] F. Ren, H. Shi. A General Ontology Based Multi-Lingual Multi-Function Multi-Media Intellgent System. *Proceedings of the IEEE SMC International Conference*, pages 2362–2368, 2000.

[21] F. Ren, Y. Takehara. Tool MKSF for Acquoring Super-Function in JAVA. *Proceedings of the IEEE SMC International Conference*, pages 2473–2480, 2000.

[22] F. Ren. A Hybrid Approach of Text Segmentation Based On Sensitive Word Concept for NLP. *Computational Linguistics and Intelligent Text Processing*, pages 375–388, 2001.

[23] G. Salton and J. McGill. *Introduction to Modern Information Retrieval*. McGraw-Hill Book Company, 1983.

[24] B. Smith. Ontology and the logistic analysis of reality. In *Proceedings of the International Workshop on Formal Ontology*, pages 51–68, Padua, Italy, 1993.

[25] J. Sowa. Top-level ontological categories. *International Journal of Human and Computer Studies*, 43:669–685, 1995.

[26] J. Sowa. *Knowledge representation: logical, philosophical and computational foundation*. PWS Publishing Company, Boston, MA, 1998.

[27] T. Uchibe, S. Kuroiwa, and N. Higuchi. Determination of threshold for text-prompted speaker verification. *Transactions of IEICE D-II*, J83-D-II(11):2291–2299, Nov. 2000. (in Japanese).

[28] M. Uschold and M. Gruninger. Ontologies: Principles, methods and applications. *Knowledge Engineering Review*, 11(2), June 1996.

[29] T. Yokoi, et al. Conceptual structure of EDR. *Journal of Information Processing, IPSJ*, 38(1):32–43, 1997. (in Japanese).

[30] Q. Zhou, F. Ren. Acquisitions and applications of structure preference relations in Chinese. *Natural Language Engineering*, 6(2):163–181, 2000.

In: Focus on Computational Neurobiology
Editor: Lei Li, pp. 97-104

ISBN 1-59033-915-0

SUBJECTIVE CONTOURS STRENGTH DEPENDENCE ON THE CURVATURE OF ILLUSORY FORM

SHENG GE*, JING-LONG WU†, SHUNICHI KAWANO , AND TAKASHI SAITO

Abstract. Two experiments were designed in order to investigate the relationship between the subjective contours strength and the curvature of the illusory form. Both of the two experiments used the partial eclipse disc as the inducing elements, while the illusory form was an ellipse. Experimental stimuli are those figures whose one inducing element is randomly omitted from the standard figure. In Experiment 1, the area of the inducing element was bigger where the curvature of the illusory form was smaller. We found that the mean subjective contours strength is stronger when the curvature of illusory form of omitted inducing element is smaller. In Experiment 2, the area of the inducing element is bigger where the curvature of the illusory form is bigger. The experimental results show that the conclusion of experiment 1 is still tenable in this different case.

Key words. subjective contours, inducing elements, subjective contours strength, illusory form

AMS subject classifications. 92J30

1. Background. As one important characteristic of human vision, many previous investigators have studied the field of subjective contours (illusory figures). Since subjective contours have a subtle relation with real contours in optical illusions, binocular rivalry, figural aftereffect and tilt aftereffect, etc, the study of subjective contours also could explain the mechanism of human vision. On the other hand, the pattern recognition systems, which are used currently, don't comply with human visual characteristics very well. In order to develop new pattern recognition algorithms which comply with the human visual characteristics, it is necessary to gather the basic data for human visual characteristics. For these reasons, subjective contours as one of the visual characteristics, attracted much attention.

Day & Kasperczyk [1] suggested that incomplete inducing elements resulted in stronger apparent strength of subjective contours. Coren [2] found that implicit interposition cues could make subjects observed the subjective contours. Rock & Anson [3] considered that the edges of interior angles played an important role in the perception of subjective contours. Dumais & Bradley [4] suggested that the apparent strength of subjective contours acts as a function of the retinal size, and that with the retinal size decreased the apparent strength increased. They also thought the illumination level was a powerful determinant of the strength of subjective contours. Brigner & Gallagher [5] noted that the perception of subjective contours requires proximity and alignment of the converging edges, and they suggested that the subjective contours were due in part to induce the differences in brightness.

Some studies involved the relationship between the apparent strength of subjective contours and the size or the span of inducing elements. Petry, Harbeck, Conway and Levey [6] required the subjects to rate the apparent strength of subjective contours while the number and size of inducing elements of the displays were varied. The results showed that increasing the size and number of inducing elements resulted in an increase in the apparent strength of subjective contours. Since all the figures they used were the same in size, it was hard to affirm that the above-monitored result was independent of the figure size. Siegel

*Graduate School of Science and Engineering, Yamaguchi University 2-16-1 Tokiwadai, Ube City, Yamaguchi 755-8611, Japan (c2511@stu.cc.yamaguchi-u.ac.jp).

†Faculty of Engineering, Kagawa University 2217-20 Hayashi-cho, Takamatsu City, Kagawa 760-8526, Japan (wu@eng.kagawa-u.ac.jp).

& Petry [7] found evidence to explain the independent processing of subjective contours brightness and sharpness. Their experiments showed that there was an indication of a relationship between the amount of inducing elements and the contour sizes. Distinctness or subjective contours strength was greater at smaller sizes, and the figures which had more inducing elements would be judged to be more distinctive.

Siegel & Petry's study gave Shipley & Kellman [8] good inspiration. Shipley & Kellman thought that the interpolation, which is determined by both the size of inducing elements and the spacing between inducing elements, affect the subjective contours strength.

From the above-mentioned account, it can be found that most of the studies laid emphasis on the inducing elements or the spacing between the inducing elements. A few studies involved the relations between subjective contours strength and the illusory form. We thought that as the two basic factors (inducing elements and illusory form) of subjective contours, the characteristics of illusory form should play a very important role in the evaluation of the subjective contours strength. There were some factors that included the characteristics of illusory form: the shape of illusory form, the angle of the illusory form, the complexity of the illusory form and the curvature of the illusory form, etc.

In this study, we designed two experiments in order to investigate the relationship between the subjective contours strength and the curvature of the illusory form.

2. Experiment 1.

2.1. Subjects. Ten male subjects who experienced psychophysical observers but ignored the purpose of the experiment were randomly enrolled into our study group. All of them had previous practice before the experiment in order to make them understand subjective contours and be familiar with judging the subjective contours strength. They all had a normal or corrected-to-normal visual acuity. Subjects ranged in age from 21 to 36 years.

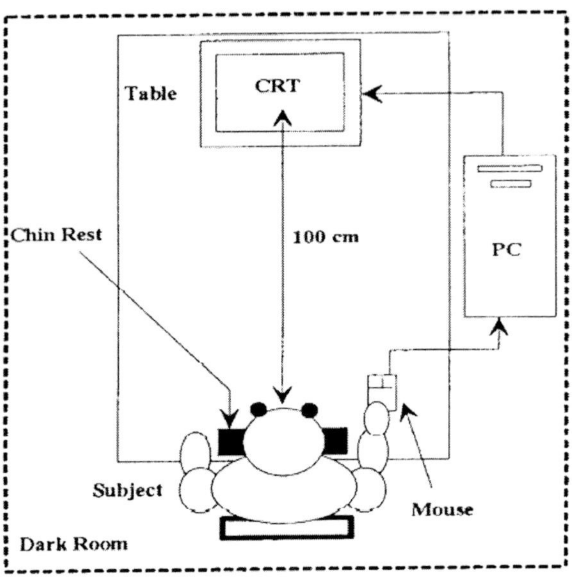

FIG. 1. *Outline of the experimental system.*

2.2. Apparatus. As shown in Fig. 1, a personal computer (NEC PC9812) was used to produce the stimuli displays, and a SONY (CPD-17SF7) RGB monitor (20 × 25cm), set at middle resolution (800 × 600pixels), was used to display the stimuli.

All stimuli were presented to each subject in a random order. A chin rest was used to keep the subjects head stationary and aligned with the screen. The subjects viewed the stimuli binocularly from a distance of 100cm. All the experiments were done in a darkroom.

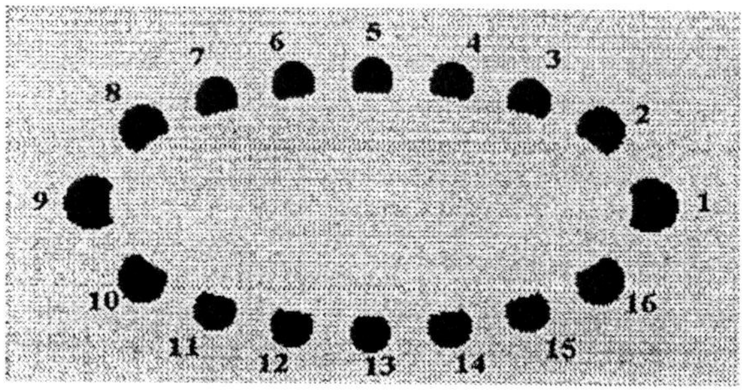

FIG. 2. *Standard stimulus of Experiment 1.*

2.3. Stimuli. The standard figure is shown as Fig. 2. The illusory form is an ellipse, and the inducing elements are a series of "partial eclipse discs" which differ in radii. The radii of inducing elements are decreased gradually from *No.1* to *No.5*, then increased gradually from *No.6* to *No.9*. The figure is symmetric both in the horizontal and vertical directions. All the spans (arc length) between the inducing elements and the arc lengths of every "partial eclipse disc" which border on the illusory form are set in same length.

FIG. 3. *The No.2 experimental stimulus.*

The experimental stimuli are the series of figures each one of which removes one inducing element of the standard figure from *No.1* to *No.16* consecutively. An example of the experimental stimulus is shown in Fig. 3.

2.4. Procedure. In this study, the method of magnitude estimation procedure(Day & Kasperczyk [1]) was used to rate the strength of the subjective contours.

A screen-copy of Experiment 1 is shown in Fig. 4. All the inducing elements were white ($40.5cd/m^2$, here, for the sake of print, the color of inducing elements are set as black.) and the background was gray ($16.5cd/m^2$). The left figure is a standard figure. The right figure is an experimental figure. The 11 buttons at the bottom of the screen are for subjects to rate the subjective contours strength of the experimental figures. The button at the upper-left of screen is for ending the experiment at one critical situation, and the upper-right button

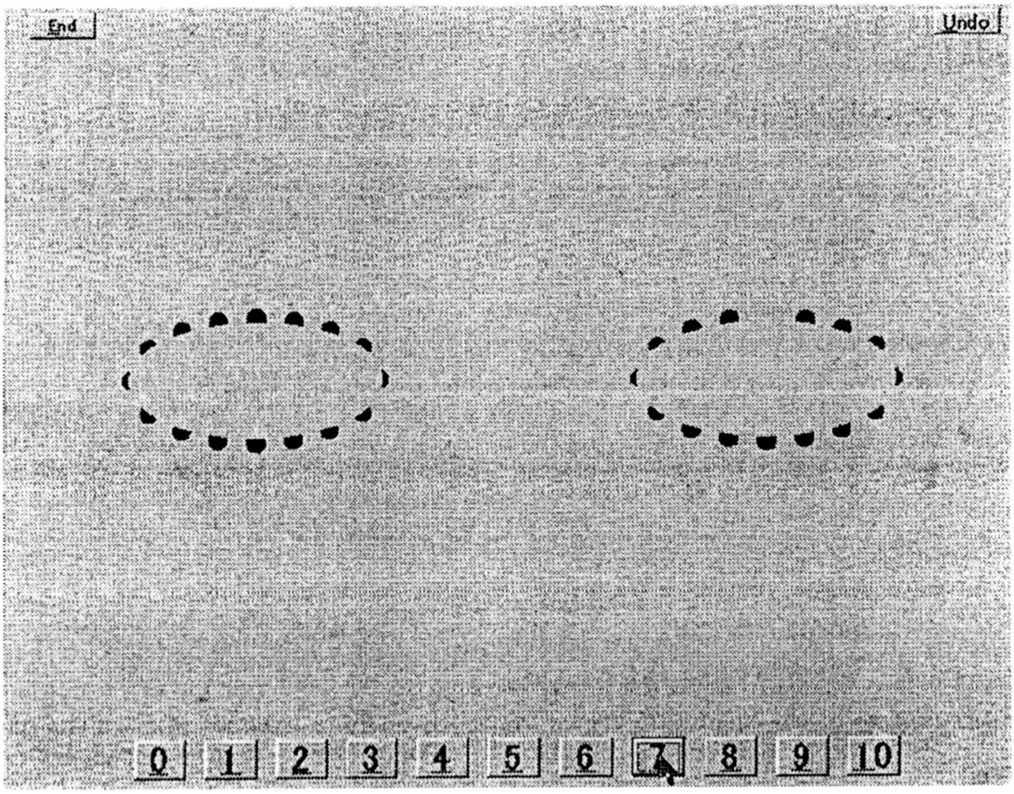

FIG. 4. *A screen copy of Experiment 1.*

is for canceling the last selection when the subjects felt it was unsuitable. All the buttons are selected by the mouse.

Subjects are required to evaluate the subjective contours strength of experimental figures, compared to the basic standard figures, from rate 0 to rate 10 by clicking the buttons at the bottom of the screen. The displays would not be removed until the subject gives response. And there is a five seconds interval before the next stimulus is displayed. During this period the screen is gray ($16.5cd/m^2$) and no stimulus is shown.

2.5. Results. The results of Experiment 1 are shown in Fig. 5. The horizontal axis of Fig. 5 stands for the mode of stimuli, and the vertical axis represents the mean subjective contours strength.

Here, mode X stands for the stimulus whose *No.* X inducing element is emitted. It is obvious that the subjective contours strength is weaker at modes 1 and 9. Oppositely, the subjective contours strength is stronger near modes 5 and 13.

It also can be found that the curvature of the illusory form which is adjacent to the *No.1* (or *No.9*) inducing element is the biggest. On the other hand, the curvature of the illusory form which is adjacent to the *No.5* (or *No.13*) inducing element is the smallest.

Therefore, based on results of Experiment 1, we can conclude that the mean subjective contours strength is stronger when the curvature of illusory form of the omitted inducing

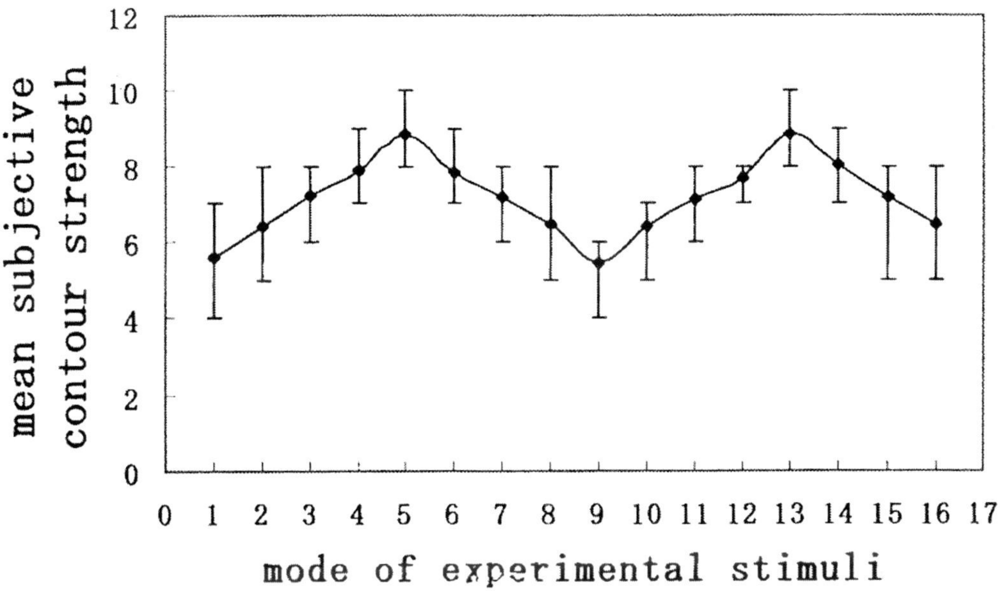

FIG. 5. *Results of Experiment 1. Mean contour strength plotted as a regular function while the mode of the stimuli was changed.*

element is smaller.

Using the of chi-square test, it can be found that the regularity of the curve of Fig. 5 is symmetric in the horizontal ($\chi^2 = 0.00482, p = 1.0$) and vertical ($\chi^2 = 0.00843, p = 1.0$) directions.

3. Experiment 2. The experimental apparatus and method were the same as for Experiment 1. And eight of the ten subjects were changed in Experiment 2.

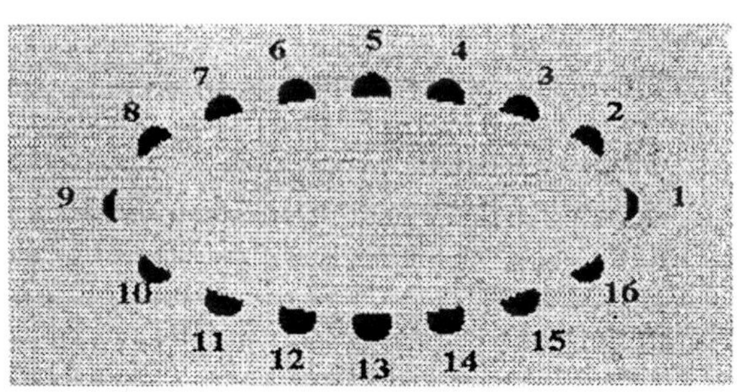

FIG. 6. *Standard stimulus of Experiment 2.*

3.1. Stimuli. The standard figure and the screen-copy of Experiment 2 are shown in Fig. 6 and Fig. 7 respectively. And the other conditions are the same as those in Experiment 1.

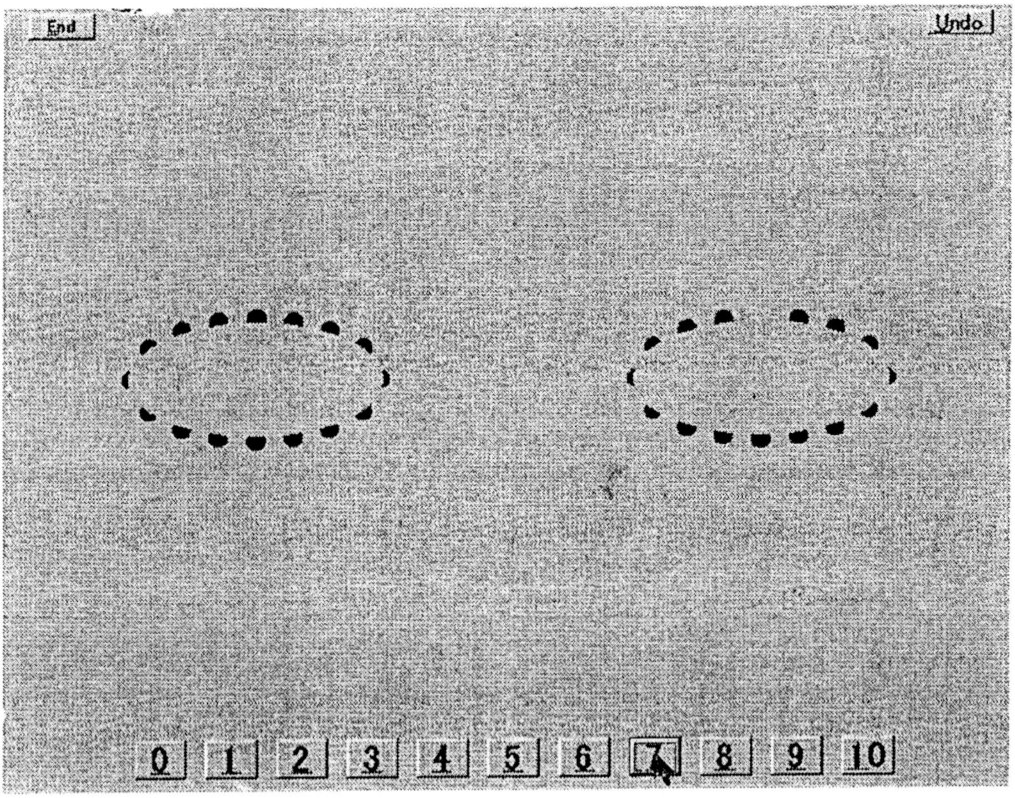

FIG. 7. *A screen copy of Experiment 2.*

TABLE 1
The data of Experiments 1 and 2.

mode	1	2	3	4	5	6	7	8
Exp.1	5.94	6.90	7.51	8.03	8.69	7.99	7.46	6.78
Exp.2	5.62	6.41	7.24	7.88	8.86	7.85	7.15	6.45
mode	9	10	11	12	13	14	15	16
Exp.1	5.67	6.63	7.29	7.95	8.67	7.95	7.19	6.77
Exp.2	5.42	6.41	7.13	7.65	8.86	8.01	7.17	6.46

3.2. Results. The result of Experiment 2 is shown in Fig. 8. It shows that the relationship between subjective contours strength and curvature of illusory form is the same as that found in Experiment 1. That is, the bigger the curvature of illusory form of omitted inducing element is, the weaker the subjective contours strength will be.

It can also be found that the regularity of the curve of Fig. 8 is symmetric in the horizontal ($\chi^2 = 0.01780, p = 1.0$) and vertical ($\chi^2 = 0.00843, p = 1.0$) directions.

4. Discussion. Based on the results of Experiments 1 and 2, the contours strength data can be summarized as in Table 1.

In our experiments, there are some factors that play significant roles in the evaluation of the subjective contours strength. Since the spans between the inducing elements and

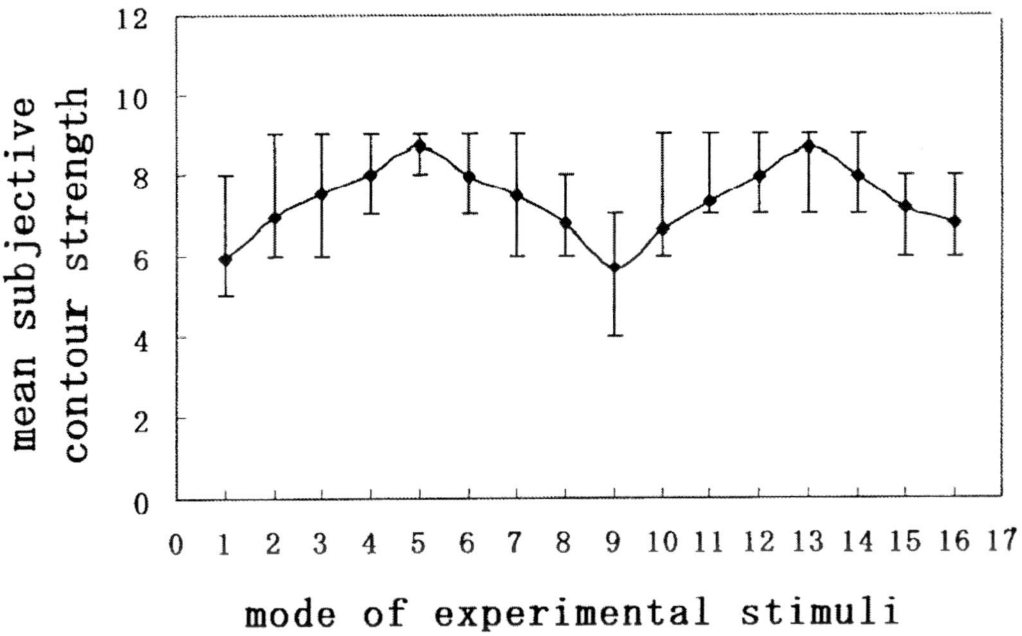

FIG. 8. *Results of Experiment 2. Mean contour strength plotted as a regular function while the mode of the stimuli was changed.*

the arc lengths of every "partial eclipse disc" which border on the illusory form are set at the same length, there remained two factors, i.e. the variation of the size of the inducing elements and the pattern of the stimuli (i.e., the mode of the experimental stimuli).

Using the method of two-way analysis of variance (two-way ANOVA), we found that there is no statistical difference of variation of the size of the inducing elements in Experiments 1 and 2 ($p = 0.1623$). And, there is a statistical difference of the mode of stimuli in Experiments 1 and 2 ($p < 0.0001$).

Therefore, based on the results of Experiments 1 and 2, we conclude that the subjective contours strength is stronger when the curvature of illusory form of omitted inducing element is smaller. We also consider that the subjective contours strength is depended on the curvature of illusory form. When an inducing element is omitted, the subjective contours strength will be reduced. The bigger the curvature of illusory form of the omitted inducing element is, the weaker the subjective contours strength will be. So we can draw a conclusion that the subjective contours strength is an inverse proportion of the curvature of illusory form.

REFERENCES

[1] R. H. DAY AND R. T. KASPERCZYK, *Amodal completion as a basis for illusory contours*, Perception And Psychophysics, 33 (1983), pp. 355–364.

[2] S. COREN, *Subjective contours and apparent depth*, Psychological Review, 79 (1972), pp. 359–369.

[3] I. ROCK AND R. ANSON, *Illusory contours as the solution to a problem*, Perception, 8 (1979), pp. 665–681.

[4] S. T. DUMAIS AND D. R. BRADLEY, *The effect of illumination level and retinal size on the apparent strength of subjective contours*, Perception And Psychophysics, 19 (1976), pp. 339–345.

[5] W. L. BRIGNER AND M. B. GALLAGHER, *Subjective contour: Apparent depth or simultaneous brightness contrast ?* , Perceptual And Motor Skills, 38 (1974), pp. 1047–1053.
[6] S. PETRY, A. HARBECK, J. CONWAY, AND J. LEVEY, *Stimulus determinants of brightness and distinctness of subjective contours*, Perception And Psychophysics, 34 (1983), pp. 169–174.
[7] S. SIEGEL AND S. PETRY, *Evidence for independent processing of subjective contour brightness and sharpness*, Perception, 20 (1991), pp. 233–241.
[8] T. SHIPLEY AND P. KELLMAN, *Strength of interpolated illusory contours depends on the ratio of physically specified to total edge length*, Perception And Psychophysics, 52 (1992), pp. 97–106.

In: Focus on Computational Neurobiology
Editor: Lei Li, pp. 105-113
ISBN 1-59033-915-0

PRESENCE OF CEREBRAL FACTORS TERMINATING ADULT REPRODUCTIVE DIAPAUSE IN TWO SPECIES OF NYMPHALID BUTTERFLIES *

KIYOTOSHI NURANAKA†, AKIRA YAMANAKA† , HIROSHI TANAKA† , REZA MD. SHAHJAHAN‡, AND KATSUHIKO ENDO†

Abstract. The Asian comma butterfly, *Polygonia c-aureum*, exhibits seasonal dimorphism, i.e. summer and autumn morphs, whose development is determined by photoperiod and temperature during the larval stages. The physiological mechanism of *P. c-aureum* underlying the photoperiodic control of seasonal morph development involves a cerebral factor, named summer-morph-producing hormone (SMPH).

Autumn-morph females of *P. c-aureum* as well as females of univoltine butterfly, *Nymphalis xanthomelas japonica*, do not start ovarian maturation after adult emergence and enter reproductive diapause. Diapausing female adults of these two butterfly species started ovarian maturation, a sign of the termination of reproductive diapause, when they were injected with juvenile hormone-I (JH-I). With the injection of JH-I, ovarian maturation of decapitated females and isolated female abdomens was also stimulated in both of *P. c-aureum* and *N. xanthomelas japonica*.

In diapause females of *P. c-aureum* and *N. xanthomelas japonica* ovarian maturation also started when they were injected with 2% NaCl extracts of the adult brain-suboesophageal ganglion (Br-SG) complexes of their own species. However, acetone and 80% ethanol extracts of their adult Br-SG complexes failed to stimulate ovarian maturation.

Female adults of *P. c-aureum* and *N. xanthomelas japonica*, corpora allata (CA) of which remain inactive after adult emergence to enter reproductive diapause in the absence of JH as has been demonstrated in *Leptinotarsa decemlineata* (De Wilde, 1954).

A factor(s) stimulating ovarian maturation in diapausing female adults may exist in the adult Br-SG complexes of *P. c-aureum* and *N. xanthomelas japonica*. The Br-SG factor(s) extracted with 2% NaCl may stimulate the CA *in vivo* to secrete the JH essential for ovarian maturation.

Key words. juvenile hormone, brain-suboesophageal ganglion factor, ovarian maturation, termination, reproductive diapause, *Polygonia* and *Nymphalis*

1. Introduction. In insects, the corpora allata (CA) secrete the juvenile hormone (JH) essential for larval-larval ecdysis and ovarian maturation. Many insects, the CA of which remain inactive after adult emergence, enter reproductive diapause in the absence of JH [1].

The Colorado beetle, *Leptinotarsa decemlineata*, enters reproductive diapause determined by photoperiod and temperature imposing during the larval, pupal and adult stages. Female beetles, the CA of which remain inactive after adult emergence under short-day conditions, enter reproductive diapause in the absence of JH. However, under long-day conditions, the CA of female adults become active after adult emergence and they produce eggs few days later [2, 3].

The Asian comma butterfly, *Polygonia c-aureum* L., exhibits seasonal dimorphism, i. e. summer and autumn morphs, whose development is determined by photoperiod and temperature imposing during the larval stages [4, 5, 6, 7]. *P. c-aureum* larvae develop into summer-mor9h adults under long-day conditions at 20. Summer-morph female adults start ovarian maturation soon after adult emergence and lay eggs a few days later. Autumn-morph

* This work was supported in part by a Grant-in Aid for Scientific Research Priority Areas (No. 09265211) and a Grant-in-Aid for Scientific Research (C) (No. 12640662) from the Ministry of Education, Science and Culture of Japan to K. E., and in part by the Naito Foundation to A. Y.

†Environmental Biology Laboratory, Institute of Biological Science, Faculty of Science, Yamaguchi University, Yamaguchi 753-8512, Japan (endo@po.cc.yamaguchi-u.ac.jp).

‡Institute of Food and Radiation Biology, AERE, Savar, GPO Box-3787, Dhaka-1000, Bangladesh.

female adults whose CA remain inactive after adult emergence, enter reproductive diapause and do not produce eggs within 15 days at 27 [7]. Summer-morph development has been shown to be determined by a cerebral factor, named the summer-morph-producing hormone (SMPH), which is produced in the medial neurosecretory cells of the brain, transported *vir* nerves and secreted from the corpora cardiaca (or the CA) in the early pupal stage [4, 5, 8].

In female adults of *P. c-aureum*, ovarian maturation and accumulation of ovarian accessory gland (OAG) fluid was shown to be suppressed by either allatectomy or by the severance of the nervi corporis allati in the 5th-instar larval stage. Ovarian maturation and OAG-fluid accumulation suppressed by allatectomy were recovered by the transplantation of the active CA of summer-morph adults in the abdomens [9, 5, 10].

In the univoltine nymphalid butterfly, *Nymphalis xanthomelas japonica*, female adults enter reproductive diapause and do not start ovarian maturation for at least 6 months after adult emergence in the laboratory [11].

A cerebral neuropeptide activating the CA of *Manduca sexta* adults *in vitro* was purified from brains of *M. sexta* adults and sequenced to be 13-amino acids [12]. In *Galleria mellonella*, a 20 kD factor extracted from larval brains was shown to activate the larval CA of the same species *in vitro* [13].

In addition, a factor, named the egg development neurosecretory hormone (EDNH), is essential for ovarian maturation in the yellow-fever mosquito, *Aedes aegypti*. The EDNH is produced in the median neurosecretory cells of the brain and secrete after blood feeding for the stimulation of ovarian maturation [14, 15].

In the present study, we attempted to confirm whether JH is a essential factor (or one of major factors) for reproductive diapause in female adults of *P. c-aureum* and *N. xanthomelas japonica*. Subsequently, the study was extended to the question of whether factors terminating reproductive diapause in female adults exist in the adult brain-suboesophageal ganglion (Br-SG) complexes of *P. c-aureum* and *N. xanthomelas japonica*.

2. Materials and methods.

2.1. Animals. Two species of nymphalid butterflies, *P. c-aureum* and *N. xanthomelas japonica*, were collected near the town of Yamaguchi. *P. c-aureum* eggs were obtained from summer-morph female adults and *P. c-aureum* larvae were subjected to either long-day conditions, alternating 16-hr light and 8-hr dark periods (16L-8D) at 23°C, or short-day conditions (8L-16D) at 20°C. They were fed on *Humulus japonicus* leaves which were changed every day. *P. c-aureum* larvae developed into summer-morph adults under 16L-8D at 23°C and into autumn-morph adults under 8L-16D at 20°C.

Summer-morph female adults of *P. c-aureum* started ovarian maturation after adult emergence and laid eggs within 4 days. Autumn-morph female adults entered reproductive diapause and did not produce eggs within 15 days of adult emergence at 25°C.

Fourth- and fifth-instar larvae of *N. xanthomelas japonica* collected in the field were fed on *Celtis sinensis* leaves in the laboratory. They all entered reproductive daipause after adult emergence and did not produce eggs for at least 6 months in the laboratory (about 25°C).

2.2. Decapitation and isolation of abdomens. One-day-old autumn-morph female adults of *P. c-aureum* and diapausing female adults of *N. xanthomelas japonica* were chilled at 4°C for 2 hr. Then, the head (or the complex of head and thorax) was removed with fine scissors and the wound was sealed with melted paraffin.

2.3. Injection of juvenile hormone-I (JH-I). JH-I, obtained from Sigma-Aldrich Japan Co. Ltd., Tokyo, was dissolved in 5% ethanol at concentrations ranging from 1×10^{-3} to 400 μg/ml, 10μl of which was injected into the abdomens of 1-day-old autumn-morph female adults of *P. c-aureum* and the abdomens of diapausing female adults of *N. xanthomelas japonica*. The injection was made into a dorso-lateral intersegmental region between the 6th and 7th abdominal segments. The wound was sealed with melted paraffin. They were allowed to develop at 25°C, and subjected to a dissection 4 days after injection in the case of *P. c-aureum* (8 days after injection in the case of *N. xanthomelas japonica*) to see whether they had produced eggs. JH-I was also injected into decapitated female adults and isolated abdomens of diapausing female adults, in the same manner as above, in doses of 1.0μg in *P. c-aureum* females and 4.0μg in *N. xanthomelas* japonica females, respectively. They were allowed to develop at 25°C for 4 days (for 8 days in the case of *N. xanthomelas japonica*) and subjected to a dissection to examine their ovaries.

2.4. Preparation and injection of adult Br-SG (or pupal brain) extracts. Br-SG complexes were obtained from summer-morph and autumn-morph adults of *P. c-aureum* by dissection in 0.9% NaCl and were stored at -85°C. Br-SG complexes were also obtained from diapausing adults of *N. xanthomelas japonica*. A batch of 100 Br-SG complexes were homogenized in 2.4 ml of ice-cold acetone with a glass homogenizer, and washed in 1.0 ml of ice-cold 80% ethanol. At each step, insoluble materials were removed by centrifugation at 12,000$\times g$ for 15 min at 4°C. The precipitate was extracted with 1.0 ml of 2% NaCl for 3 min at 95°C, cooled rapidly, and centrifuged at 12,000$\times g$ for 30 min at 4°C. The 2% NaCl Br-SG extracts were applied toSep-Pak Plus C18 cartridge column (Waters Co., Milford) for desaltion. Eluate of 50% acetonitril in 0.01 M ammonium sulfate was lyophilized and served as crude Br-SG extracts of 2% NaCl in addition to crude Br-SG extracts (or washings) of acetone and 80% ethanol lyophilized. Each extract was dissolved in distilled water at concentrations of 5, 10, 15, 25 and 50 Br-SG equivalents/10μl, and were injected into the abdomens of 1-day-old autumn-morph female adults of *P. c-aureum* (n=5-10) and those of diapausing female adults of *N. xanthomelas japonica* (n=5-10), respectively. The recipient female adults were kept at 25°C for 4 days (8 days for *N. xanthomelas japonica*) and were subjected to dissection to see whether they had produced eggs.

3. Results.

3.1. Effects of JH-I injection on ovarian maturation in diapausing female adults of *P. c − aureum* and *N. xanthomelas japonica*. To investigate whether JH-I stimulates ovarian maturation in reproductive diapausing females of *P. c-aureum* and *N. xanthomelas japonica*, JH-I was injected into the abdomens of 1-day-old autumn-morph female adults of *P. c-aureum* and diapausing female adults of *N. xanthomelas japonica*. The JH-I dose was raised incrementally from $1\times10^{-5}\mu$g to 1.0μg in *P. c-aureum* and from $1\times10^{-2}\mu$g to 4.0μg in *N. xanthomelas japonica*. The recipients were allowed to develop at 25°C for 4 days in the case of *P. c-aureum* and for 8 days in the case of *N. xanthomelas japonica*. They were then subjected to dissection to see whether they had produced eggs.

A few autumn-morph females of *P. c-aureum* which had been treated with $1\times10^{-3}\mu$g of JH-I had produced eggs (Table 3.1) and accumulated OGA fluid 4 days after injection. The proportion of females having eggs and accumulating OAG-fluid increased with the increment of JH-I doses and reached 100% with the injection of JH-I doses larger than 1.0μg (Fig. 3.1: upper panel). The critical dose of JH-I for stimulating ovarian maturation and OAG-fluid accumulation in 50% of diapausing female adults was estimated to be about $1\times10^{-1}\mu$g. No

TABLE 3.1

Effects of the injection of JH-I and 2% NaCl Br-SG extracts of P. c-aureum adults on ovarian maturation of diapausing females, decapitated diapausing females and isolated abdomens of diapausing females in P. c-aureum.

Insects/Traetments	No. of insects examined	No. of insects having eggs	no eggs
Diapausing females			
distilled water	10	0	10
JH-I(0.001μg)	20	4	16
JH-I(0.1μg)	10	6	4
Decapitated diapausing females			
distilled water	10	0	10
JH-I(0.1μg)	8	8	0
Isolated abdomens of diapausing females			
distilled water	10	0	10
JH-I(0.1μg)	8	8	0
Diapausing females			
distilled water	10	0	10
S-Ext.(25 Br-SG)	10	6	4
S-Ext.(50 Br-SG)	5	5	0
A-Ext.(25 Br-SG)	9	6	3
A-Ext.(50 Br-SG)	5	5	0

*Females were treated with JH-I and Br-SG extracts one day after adult emergence.
**S- and A-Ext. show Br-SG extracts of summer- and autumn-morph adults, respectively.
Figures in parentheses show the doses of JH-I and 2% NaCl extracts (Br-SG equivalents) of *P. c-aureum adults*.

females injected with (or without) distilled water produced eggs and accumulated OAG-fluid within 15 days of injection.

With a JH-I injection of 0.1μg, a few females of *N. xanthomelas japonica* had produced eggs 8 days later (Table 3.2). The proportion of females having eggs increased with the increment of the JH-I doses and reached 100% (or almost 100%) with the injection of JH-I doses larger than 4.0μg (Fig. 3.1: lower panel). The critical dose for stimulating ovarian maturation in 50% of diapausing female adults was estimated to be about 1.5μg in *N. xanthomelas japonica*. No female adults injected with JH-I doses smaller than $1\times10^{-2}\mu$g had produced eggs 8 days after JH-I injection.

The results indicate that in female adults of *P. c-aureum* and *N. xanthomelas japonica* ovarian maturation was stimulated by the JH-I injection. Diapausing female adults of *P. c-aureum* and *N. xanthomelas japonica* may require $1\times10^{-1}\mu$g and 1.5μg of JH-I for starting ovarian maturation, respectively.

3.2. Effects of JH-I injection on ovarian maturation in decapitated females and isolated female abdomens of *P. c − aureum* and *N. xanthomelas japonica*. To investigate whether JH-I stimulates ovarian maturation without the assistance of cephalic (or thoracic) factors in diapausing female adults of *P. c-aureum*, 1-day-old autumn-morph female adults of *P. c-aureum* were decapitated and isolated abdomens, and injected with 1.0μg of JH-I. Four days later, they were subjected to dissection to see whether they had produced eggs with the controls injected with distilled water. The decapitation and isolation of the abdomens were also carried out in the diapausing female adults of *N. xanthomelas japonica*, and 4.0μg of JH-I injected. Eight days later they were subjected to dissection in the same manner as above.

All the decapitated female adults and all the isolated abdomens produced eggs 4 days after JH-I injection in *P. c-aureum* (Table 3.1), and 8 days after JH-I injection in *N. xan-*

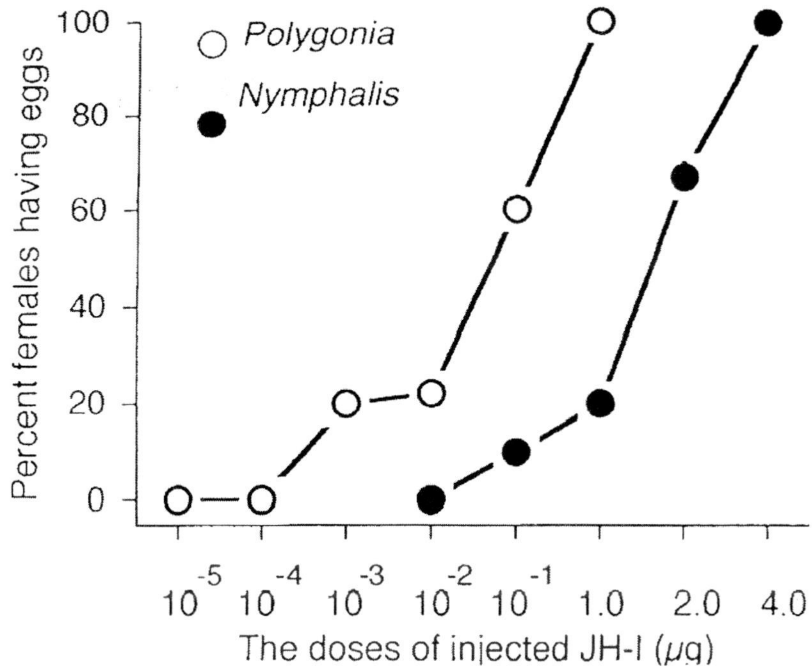

FIG. 3.1. *Dose-dependent effect of juvenile hormone I (JH-I) on egg-production of diapausing female adults of P. c-aureum. Open and solid circles show the percentages of JH-I treated female adults of Polygonia c-aureum and Nymphalis xanthomelas japonica which produced eggs 4 and 8 days later, respectively.*

thomelas japonica (Table 3.2). However, the isolated female abdomens and the decapitated females injected with distilled water had not produced eggs 4 days (or 8 days) after injection (Tables 3.1, 3.2).

It may be that JH-I stimulates ovarian maturation in diapausing the female adults of *P. c-aureum* and *N. xanthomelas japonica* without assistance of cephalic (or thoracic) factor(s).

3.3. Effects of the injection of adult Br-SG extracts on ovarian maturation in reproductive diapausing female adults of *P. c − aureum*. To examine whether Br-SG extracts contain a factor stimulating ovarian maturation in autumn-morph female adults of *P. c-aureum*, 2% NaCl, acetone and 80% ethanol extracts were made from 500 Br-SG complexes of summer- and autumn-morph adults and injected into the abdomens of 1-day-old autumn-morph female adults. The extract doses injected were raised incrementally (5, 10, 15, 25 and 50 Br-SG equivalents). Extracts of 2% NaCl were also made from 500 brains of 0-day-old long-day pupae, 25 brain-equivalents of which were injected into the abdomens of 1-day-old autumn-morph female adults. They were kept at 15°C for 4 days and subjected to dissection to observe whether they had produced eggs.

A few autumn-morph female adults injected with 15 (or 10) Br-SG equivalents of 2% NaCl extracts of summer (or autumn) morphs had eggs 4 days after injection (Table 3.1). The proportion of the females with eggs increased with the increment of the extract doses and reached 100% with a dose of 50 Br-SG equivalents in 2% NaCl extracts of both summer- and autumn-morph adults (Fig. 3.2: upper panel). However, the autumn-morph female adults injected with Br-SG extracts of acetone and 80% ethanol, and those injected with 2% NaCl summer-morph (or autumn-morph) extracts of 10 (or 5) Br-SG equivalents, did

TABLE 3.2

Effects of the injection of JH-I and 2% NaCl Br-SG extracts of N. xanthomelas japonica adults on ovarian maturation of diapausing females, decapitated diapausing females and isolated abdomens of diapausing females in N. xanthomelas japonica.

Insects/Traetments	No. of insects examined	No. of insects having eggs	no eggs
Diapausing females			
distilled water	10	0	10
JH-I(0.01μg)	20	0	20
JH-I(2.0μg)	25	9	16
Decapitated diapausing females			
distilled water	10	0	10
JH-I(10μg)	8	8	0
Isolated abdomens of diapausing females			
distilled water	10	0	10
JH-I(10μg)	8	8	0
Diapausing females			
distilled water	10	0	10
Ext.(25 Br-SG)	10	5	5
Ext.(50 Br-SG)	5	5	0

*Figures in parentheses show the doses of JH-I and 2% NaCl extracts (Br-SG equivalents) of *N. xanthomelas japonica* adults.

not produce eggs 4 days after injection (Fig. 3.2: upper panel). The autumn-morph female adults also did not produced eggs when they were injected with 2% NaCl brain extracts of 0-day-old long-day pupae (25 brain-equivalents).

There may be a factor stimulating ovarian maturation in reproductive diapausing female adults in the Br-SG complexes of summer-morph and autumn-morph adults. But, the factor may be small amount, even when it exists in the brains of 0-day-old long-day pupae.

3.4. Effects of the injection of adult Br-SG extracts on ovarian maturation in reproductive diapausing female adults of *N. xanthomelas japonica*. To examine whether adult Br-SG complexes of *N. xanthomelas japonica* contain a factor stimulating ovarian maturation in diapausing female adults of the same species, extracts of 2% NaCl, 80% ethanol and acetone were made from 500 Br-SG complexes of diapausing adults of *N. xanthomelas japonica* and injected into the abdomens of diapausing female adults of *N. xanthomelas japonica* (50 Br-SG equivalents). The extract doses were 5, 10, 15, 25 and 50 Br-SG equivalents. Br-SG extracts were also made with 2% NaCl from *N. xanthomelas japonica* adults and injected into the abdomens of 1-day-old autumn-morph females of *P. c-aureum* (50 Br-SG equivalents). Eight days (4 days in the case of *P. c-aureum*) later, they were subjected to dissection.

A few diapausing female adults of *N. xanthomelas japonica* produced eggs by the injection of 10 Br-SG equivalents of 2% NaCl extracts (Table 3.2). The proportion of female adults producing eggs increased with the increment of the extract dose and reached 100% with the injection of 50 Br-SG equivalents of 2% NaCl extracts (Fig. 3.2:lower panel).

However, female adults did not produce eggs when they were injected with acetone and 80% ethanol extracts of the Br-SG complexes of *P. c-aureum* adults (50 Br-SG equivalents) (Table 3.2). Adult Br-SG extracts of *N. xanthomelas japonica* (2% NaCl) failed to stimulate ovarian maturation in the 1-day-old autumn-morph females of *P. c-aureum*.

The results indicate that in the Br-SG complexes of diapausing female adults of *N. xanthomelas japonica* there may be a factor stimulating ovarian maturation *in vivo* in diapausing adults of *N. xanthomelas japonica*. The factor may not stimulate ovarian maturation in the diapausing female adults of *P. c-aureum*.

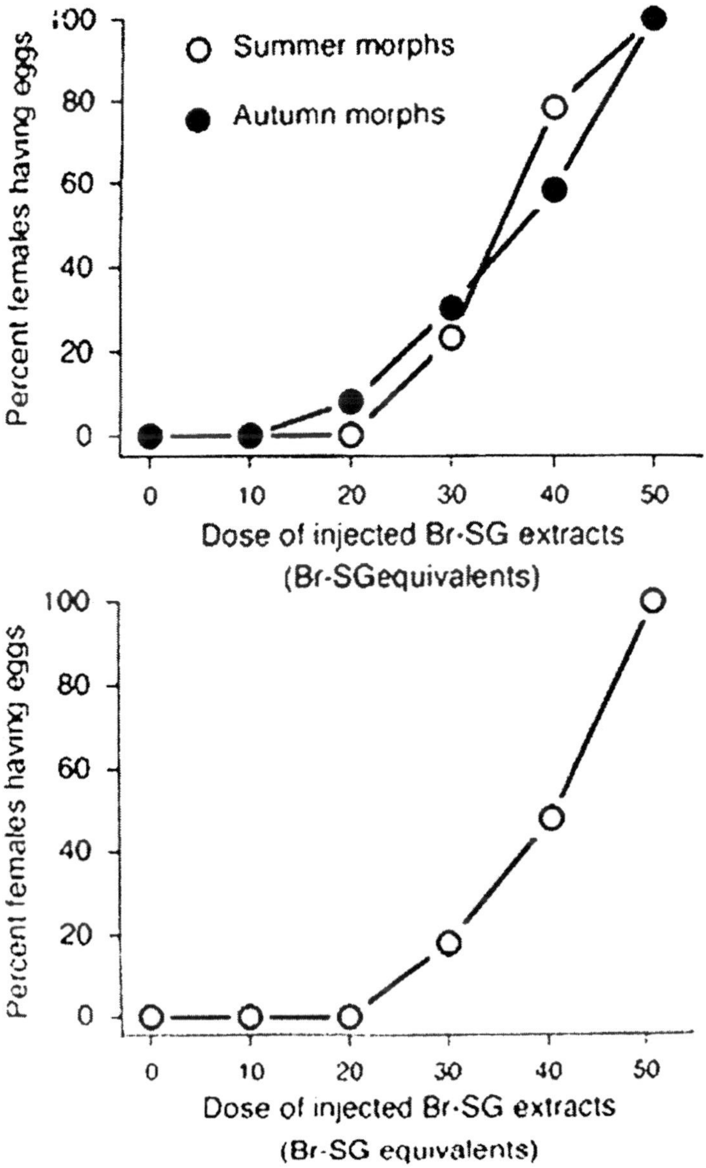

FIG. 3.2. *Dose-dependent response curves of adult Br-SG extracts in ovarian maturation of reproductive diapausing female adults of P. c-aureum (upper panel) and N. xanthomelas japonica (lower panel). Upper panel: Solid and open circles show the percentages of autumn-morph female adults producing eggs 4 days after the treatment of 2% NaCl Br-SG extracts of summer- and autumn-morph adults of P. c-aureum, respectively.*
Lower panel: Open circles show the percentages of egg-produced female adults 8 days after the treatment of 2% NaCl Br-SG extracts of N. xanthomelas japonica adults.

4. Discussion. Autumn-morph female adults of *P. c-aureum* and female adults of *N. xanthomelas japonica* entered reproductive diapause and did not produce eggs within 20 days of adult emergence. When injected with a JH-I dose larger than 1.0μg/insect, the autumn-morph female adults started ovarian maturation and produced eggs within 4 days after JH-I injection. The diapausing female adults of *P. c-aureum* and *N. xanthomelas japonica* produced eggs by JH-I injection, as has previously been demonstrated in two nymphalid butterflies, *Inachis io* and *Aglais urticae* [16].

It may be that autumn-morph female adults of *P. c-aureum* and female adults of *N. xanthomelas japonica* enter (or maintain) reproductive diapause in the absence or at a low titer of hemolymph JH. The JH-I dose required for starting ovarian maturation (or for terminating reproductive diapause) in 50% of the autumn-morph female adults of *P. c-aureum* was estimated to be $1\times10^{-1}\mu$g/insect. This was estimated to correspond to 1/15 of the JH-I dose required for stimulating ovarian maturation in the diapausing female adults of *N. xanthomelas japonica* (1.5μg).

The Br-SG complexes of the summer- and autumn-morph adults of *P. c-aureum* and the diapausing adults of *N. xanthomelas japonica* may contain a factor stimulating ovarian maturation in diapausing females of their own species *in vivo* as has been demonstrated in the EDNH of the yellow-fever mosquito, *A. aegypti* [14, 15].

The Br-SG factor of *P. c-aureum* stimulating ovarian maturation *in vivo* can be extracted, and its secretion is regulated by photoperiod and temperature during the larval stage in the same manner as reported in *P. c-aureum* SMPH [9, 17, 18, 19] But, the Br-SG factor may not be the SMPH, since the autumn-morph female adults developed in the absence of the SMPH under short-day conditions did not always enter reproductive diapause in *P. c-aureum* [7]. In addition, the action of *N. xanthomelas japonica* factor failing to stimulate ovarian maturation in *P. c-aureum* may be species-specific.

A cerebral neuropeptide activating adult corpora allata of *M. sexta* (or larval corpora allata of *Galleria mellonella*) *in vitro* has already been purified (or purified partially) from their adult (or larval) brains [12, 13]. The cerebral neuropeptides of 13 amino acids and 20kD may be allatotropins playing significant role in the regulation of reproductive activity in *M. sexta* female adults and in the regulation of the post-embryonic development in *G. mellonella* larvae, respectively.

We could not provide any evidence about the physicochemical characteristics of the Br-SG factor of *P. c-aureum* and *N. xanthomelas japonica* stimulating ovarian maturation in their diapausing female adults. The adult Br-SG factors may be allatotropins regulating reproductive diapause in these two butterfly species. The nature of these factors may appear on a course of study about neuroendocrine regulation of reproductive diapause in these two species of nymphalid butterflies.

REFERENCES

[1] D. L. Denlinger, *Hormonal control of diapause*, in Comprehensive Insect Physiology, Biochemistry and Pharmacology, G. A. Kerkut and L. I. Gilbert, eds., Pergamon Press, Oxford, 18 (1985), pp. 353-412.

[2] De J. Wilde, *Aspects of diapause in adult insects with special regard to the Colorado beetle, Leptinotarsa decemlineata.*, Archiev der Neederland Zoologie, 10 (1954), pp. 375-385.

[3] De J. Wilde and De J. Boer, *Physiology of diapause in the adult Colorado beetle — II. Diapause as a case of pseudoallatectomy.*, Journal of Insect Physiology, 6 (1961), pp. 152-161.

[4] S. Fukuda and K. Endo, *Hormonal control of the development of seasonal forms in the butterfly, Polygonia c-aureum L.*, Proceeding of Japan Academy, 42 (1966), pp. 1082-1087.

[5] K. Endo, *Activation of corpora allata in relation to ovarian maturation in the seasonal forms of the butterfly, Polygonia c-aureum L.*, Development, Growth and Differentiation, 11 (1972), pp. 263-274.

[6] T. Hidaka and H. Takahashi, *Temperature condition and maternal effect as a modifying factor in the photoperiodic control of seasonal forms in Polygonia c-aureum (Lepidoptera, Nymphalidae).*, Annotationes Zoologicae Japonenses, 40 (1967), pp. 200-204.

[7] K. Endo, S. Ueno, M. Matsufuji, and Y. Kakuo, *Photoperiodic control of the determination of two different seasonal diphenisms of the Asian comma butterfly, Polygonia c-aureum L.*, Zoological Science, 9 (1992), pp. 725-731.

[8] K. Endo, *Neuroendocrine regulation of the development of seasonal forms in the Asian comma butterfly, Polygonia c-aureum L.*, Development, Growth and Differentiation, 26 (1984), pp. 212-222.

[9] K. Endo, *Relation between ovarian maturation and activity of the corpora allata in seasonal forms of the butterfly, Polygonia c-aureum L.*, Development, Growth and Differentiation, 11 (1970), pp. 297-304.

[10] K. Endo, *Relation between accumulation of secretory fluid in the accessory gland of female genital organ and activity of the corpus allatum in Polygonia c-aureum L.*, Zoological Magazine, 82 (1973), pp. 53-58 (in Japanese with English summary).

[11] K. Endo, unpublished data.

[12] H. Kataoka, A. Toschi, J. P. Li, R. L. Carney, D. A. Schooly, and S. J. Kramer, *Identification of an allatotropin from adult Manduca sexta.*, Science, 243 (1989), pp. 1481-1483.

[13] M. I. Bogus and K. Scheller, *Identification of allatotropin-secreting cells in the brain of an insect larva.*, Naturwissenschaften, 81 (1994), pp. 87-89.

[14] A. O. Lea, *Regulation of egg maturation in the mosquito by the neurosecretory system: The role of the corpus cardiacum.*, General and Comparative Endocrinology (suppl.), 3 (1972), pp. 602-608.

[15] H. H. Hagedorn, J. P. Shapirio, and K. Hanaoka, *Ovarian ecdysone secretion is controlled by a brain hormone in an adult mosquito.*, Nature, 282 (1979), pp. 92-94.

[16] G. Benz, *Juvenile hormone breaks ovarian diapause in two Nymphalide butterflies.*, Experienta, 28 (1972), pp. 1507.

[17] K. Endo, T. Masaki, and K. Kumagai, *Neuroendocrine regulation of the development of seasonal morphs in the Asian comma butterfly, Polygonia c-aureum L.: Difference in activity of summer-morph-producing hormone from brain-extracts of long-day and short-day pupae.*, Zoological Science, 5 (1988), pp. 145-152.

[18] T. Masaki, K. Endo, and K. Kumagai, *Neuroendocrine regulation of the development of seasonal morphs in the Asian comma butterfly, Polygonia c-aureum L.: Is the factor producing summer-morphs (SMPH) identical to the small Prothoracicotropic hormone (4K-PTTH)?*, Zoological Science, 5 (1988), pp. 1051-1057.

[19] T. Masaki, K. Endo, and K. Kumagai, *Neuroendocrine regulation of the development of seasonal morphs in the Asian comma butterfly, Polygonia c-aureum L.: Stage-dependent changes in the activity of summer-morph-producing Hormone of the brain-extracts.* Zoological Science, 6 (1989), pp. 113-119.

In: Focus on Computational Neurobiology
Editor: Lei Li, pp. 115-132
ISBN 1-59033-915-0

GENERATING AND DETECTING MATRICES WITH POSITIVE PRINCIPAL MINORS

MICHAEL J. TSATSOMEROS*

Abstract. A brief but concise review of methods to generate P-matrices (i.e., matrices having positive principal minors) is provided and motivated by open problems on P-matrices and the desire to develop and test efficient methods for the detection of P-matrices. Also discussed are operations that leave the class of P-matrices invariant. Some new results and extensions of results regarding P-matrices are included.

Key words. P-matrix, positive definite matrix, M-matrix, MMA-matrix, H-matrix, B-matrix, totally positive matrix, mime, Schur complement, principal pivot transform, Cayley transform, linear complementarity problem, P-problem.

1. Introduction. An $n \times n$ complex matrix $A \in \mathcal{M}_n(\mathbb{C})$ is called a *P-matrix* if all its principal minors are positive. Recall that a *principal minor* is simply the determinant of a submatrix obtained from A when the same set of rows and columns are stricken out. The diagonal entries and the determinant of A are thus among its principal minors. We shall denote the class of complex P-matrices by $\mathbb{P}$.

The P-matrices encompass such notable classes as the Hermitian positive definite matrices, the M-matrices, the totally positive matrices and the real diagonally dominant matrices with positive diagonal entries. The first systematic study of P-matrices appears in the work of Fiedler and Ptak [15]. Since then, the class $\mathbb{P}$ and its subclasses have proven a fruitful subject, judged by the attention received in the matrix theory community and the interest generated (or motivated) by their applications in the mathematical and social sciences; see [3, 14, 25]. Of particular concern is the ability to decide as efficiently as possible whether an n-by-n matrix is in $\mathbb{P}$ or not, known as the *P-problem*. It is receiving attention due to its inherent computational complexity (it is known to be NP-hard [5, 6]), and due to the connection of P-matrices to the linear complementarity problem and to self-validating methods for its solution; see, e.g. [4, 26, 42, 43]. A recursive $O(2^n)$ algorithm for the P-problem that is simple to implement and lends itself to computation in parallel is provided in [48] and reviewed here. More recently [44], a strategy is provided for detecting P-matrices, which is not a priori exponential, although it can be exponential in the worst case.

Motivated by the P-problem and other questions about P-matrices, in this article we address the need to generate P-matrices for purposes of experimentation as well as theoretical and algorithmic development. To this end, we provide a review of (i) operations that preserve P-matrices and (ii) techniques that can be used to generate P-matrices. This affords us an opportunity to survey well-known results and to present some new and some less known results on P-matrices. An important goal remains a method to generate 'random' or 'generic' P-matrices. This is meant in the sense of having at our disposal a property shared by all P-matrices, other than the defining property, which would then allow us to easily construct

*Department of Mathematics, Washington State University, Pullman, Washington 99164-3113 (tsat@math.wsu.edu). Work partially supported by a Natural Sciences and Engineering Research Council of Canada grant.

them and possibly detect them.

The presentation unfolds as follows: Section 2 contains all the notation and definitions. Section 3 reviews mappings of $\mathbb{P}$ into itself, which can therefore be viewed as methods of generating P-matrices from other P-matrices. It also contains some background material used in subsequent sections. Section 4 contains methods to generate P-matrices, some of which yield P-matrices with additional properties. Section 5 contains a closer examination of mimes, a special subclass of the P-matrices. In section 6, we briefly discuss some related topics such as P-matrix completions and interval P-matrices. In section 7, we provide an accelerated Matlab implementation of the P-matrix test algorithm in [48]; its ability is also extended to complex matrices.

2. Notation, definitions and preliminaries. We group the contents of this section in several categories for convenience.

General notation

The transpose of a complex array X is denoted by X^T and its conjugate transpose by X^*. Entrywise ordering of arrays of the same size is indicated by $\geq$. We write $X > Y$ if X, Y are real and every entry of $X - Y$ is positive. The indication of a matrix interval $[X, Y]$ presumes that $Y \geq X$ and denotes the set of all real matrices each of whose entry lies in the interval of the corresponding entries of X and Y. When $X \geq 0$ (resp., $X > 0$), we refer to X as *nonnegative* (resp., *positive*).

A vector $x \in \mathbb{C}^n$ is called a *unit* vector if $\|x\|_2 = 1$. Let n be a positive integer and $A \in \mathcal{M}_n(\mathbb{C})$. The following notation is also used:

- $\langle n \rangle = \{1, \ldots, n\}$.
- The i-th entry of a vector x is denoted by x_i.
- $\sigma(A)$ denotes the spectrum of A.
- $\rho(A) = \max\{|\lambda| : \lambda \in \sigma(A)\}$ is the spectral radius of A.
- $\mathrm{diag}\,(d_1, \ldots, d_n)$ is the diagonal matrix with diagonal entries $d_1, \ldots, d_n$.
- For $\alpha \subseteq \langle n \rangle$, $|\alpha|$ denotes the cardinality of α and $\overline{\alpha} = \langle n \rangle \setminus \alpha$.
- $A[\alpha, \beta]$ is the submatrix of A whose rows and columns are indexed by $\alpha, \beta \subseteq \langle n \rangle$, respectively; the elements of α, β are assumed to be in ascending order. When a row or column index set is empty, the corresponding submatrix is considered vacuous and by convention has determinant equal to 1. We abbreviate $A[\alpha, \alpha]$ by $A[\alpha]$.

Matrix Transforms

Given $A \in \mathcal{M}_n(\mathbb{C})$ and $\alpha \subseteq \langle n \rangle$ such that $A[\alpha]$ is invertible, $A/A[\alpha]$ denotes the *Schur complement* of $A[\alpha]$ in A, that is,

$$A/A[\alpha] \; = \; A[\overline{\alpha}] \; - \; A[\overline{\alpha}, \alpha]A[\alpha]^{-1}A[\alpha, \overline{\alpha}].$$

DEFINITION 2.1. Given a nonempty $\alpha \subseteq \langle n \rangle$ and provided that $A[\alpha]$ is invertible, we define the *principal pivot transform of* $A \in \mathcal{M}_n(\mathbb{C})$ *relative to* α as the matrix $\mathrm{ppt}\,(A, \alpha)$ obtained from A by replacing

$$\begin{array}{llll} A[\alpha] & \text{by } A[\alpha]^{-1}, & A[\alpha,\overline{\alpha}] & \text{by } -A[\alpha]^{-1}A[\alpha,\overline{\alpha}], \\ A[\overline{\alpha},\alpha] & \text{by } A[\overline{\alpha},\alpha]A[\alpha]^{-1} & A[\overline{\alpha}] & \text{by } A/A[\alpha]. \end{array}$$

By convention, ppt $(A,\emptyset) = A$.

To illustrate this definition, when $\alpha = \{1,\ldots,k\}$ $(0 < k < n)$,

$$\text{ppt}\,(A,\alpha) = \begin{bmatrix} A[\alpha]^{-1} & -A[\alpha]^{-1}A[\alpha,\overline{\alpha}] \\ A[\overline{\alpha},\alpha]A[\alpha]^{-1} & A/A[\alpha] \end{bmatrix}.$$

DEFINITION 2.2. For $A \in \mathcal{M}_n(\mathbb{C})$ with $-1 \notin \sigma(A)$, consider the fractional linear map $F_A \equiv (I+A)^{-1}(I-A)$. This map is an involution, namely, $A = (I+F_A)^{-1}(I-F_A)$. The matrix F_A is referred to as the *Cayley transform* of A.

Conditions on the entries and stability

We call $A = [a_{ij}] \in \mathcal{M}_n(\mathbb{C})$ *row diagonally dominant* if for all $i \in \langle n \rangle$,

$$|a_{ii}| > \sum_{j\neq i} |a_{ij}|.$$

Note that in our terminology the diagonal dominance is strict. Due to the Geršgorin Theorem [24, Theorem 6.1.1], row diagonally dominant matrices with positive diagonal entries are *positive stable*, namely, their eigenvalues lie in the open right half-plane.

Matrix $A = [a_{ij}] \in \mathcal{M}_n(\mathbb{R})$ is called a *B-matrix* if

$$\sum_{k=1}^{n} a_{ik} > 0 \quad \text{and} \quad \frac{1}{n}\sum_{k=1}^{n} a_{ik} > a_{ij} \quad \text{for all } j \neq i.$$

The properties and applications of B-matrices are studied in [39].

Positivity classes

Recall that $\mathbb{P}$ denotes the complex P-matrices (of a given order), that is, matrices all of whose principal minors are positive. We also let $\mathbb{P}_{\mathrm{M}}$ denote the class of matrices all of whose positive integer powers are in $\mathbb{P}$.

We call a matrix A *semipositive* if there exists $x \geq 0$ such that $Ax > 0$. Notice that by continuity of the map $x \to Ax$, semipositivity of A is equivalent to the existence of $u > 0$ such that $Au > 0$

A *positive definite* matrix A is simply an Hermitian (i.e., $A = A^*$) P-matrix. A *totally positive* matrix is a matrix all of whose minors (principal and non-principal) are positive.

A *Z-matrix* is a square matrix all of whose off-diagonal entries are non-positive. An (invertible) *M-matrix* is a positive stable Z-matrix or, equivalently, a semipositive Z-matrix. An *inverse M-matrix* is the inverse of an M-matrix (see [3, 25] for general background on M-matrices). An *MMA-matrix* is a matrix all of whose positive integer powers are irreducible M-matrices (see below for the definition of irreducibility).

It is known that an M-matrix A can be written as $A = sI - B$, where $B \geq 0$ and $s > \rho(B)$. The Perron-Frobenius Theorem applied to B and B^T implies that A possesses right and left nonnegative eigenvectors x, y, respectively, corresponding to the eigenvalue $s - \rho(B)$. We refer to x and y as the *right* and *left Perron* eigenvectors of A, respectively. When B is also irreducible, it is known that $s - \rho(B)$ is a simple eigenvalue of A and that $x > 0$ and $y > 0$.

The *companion matrix* of $A = [a_{ij}]$, denoted by $\mathcal{M}(A) = [b_{ij}]$, is defined by

$$b_{ij} = \begin{cases} -|a_{ij}| & \text{if } i \neq j \\ |a_{ii}| & \text{otherwise.} \end{cases}$$

We call $A \in \mathcal{M}_n(\mathbb{C})$ an *H-matrix* if $\mathcal{M}(A)$ is an M-matrix.

A less known class of matrices is defined next; it was introduced by Pang in [37, 38], extending notions introduced by Mangasarian and Dantzig. Such matrices were called 'hidden Minkowski matrices' in [38]; we adopt a new name for this class of matrices, indicative of their matricial nature and origin:

DEFINITION 2.3. Consider a matrix $A \in \mathcal{M}_n(\mathbb{R})$ of the form

$$A = (s_1 I - P_1)\,(s_2 I - P_2)^{-1},$$

where $s_1,\ s_2 \in \mathbb{R}$, $P_1,\ P_2 \geq 0$, and for some vector $u \geq 0$,

$$P_1 u < s_1 u \quad \text{and} \quad P_2 u < s_2 u.$$

We call A a *mime*, an acronym for '**M**-matrix and **I**nverse **M**-matrix **E**xtension', because the class of mimes contains the M-matrices (by taking $P_2 = 0, s_2 = 1$) and their inverses (by taking $P_1 = 0, s_1 = 1$). We refer to the positive vector u above as a *common semipositivity vector* of A.

We continue with a definition of a type of orthogonal matrix to be used in generating matrices in $\mathbb{P}_{\mathrm{M}}$. An n-by-n *Soules matrix* R is an orthogonal matrix with columns $\{w_1, \ldots, w_n\}$ such that $w_1 > 0$ and $R \Lambda R^T \geq 0$ for every

$$\Lambda = \operatorname{diag}(\lambda_1, \ldots, \lambda_n)$$

with $\lambda_1 \geq \ldots \geq \lambda_n \geq 0$. Soules matrices can be constructed starting with an arbitrary positive vector w_1 such that $\|w_1\|_2 = 1$; see [9, 45].

Sign patterns and directed graphs

There are two fundamental methods of generating P-matrices based on the notion of the *sign pattern* of a real matrix A, namely, the corresponding array consisting of $(0, +, -)$ entries according to the sign of each entry of A. In preparation for describing these methods, we need the following definitions.

We call a diagonal matrix S whose diagonal entries equal ± 1 a *signature (matrix)*. Note that $S = S^{-1}$; thus we refer to SAS as a *signature similarity* of A.

Matrix $A \in \mathcal{M}_n(\mathbb{R})$ is called *sign nonsingular* if every matrix with the same sign pattern as A is nonsingular.

The *directed graph*, $D(A)$, of $A = [a_{ij}] \in \mathcal{M}_n(\mathbb{R})$ consists of the set of vertices $\{1, \ldots, n\}$ and the set of directed edges (i, j) connecting vertex i to vertex j if and only if $a_{ij} \neq 0$. We say $D(A)$ is *strongly connected* if any two distinct vertices i, j are connected by a path of edges $(i, i_1), (i_1, i_2), \ldots, (i_{k-1}, i_k), (i_k, j)$; we then refer to A as an *irreducible matrix*. A *cycle of length* k in $D(A)$ consists of edges

$$(i_1, i_2), (i_2, i_3), \ldots, (i_{k-1}, i_k), (i_k, i_1),$$

where the vertices $i_1, \ldots, i_k$ are distinct. The nonzero diagonal entries of A correspond to cycles of length 1 in $D(A)$. The *signed directed graph* of A, $S(A)$, is obtained from $D(A)$ by labeling each edge (i, j) with the sign of a_{ij}. We define the sign of the above cycle on the vertices $\{i_1, \ldots, i_k\}$ to be the sign of the product $a_{i_1 i_2} a_{i_2 i_3} \cdots a_{i_{k-1} i_k} a_{i_k i_1}$.

Denote by $M_{n,k}$ the set of matrices $A \in \mathcal{M}_n(\mathbb{R})$ with nonzero diagonal entries such that the length of the longest cycle in $D(A)$ is no more than k. For matrices in $M_{n,k}$ we adopt the following further notation: $A \in \mathbb{P}_{n,k}$ if A is, in addition, a P-matrix, and $A \in S_{n,k}$ if all the cycles in $S(-A)$ are signed negatively.

3. Mapping $\mathbb{P}$ into $\mathbb{P}$. First, it is worth noting that if $A_1, \ldots, A_k \in \mathbb{P}$, then any block triangular matrix with diagonal blocks $A_1, \ldots, A_k$ is a P-matrix. In particular, the direct sum of P-matrices is a P-matrix. We proceed with transformations that map $\mathbb{P}$ into itself.

THEOREM 3.1. *Assume that $A \in \mathcal{M}_n(\mathbb{C})$ is a P-matrix. Then the following hold.*

(1) $A^T \in \mathbb{P}$.

(2) $QAQ^T \in \mathbb{P}$ *for every permutation matrix* Q.

(3) $SAS \in \mathbb{P}$ *for every signature matrix* S.

(4) $DAE \in \mathbb{P}$ *for all diagonal matrices* D, E *such that* DE *has positive diagonal entries.*

(5) $A + D \in \mathbb{P}$ *for all diagonal matrices* D *with nonnegative diagonal entries.*

(6) $A[\alpha] \in \mathbb{P}$ *for all nonempty* $\alpha \subseteq \langle n \rangle$.

(7) $A/A[\alpha] \in \mathbb{P}$ *for all* $\alpha \subseteq \langle n \rangle$.

(8) $\mathrm{ppt}\,(A, \alpha) \in \mathbb{P}$ *for all* $\alpha \subseteq \langle n \rangle$.
In particular, when $a = \langle n \rangle$, *we obtain that* $\mathrm{ppt}\,(A, \langle n \rangle) = A^{-1} \in \mathbb{P}$.

(9) $I + F_A$, $I - F_A \in \mathbb{P}$.

(10) $TI + (I - T)A \in \mathbb{P}$ *for all* $T \in [0, I]$.

Proof. Clauses (1)–(4) and (6) are direct consequences of determinantal properties and the definition of a P-matrix.

(5) Notice that if $A = [a_{ij}] \in \mathbb{P}$, then $\dfrac{\partial \det A}{\partial\, a_{ii}} = \det A[\overline{\{i\}}] > 0$, that is, $\det A$ is an increasing function of the diagonal entries. Thus, as the diagonal entries of D are added in succession to the diagonal entries of A, the determinant of A, and similarly every principal minor of A, remains positive.

(7) Since A is a P-matrix, $A[\alpha]$ is invertible and A^{-1}, up to a permutation similarity, has

the block representation (see e.g., [24, (0.7.3) p. 18])

$$\begin{bmatrix} (A/A[\overline{\alpha}])^{-1} & -A[\alpha]^{-1}A[\alpha,\overline{\alpha}](A/A[\alpha])^{-1} \\ -(A/A[\alpha])^{-1}A[\overline{\alpha},\alpha]A[\alpha]^{-1} & (A/A[\alpha])^{-1} \end{bmatrix}.$$

Therefore, every principal submatrix of A^{-1} is of the form $(A/A[\alpha])^{-1}$ for some $\alpha \subseteq \langle n\rangle$ and has determinant $\det A[\alpha]/\det A > 0$. This shows that A^{-1} is a P-matrix and, in turn, that $(A/A[\alpha])^{-1}$ and thus $A/A[\alpha]$ are P-matrices for every $\alpha \subseteq \langle n\rangle$.

(8) Let A be a P-matrix and consider first the case where α is a singleton; without loss of generality assume that $\alpha = \{1\}$. Let $B = \text{ppt}\,(A,\alpha) = [b_{ij}]$. By definition, the principal submatrices of B that do not include entries from the first row coincide with the principal submatrices of $A/A[\alpha]$ and thus, by (7), have positive determinants. The principal submatrices of B that include entries from the first row of B are equal to the corresponding principal submatrices of the matrix B' obtained from B using $b_{11} = (A[\alpha])^{-1} > 0$ as the pivot and eliminating the nonzero entries below it. Notice that

$$B' = \begin{bmatrix} 1 & 0 \\ -A[\overline{\alpha},\alpha] & I \end{bmatrix} \begin{bmatrix} b_{11} & -b_{11}A[\alpha,\overline{\alpha}] \\ A[\overline{\alpha},\alpha]b_{11} & A/A[\alpha] \end{bmatrix} = \begin{bmatrix} b_{11} & -b_{11}A[\alpha,\overline{\alpha}] \\ 0 & A[\overline{\alpha}] \end{bmatrix}.$$

That is, B' is itself a P-matrix for it is block upper triangular and the diagonal blocks are P-matrices. It follows that all the principal minors of B are positive and thus B is a P-matrix. Next, consider the case $\alpha = \{i_1,\ldots,i_k\} \subseteq \langle n\rangle$ with $k \geq 1$. By our arguments so far, the sequence of matrices

$$A_0 = A, \quad A_j = \text{ppt}\,(A_{j-1},\{i_j\}),\ j = 1,\ldots,k$$

is well defined and comprises P-matrices. Moreover, from the uniqueness of $B = \text{ppt}\,(A,\alpha)$ shown in [47, Theorem 3.1] it follows that $A_k = \text{ppt}\,(A,\alpha) = B$ and thus B is a P-matrix.

(9) First, since A is a P-matrix, A is nonsingular and has no negative real eigenvalues. Hence F_A is well-defined. It can also be verified that

$$I + F_A = 2(I+A)^{-1} \quad \text{and} \quad I - F_A = 2(I+A^{-1})^{-1}.$$

As addition of positive diagonal matrices and inversion are operations that preserve P-matrices (see (5) and (8)), it follows that $I - F_A$ and $I + F_A$ are P-matrices.

(10) Let $A \in \mathbb{P}$ and $T = \text{diag}(t_1,\ldots,t_n) \in [0,I]$. Since T and $I-T$ are diagonal,

$$\det(TI + (I-T)A) = \sum_{\alpha\subseteq\langle n\rangle} \prod_{i\notin\alpha} t_i \,\det\left(((I-T)A)\,[\alpha]\right).$$

As $t_i \in [0,1]$ and $A \in \mathbb{P}$, all summands in this determinantal expansion are nonnegative. Unless $T = 0$, in which case $TI + (I-T)A = A$, one of these summands is positive. Hence $\det(A) > 0$. The exact same argument can be applied to any principal submatrix of A, proving that $A \in \mathbb{P}$. □

REMARK 3.2. The following comments pertain to the above theorem.

(i) It is quite clear that each one of the clauses (1)–(5), (7) and (10) represents a necessary and sufficient condition that A be a P-matrix.

(ii) Clause (8) is also a necessary and sufficient condition that A be a P-matrix. Sufficiency follows by taking $\alpha = \emptyset$. A stronger result is, however, true: The principal pivot transform of A relative to any one subset α of $\langle n \rangle$ being a P-matrix is necessary and sufficient for **all** principal pivot transforms of A to be in $\mathbb{P}$; see [47].

(iii) A more extensive analysis of the relation between the Cayley transforms implicated in (9), P-matrices and other matrix positivity classes is undertaken in [12].

We conclude this section with a few more basic facts and characterizations of P-matrices with proofs, which are quoted in the remainder.

THEOREM 3.3. *If $A \in \mathcal{M}_n(\mathbb{C})$ is a P-matrix, then for every nonzero $x \in \mathbb{R}^n$, there exists $j \in \langle n \rangle$ such that $x_j(Ax)_j > 0$. If $A \in \mathcal{M}_n(\mathbb{R})$, then A is a P-matrix if and only if for every nonzero $x \in \mathbb{R}^n$, there exists $j \in \langle n \rangle$ such that $x_j(Ax)_j > 0$.*

Proof. Suppose that $A \in \mathcal{M}_n(\mathbb{C})$ and that there exists $x \in \mathbb{R}^n$ such that for all $j \in \langle n \rangle$, $x_j(Ax)_j \leq 0$. Then there exists positive diagonal matrix D such that $Ax = -Dx$, i.e., $(A+D)x = 0$. By Theorem 3.1 (5), A is not a P-matrix. This proves that when $A \in \mathcal{M}_n(\mathbb{C})$ is a P-matrix, then for every nonzero $x \in \mathbb{R}^n$, there exists $j \in \langle n \rangle$ such that $x_j(Ax)_j > 0$.

Suppose now that $A \in \mathcal{M}_n(\mathbb{R})$ and that for every nonzero $x \in \mathbb{R}^n$, there exists $j \in \langle n \rangle$ such that $x_j(Ax)_j > 0$. Notice that the same holds for every principal submatrix $A[\alpha]$ of A, by simply considering vectors x such that $x[\overline{\alpha}] = 0$. Thus all the real eigenvalues of $A[\alpha]$ are positive, for all nonempty $\alpha \subseteq \langle n \rangle$. As complex eigenvalues come in conjugate pairs, it follows that all the principal minors of A are positive, completing the proof of the theorem. □

THEOREM 3.4. *Let $A \in \mathcal{M}_n(\mathbb{R})$ be a P-matrix. Then A is a semipositive matrix.*

Proof. We will prove the contrapositive. Recall the following Theorem of the Alternative (see [34]), stating that for a real matrix A, exactly one of the following is true:

(i) There is an $x \geq 0$, $x \neq 0$, such that $A^T x \leq 0$.
(ii) There is a $y \geq 0$ such that $Ay > 0$.

Thus, if A is not semipositive, then there is a nonzero $x \geq 0$ such that $A^T x \leq 0$. By Theorem 3.3, A^T is not a P-matrix and so A is not a P-matrix. □

THEOREM 3.5. [31, Theorem 3.1] *Let $A = BC^{-1}\mathcal{M}_n(\mathbb{R})$. Then $A \in \mathbb{P}$ if and only if the matrix $TB + (I - T)C$ is invertible for every $T \in [0, I]$.*

Proof. If $A \in \mathbb{P}$, by Theorem 3.1 (10), $TI + (I - T)BC^{-1} \in \mathbb{P}$ for every $T \in [0, I]$. Thus $TC + (I - T)B$ is invertible for every $T \in [0, I]$.

For the converse, suppose $TI + (I - T)BC^{-1}$ is invertible for every $T \in [0, I]$ and, by way of contradiction, suppose $BC^{-1} \notin \mathbb{P}$. By Theorem 3.3, there exists nonzero $x \in \mathbb{R}^n$ such that $y_j x_j \leq 0$ for every $j \in \langle n \rangle$, where $y = BC^{-1}x$. Consider then $T = \text{diag}(t_1, \ldots, t_n)$, where $t_j \in [0, 1]$ are selected so that $t_j x_j + (1 - t_j)y_j = 0$ for all j. It follows that

$$Tx + (I - T)BC^{-1}x = 0,$$

a contradiction that completes the proof. □

4. Generating matrices in $\mathbb{P}$. Below we originate a list of P-matrix generating methods. We indicate any special properties these P-matrices have and provide or outline proofs as necessary.

GENERATING METHOD 4.1. *Every row diagonally dominant matrix $A \in \mathcal{M}_n(\mathbb{R})$ with positive diagonal entries is a positive stable P-matrix.*

Proof. Every principal submatrix $A[\alpha]$ is row diagonally dominant with positive diagonal entries and thus positive stable. In particular, every real eigenvalue of $A[\alpha]$ is positive. As the complex eigenvalues come in conjugate pairs, it follows the $\det A[\alpha] > 0$ for all nonempty $\alpha \subset \langle n \rangle$. □

GENERATING METHOD 4.2. *Let $A \in \mathcal{M}_n(\mathbb{R})$ such that $A + A^T$ is positive definite. Then A is a positive stable P-matrix.*

Proof. As is well-known, every principal submatrix $A[\alpha] + A[\alpha]^T$ of $A + A^T$ is also positive definite. Thus for every $x \in \mathbb{C}^{|\alpha|}$,

$$x^* \, A[\alpha] \, x = x^* \, \frac{A[\alpha] + A[\alpha]^T}{2} \, x \, + \, x^* \, \frac{A[\alpha] - A[\alpha]^T}{2} \, x$$

has positive real part. It follows that every eigenvalue of $A[\alpha]$ has positive real part and thus every principal submatrix of A is positive stable. As above, this implies that A is a positive stable P-matrix. □

The following is stated and proved in [39].

GENERATING METHOD 4.3. *Let $A \in \mathcal{M}_n(\mathbb{R})$ be a B-matrix. Then $A \in \mathbb{P}$.*

GENERATING METHOD 4.4. *For every nonsingular matrix $A \in \mathcal{M}_n(\mathbb{C})$, the matrices A^*A, AA^* are positive definite and thus P-matrices.*

GENERATING METHOD 4.5. *Given a square matrix $B \geq 0$ and $s > \rho(B)$, $A = sI - \rho(B) \in \mathbb{P}$. In particular, A is an M-matrix.*

Proof. Consider $B = [b_{ij}] \geq 0$ and $s > \rho(B)$. By [24, Theorem 8.1.18], $s > \rho(B[\alpha])$ for every nonempty $\alpha \subseteq \langle n \rangle$. Thus every principal submatrix $A[\alpha]$ of A is positive stable and, as in the proof of Generating Method 4.1, it must have positive determinant. □

GENERATING METHOD 4.6. *Let $B, C \in \mathcal{M}_n(\mathbb{R})$ be row diagonally dominant matrices with positive diagonal entries. Then $BC^{-1} \in \mathbb{P}$.*

Proof. Let B and C be as prescribed and notice that by the Levy-Desplanques theorem (see [24, Corollary 5.6.17]), $TB + (I - T)C$ is invertible for every $T \in [0, I]$. Thus, by Theorem 3.5, $BC^{-1} \in \mathbb{P}$. □

REMARK 4.7. It is easy to construct examples showing that the above result fails to be true when B or C are not real matrices. At the Oberwolfach meeting [51], C.R. Johnson stated the above result and conjectured that every real P-matrix A can be factored into BC^{-1}, where $B, C \in \mathcal{M}_n(\mathbb{R})$ are row diagonally dominant matrices with positive diagonal entries.

We continue with results on mimes. We will restate in our context a result from [37] as well as a remarkable method for constructing entrywise nonnegative mimes. The proofs of these results in [37] rely on (hidden) Leontief matrices and principal pivot transforms. In particular, the proof of the latter construction method is attributed to Mangasarian [35], who also used ideas from mathematical programming. We include here shorter proofs that are based on what is now considered standard M-matrix and P-matrix theory.

GENERATING METHOD 4.8. *Let $A \in \mathcal{M}_n(\mathbb{R})$ be a mime. Then $A \in \mathbb{P}$.*

Proof. Let A be a mime and s_1, s_2, P_1, P_2 and $u > 0$ be as in Definition 2.3. Then, for every $T \in [0, I]$, the matrix

$$C = T(s_2 I - P_2) + (I - T)(s_1 I - P_1)$$

is a Z-matrix and $Cu > 0$ (i.e., C is a semipositive Z-matrix). This means that C is an M-matrix. In particular, C is invertible for every $T \in [0, I]$. By Theorem 3.5, we can now conclude that $A = (s_1 I - P_1)(s_2 I - P_2)^{-1} \in \mathbb{P}$. □

GENERATING METHOD 4.9. *Let $B \geq 0$ with $\rho(B) < 1$. Let $\{a_k\}_{k=1}^{m}$ be a sequence such that $0 \leq a_{k+1} \leq a_k \leq 1$ for all $k = 1, \ldots, m-1$. Then*

$$A = I + \sum_{k=1}^{m} a_k B^k \in \mathbb{P}.$$

If m is infinite, under the additional assumption that $\sum_{k=1}^{\infty} a_k$ is convergent, we can still conclude that $A \in \mathbb{P}$. More specifically, A is a mime.

Proof. Consider the matrix $C \equiv A(I - B)$ and notice that C can be written as

$$C = I - G, \quad \text{where } G \equiv B - \sum_{k=1}^{m} a_k (B^k - B^{k+1}).$$

First we show that G is nonnegative: Indeed, as $0 \leq a_{k+1} \leq a_k \leq 1$, we have

$$\begin{aligned} G &\geq B - \sum_{k=1}^{m} a_k B^k + \sum_{k=1}^{m-1} a_{k+1} B^{k+1} + a_k B^{k+1} \\ &= B - \sum_{k=1}^{m} a_k B^k + \sum_{k=2}^{m} a_k B^k + a_k B^{k+1} \\ &= B - a_1 B + a_m B^{m+1} = (1 - a_1)B + a_m B^{m+1} \geq 0. \end{aligned}$$

Next we show that $\rho(G) < 1$. For this purpose, consider the function

$$\begin{aligned} f(z) &= z - \sum_{k=1}^{m} a_k (z^k - z^{k+1}) \\ &= z(1 - a_1) + z^2(a_1 - a_2) + \ldots + z^m(a_{m-1} - a_m) + a_m z^{m+1}, \end{aligned}$$

in which expression all the coefficients are by assumption nonnegative. Thus $|f(z)| \leq f(|z|)$. However, for $|z| < 1$, we have

$$f(|z|) = |z| - \sum_{k=1}^{m} a_k (|z|^k - |z|^{k+1}) \leq |z|.$$

That is, for all $|z| < 1$,

$$|f(z)| \leq f(|z|) \leq |z|.$$

We can now conclude that for every $\lambda \in \sigma(B)$,

$$|f(\lambda)| \leq |\lambda| \leq \rho(B) < 1;$$

that is, $\rho(G) < 1$. We have thus shown that

$$A = (I - G)(I - B)^{-1},$$

where B, $G \geq 0$ and $\rho(B)$, $\rho(G) < 1$. Also, as $B \geq 0$, we may consider its Perron vector $u \geq 0$. By construction, u is also an eigenvector of G corresponding to $\rho(G)$. That is, there exists vector $u > 0$ such that

$$Bu = \rho(B)\, u < u \quad \text{and} \quad Gu = \rho(G)\, u < u\,.$$

Thus A is a mime and so it belongs to $\mathbb{P}$ by Theorem 4.8. □

Generating Method 4.10. *Let $B \geq 0$. Then $e^{tB} \in \mathbb{P}$ for all $t \in [0, 1/\rho(B))$.*

Proof. It follows from Generating Method 4.9 by taking $m = \infty$ and $a_k = \frac{1}{k!}$. □

H-matrices having positive diagonal entries are mimes and thus P-matrices by the results in [37]. We include a short direct proof of this fact.

Generating Method 4.11. *Let $A \in \mathcal{M}_n(\mathbb{R})$ be an H-matrix with positive diagonal entries. Then $A \in \mathbb{P}$.*

Proof. As $\mathcal{M}(A)$ is an M-matrix, by [3, Theorem 2.3 (M_{35}), Chapter 6], there exists a diagonal matrix $D \geq 0$ such that AD is strictly row diagonally dominant. As AD has positive diagonal entries, the result follows from Theorem 3.1 (4) and Generating Method 4.1. □

We now turn our attention to P-matrices generated via sign patterns.

Generating Method 4.12. $S_{n,k} \subset \mathbb{P}_{n,k} \subset \mathbb{P}$.

Proof. Recall that by the definitions in Section 2, $A = [a_{ij}] \in S_{n,k}$ means that the longest cycle in the directed graph of A is $k \geq 1$; the cycles of odd (resp., even) length in the signed directed graph of A are positive (resp., negative). In particular, the diagonal entries of A are **all** positive. In the standard expansion of the determinant of A, the terms that appear are of the form

$$(-1)^{\text{sign}(\sigma)} \; a_{1\sigma(1)} \cdots a_{n\sigma(n)}, \tag{4.1}$$

where σ is a member of the symmetric permutation group on n elements. However, σ can be uniquely partitioned into its permutation cycles, some of odd and some of even length. In fact, $(-1)^{\text{sign}(\sigma)} = (-1)^{n+q}$, where q is the number of odd cycles. As a consequence, the quantity in (4.1) is nonnegative. One such term in $\det A$ consists of the diagonal entries of A, which are positive and thus the sign of that term is $(-1)^{2n}$. It follows that $\det A > 0$. Notice also that a similar argument can be applied to every principal minor of A. Thus A is a P-matrix, in particular a matrix in $\mathbb{P}_{n,k}$. □

REMARK 4.13. The argument in the proof above is essentially contained in the proof of [10, Theorem 1.9]. Also, notice that the matrices in $\mathbb{P}_{n,k}$ are sign nonsinular.

EXAMPLE 4.14. The sign pattern

$$\begin{bmatrix} + & + & + \\ - & + & + \\ 0 & - & + \end{bmatrix}$$

belongs to $S_{3,2}$ and thus every matrix with this sign pattern is a P-matrix.

REMARK 4.15. It has been shown [29] that if $A \in \mathbb{P}_{n,k}$, where $k < n$, then

$$\sigma(A) \subset \{z \in \mathbb{C} \, : \, -\pi + \frac{\pi}{n-1} < \arg z < \pi - \frac{\pi}{n-1}\}.$$

This generalizes a result of Kellogg [32], which states that for all $A \in \mathbb{P}$,

$$\sigma(A) \subset \{z \in \mathbb{C} \, : \, -\pi + \frac{\pi}{n} < \arg z < \pi - \frac{\pi}{n}\}.$$

GENERATING METHOD 4.16. *Let $A \in \mathcal{M}_n(\mathbb{R})$ be sign nonsingular and $B \in \mathcal{M}_n(\mathbb{R})$ any matrix with the same sign pattern as A. Then BA^{-1}, $B^{-1}A \in \mathbb{P}$.*

Proof. Since A and B are sign-nonsingular having the same sign pattern, we have that $C = TB + (I - T)A$ is also sign-nonsingular for every $T \in [0, I]$. Thus, by Theorem 3.5, $BA^{-1} \in \mathbb{P}$. The conclusion for $B^{-1}A$ follows from a result in [31] dual to the one quoted in Theorem 3.5. □

We conclude this section by mentioning that some sufficient conditions for a matrix A to be a P-matrix based on its signed directed graph are provided in [28]. In particular, if $A = [a_{ij}]$ is sign symmetric (i.e., $a_{ij}a_{ji} \geq 0$) and if its undirected graph is a tree (i.e., a connected acyclic graph) then necessary and sufficient conditions that A be a P-matrix are obtained.

5. Generating matrices all of whose powers are in $\mathbb{P}$. As is well-known, if A is positive definite, then so are all of its powers. Thus positive definite matrices belong to $\mathbb{P}_{\mathrm{M}}$. By the Cauchy-Binet formula for the determinant of the product of two matrices (see [24]), it follows that powers of totally positive matrices are totally positive and thus belong to $\mathbb{P}_{\mathrm{M}}$. Below is a constructive characterization of totally positive matrices found in [17] (see also [11]), which therefore allows us to construct matrices in $\mathbb{P}_{\mathrm{M}}$.

THEOREM 5.1. *Matrix $A \in \mathcal{M}_n(\mathbb{R})$ is totally positive if and only if there exist positive diagonal matrix D and positive numbers l_i, u_j $(i, j = 1, \ldots, k)$, $k = \binom{n}{2}$, such that $A = FDG$, where*

$$F = [E_n(l_k)\, E_{n-1}(l_{k-1}) \,\ldots\, E_2(l_{k-n+2})]\; [E_n(l_{k-n+1}) \,\ldots\, E_3(l_{k-2n+4})] \,\ldots\, [E_n(l_1)]$$

and

$$G = [E_n^T(u_1)]\; [E_{n-1}^T(u_2)\, E_n^T(u_3)] \,\ldots\, [E_2^T(u_{k-n+2}) \,\ldots\, E_{n-1}^T(u_{k-1}E_n^T(u_k)\,]\;;$$

here $E_k(\beta) = I + \beta E_{k,k-1}$, where $E_{k,k-1}$ denotes the $(k, k-1)$ elementary matrix.

Another subclass of $\mathbb{P}_M$ are the MMA-matrices, introduced in [16] (recall that these are matrices all of whose positive integer powers are irreducible M-matrices). By the results in [9] (see also [46]) combined with the notion of a Soules matrix allow us to firstly construct all symmetric (inverse) MMA-matrices:

THEOREM 5.2. *Let $A \in \mathcal{M}_n(\mathbb{R})$ be an invertible and symmetric matrix. Then A is an MMA-matrix if and only if $A^{-1} = R\Lambda R^T$, where R is a Soules matrix and $\Lambda = \mathrm{diag}\,(\lambda_1, \ldots, \lambda_n)$ with $\lambda_1 > \lambda_2 \geq \ldots \geq \lambda_n > 0$.*

It has also been shown in [16] that for every MMA-matrix $B \in \mathcal{M}_n(\mathbb{R})$ there exists a positive diagonal matrix D such that $A = D^{-1}BD$ is a symmetric MMA-matrix. In [21], D is found to be

$$D = \mathrm{diag}\,(x_1^{1/2}\, y_1^{-1/2}, \ldots, x_n^{1/2}\, y_n^{-1/2}),$$

where x, y are the unit strictly positive right and left Perron eigenvectors of B, respectively. Thus, we have a way of constructing arbitrary MMA-matrices: Determine an orthogonal Soules matrix R starting with an arbitrary unit positive vector w_1 (as described in section 2). Choose a matrix Λ as in Theorem 5.2 and form $R\Lambda R^T$. Then $A = R\Lambda^{-1}R^T$ is a symmetric MMA-matrix with unit left and right Perron eigenvectors equal to w_1. Choose now positive diagonal matrix $\hat{D}$ and let $B = \hat{D}R\Lambda^{-1}R^T\hat{D}^{-1}$. Then B is an MMA-matrix having $\hat{D}w_1$ and $\hat{D}^{-1}w_1$ are right and left Perron vectors, respectively.

REMARK 5.3.

(i) Given a matrix A in $\mathbb{P}_M$, the matrices A^T, $D^{-1}AD$ (where D is a positive diagonal matrix), QAQ^T (where Q is a permutation matrix), and SAS (where S is a signature matrix) all belong to $\mathbb{P}_M$.

(ii) As all the classes of matrices in $\mathbb{P}_M$ identified so far comprise positive stable matrices, a natural (yet unanswered) question is posed in [20]: *Are all matrices in $\mathbb{P}_M$ positive stable ?*

6. More on mimes.

In this section, we further examine mimes. It has been shown in [37] that the definition of a mime A is tantamount to A being 'hidden Z' and a P-matrix at the same time. More relevant to our context is the following result, reproven here using the language and properties of M-matrices.

PROPOSITION 6.1. *Let $A \in \mathcal{M}_n(\mathbb{R})$. Then A is a mime if and only if*
(1) $AX = Y$ for some Z-matrices X and Y, and
(2) A and X are semipositive.

Proof. Clearly, if A is a mime as in Definition 2.3, then (1) holds with the roles of X and Y being played by $(s_2 I - P_2)$ and $(s_1 I - P_1)$, respectively. That (2) holds follows from the fact that $z \equiv Xu > 0$ (i.e., X is semipositive) and $Yu > 0$, where $u > 0$ is a common semipositivity vector of A. We then have that $Az = YX^{-1}Xu = Yu > 0$; that is, A is also semipositive.

For the converse, suppose (1) and (2) hold. Then X is an M-matrix. As A is assumed semipositive, $Ax > 0$ for some $x > 0$. Let $u = A^{-1}x$. Then, $Yu = Ax > 0$; that is, Y is also semipositive and so an M-matrix as well. In fact, u is a common semipositivity vector of A and thus A is a mime. $\square$

REMARK 6.2.

(i) Based on the above result, we can assert that given a mime A and a positive diagonal matrix D, $A + D$ and DA are also mimes.

(ii) Principal pivot transforms, permutation similarities, Schur complementation and extraction of principal submatrices leave the class of mimes invariant; see [37, 47].

Recall that the mimes form a subclass of the P-matrices that includes the M-matrices, the H-matrices with positive diagonal entries, as well as their inverses. The following is another large class of mimes mentioned in [38].

THEOREM 6.3. *Every triangular P-matrix is a mime.*

Proof. We prove the claim by induction on the order k of A. If $k = 1$ the result is obviously true. Assume the claim is true for $k = n - 1$; we will prove it for $k = n$. For this purpose, consider the triangular P-matrix

$$A = \begin{bmatrix} A_{11} & a \\ 0 & a_{22} \end{bmatrix},$$

where A_{11} is an $(n-1)$-by-$(n-1)$ P-matrix, $a \in \mathbb{R}^{n-1}$ and $a_{22} > 0$. By the inductive hypothesis and Theorem 6.1, there exist Z-matrices X_{11}, Y_{11} and positive vector $u_1 \in \mathbb{R}^{n-1}$ such that $A_{11}X_{11} = Y_{11}$, $Y_{11}u_1 > 0$, and $X_{11}u_1 > 0$. Consider then the Z-matrix

$$X \equiv \begin{bmatrix} X_{11} & -X_{11}u_1 \\ 0 & x_{22} \end{bmatrix},$$

where $x_{22} > 0$ is to be chosen. Then let

$$Y \equiv AX = \begin{bmatrix} A_{11}X_{11} & -Y_{11}u_1 + x_{22}a \\ 0 & a_{22}x_{22} \end{bmatrix}.$$

Notice that $x_{22} > 0$ can be chosen so that Y is a Z-matrix. Let also $u^T = [u_1^T \; u_2]$. Choosing $u_2 > 0$ small enough, we have that $Xu > 0$ and $Yu > 0$. Thus A is a mime by Theorem 6.1. □

In relation to the conjecture in Remark 4.7, we can prove the following.

THEOREM 6.4. *Let A be a mime. Then A can be factored into $A = BC^{-1}$, where B, C are row diagonally dominant matrices with positive diagonal entries.*

Proof. Suppose that $A = (s_1I - P_1)(s_2I - P_2)^{-1}$ is a mime with semipositivity vector $u > 0$ and let $D = \text{diag}(u_1, \ldots, u_n)$. Define $B = (s_1I - P_1)D$ and $C = (s_2I - P_2)D$ so that $Be > 0$ and $Ce > 0$, where e is the all ones vector. Notice that as B and C are Z-matrices with positive diagonal entries, they are indeed row diagonally dominant and $A = BC^{-1}$. □

In view of the conjecture in Remark 4.7 and the definition of a mime, it is natural to wonder whether every P-matrix is a mime and whether the sought factorization is indeed provided by Theorem 6.4. Unfortunately, the answer is negative, i.e., not all P-matrices are mimes as shown by the construction of a counterexample in [38].

7. Miscellaneous related facts. We summarize and provide references to some facts on P-matrices that are related to the purpose of this paper: P-matrix completions, P-matrix intervals and linear transformations of $\mathbb{P}$ into $\mathbb{P}$.

In [27], the authors consider matrices some of whose entries are not specified and raise the problem of when do the unspecified entries can be chosen so that the completed matrix is in $\mathbb{P}$. They show that if the specified entries include all of the diagonal entries, if every fully specified principal submatrix is in $\mathbb{P}$, and if the unspecified entries are symmetrically placed (i.e., (i,j) entry is specified if and only if the (j,i) entry is specified), then the matrix can be completed to a P-matrix. In [8], the authors extend the aforementioned class of partially specified matrices that have a P-matrix completion by providing strategies to achieve its conditions. In [8, 27], partially specified matrices that cannot be completed to be in $\mathbb{P}$ are also discussed. General necessary and sufficient conditions for the completion of a partially specified matrix to a P-matrix are not known to date. Finally, completion problems of subclasses of $\mathbb{P}$ are studied in [1, 18, 22, 23, 30].

In the context of mathematical programming and elsewhere, the analysis of matrix intervals and interval equations play an important role and are intimately related to P-matrices. In particular, it is known that $[A, B]$ consists exclusively of n-by-n invertible matrices if and only if for each of the 2^n matrices $T \in [0, I]$ having diagonal entries in $\{0, 1\}$, $TA+(I-T)B$ is invertible [40, 41]. The case of matrix intervals that consist exclusively of P-matrices is considered in [42] (see also [26]): It is shown that $[A, B]$ consists entirely of P-matrices if and only if for every nonzero $x \in \mathbb{R}^n$, there exists $j \in \langle n \rangle$ such that $x_j\,(Cx)_j > 0$ for every $C \in [A, B]$ (cf. Theorem 3.3).

In [2, 19], the authors study *linear* transformations of $\mathbb{P}$ into $\mathbb{P}$. In [2] it is shown that the linear transformations that map $\mathbb{P}$ *onto* itself are necessarily compositions of transposition, permutation similarity, signature similarity, and positive diagonal equivalence (cf. Theorem 3.1 ((1)–(4), respectively). Under the assumption that the kernel of a linear transformation $\mathcal{L}$ intersects trivially the set of matrices with zero diagonal entries, it is shown in [19] that the linear transformations that map $\mathbb{P}$ *into* itself ($n \geq 3$) are compositions of transposition, permutation similarity, signature similarity, positive diagonal equivalence, and the map $A \rightarrow A + D$, where D is a diagonal matrix whose diagonal entries are nonnegative linear combinations of the diagonal entries of A.

Finally, we mention the open problem of studying when the Hadamard (i.e., entrywise) product of two P-matrices is a P-matrix. A related problem concerns Hadamard product of inverse M-matrices. In particular, it is conjectured that that Hadamard square of two inverse M-matrices is an inverse M-matrix; see [36, 50].

8. Detection of P-matrices. As mentioned in the introduction, the P-problem is NP-hard. The exhaustive check of all $2^n - 1$ principal minors of $A \in \mathcal{M}_n(\mathbb{R})$ using Gaussian elimination is an $O(n^3 2^n)$ task; see [48]. Later on we will describe an alternative test for complex P-matrices, which was first presented in [48] and was shown to be $O(n^3)$ when applied to real P-matrices.

Determining whether a matrix belongs or not to one of the subclasses of $\mathbb{P}$ that we have discussed in this paper is typically an easier task. To be more specific, to detect a positive definite matrix A one needs to check whether $A = A^*$ and whether the eigenvalues of A are positive or not. To detect an M-matrix A, one needs to check whether A is a Z-matrix and whether A is positive stable. An alternative $O(n^3)$ procedure for testing whether a Z-matrix is an M-matrix is described in [49]. To detect an inverse M-matrix A, one can apply a test for M-matrices to A^{-1}. Similarly, one needs to apply a test for M-matrices to $\mathcal{M}(A)$ to determine whether a matrix A with positive diagonal entries is an H-matrix or not.

Recall that an H-matrix is also characterized by the existence of a positive diagonal matrix D such that AD is row diagonally dominant. This is why H-matrices are also known in the literature as 'generalized diagonally dominant matrices'. Based on this characterization of H-matrices, an iterative method to determine whether A is an H-matrix or not is developed in [33]; this iterative method also determines a diagonal matrix D with the aforementioned scaling property.

To determine a totally positive matrix, Fekete's criterion [13] may be used: Let $S = \{i_1, \ldots, i_k\}$ with $i_j < i_{j+1}$, $(j = 1, \ldots, k-1)$ and define the *dispersion* of S to be

$$d(S) = \begin{cases} i_k - i_1 - k + 1 & \text{if } k > 1 \\ 0 & \text{if } k = 1. \end{cases}$$

Then $A \in \mathcal{M}_n(\mathbb{R})$ is totally positive if and only if $\det A[\alpha|\beta] > 0$ for all $\alpha, \beta \subseteq \langle n \rangle$ with $|\alpha| = |\beta|$ and $d(\alpha) = d(\beta) = 0$. That is, one only needs to check for positivity minors whose row and column index sets are contiguous.

Fekete's criterion is improved in [17] as follows:

THEOREM 8.1. *Matrix $A \in \mathcal{M}_n(\mathbb{R})$ is totally positive if and only if for every $k \in \langle n \rangle$*

(a) $\det A[\alpha|\langle k \rangle] > 0$ *for all $\alpha \subseteq \langle n \rangle$ with $|\alpha| = k$ and $d(\alpha) = 0$,*

(b) $\det A[\langle k \rangle|\beta] > 0$ *for all $\beta \subseteq \langle n \rangle$ with $|\beta| = k$ and $d(\beta) = 0$.*

The task of detecting mimes is less straightforward and can be based on Proposition 6.1. As argued in [38] and by noting that, without loss of any generality, the semipositivity vector of X in Proposition 6.1 can be taken to be the all ones vector e (otherwise, our considerations apply with X, Y replaced by XD, YD for a suitable positive diagonal matrix D), the following two-step test for mimes is applicable [38]:

Step 1. Determine whether A is semipositive by solving the linear program

minimize $e^T x$
subject to $x \geq 0$ and $Ax \geq e$

If this program is infeasible, then A is **not** semipositive and thus not a mime; stop.

Step 2. Check the consistency of the linear inequality system

$$x_{ij} \leq 0 \quad (i, j = 1, \ldots, n,\ i \neq j),$$
$$\textstyle\sum_{k=1}^{n} a_{ik} x_{kj} \leq 0 \quad (i, j = 1, \ldots, n,\ i \neq j),$$
$$\textstyle\sum_{j=1}^{n} x_{ij} > 0 \quad (i = 1, \ldots, n).$$

If this system is inconsistent, A is not a mime; stop. Otherwise, A is mime as it satisfies the conditions of Proposition 6.1.

REMARK 8.2. The task of detecting matrices in $\mathbb{P}_{\mathrm{M}}$ is an open problem, related to the problem of characterizing matrices in $\mathbb{P}_{\mathrm{M}}$ and their spectra.

Now we turn our attention back to the general P-problem. The following theorem (cf. Theorem 3.1 (7) and (8)) is the theoretical basis for the subsequent algorithm. Although the result is stated and proved in [48] for real P-matrices, its proof is valid for complex P-matrices and included here for completeness.

THEOREM 8.3. [48] *Let* $\alpha \in \langle n \rangle$ *with* $|\alpha| = 1$. *Then* $A \in \mathbb{P}$ *if and only if* $A[\alpha] > 0$, $A[\overline{\alpha}] \in \mathbb{P}$, *and* $A/A[\alpha] \in \mathbb{P}$.

Proof. Without loss of generality, assume that $\alpha = \{1\}$. Otherwise we can consider a permutation similarity of A. If $A = [a_{ij}]$ is a P-matrix, then $A[\alpha]$ and $A(\alpha)$ are also P-matrices. Also $A/A[\alpha]$ is a P-matrix by Theorem 3.1 (7).

For the converse, assume that $A[\alpha] = [a_{11}]$, $A[\overline{\alpha}]$ and $A/A[\alpha]$ are P-matrices. Using $a_{11} > 0$ as the pivot, we can row reduce A to obtain a matrix B with all of its off-diagonal entries in the first column equal to zero. As is well known, $B[\overline{\alpha}] = A/A[\alpha]$. That is, B is a block triangular matrix whose diagonal blocks are P-matrices. It follows readily that B is a P-matrix. The determinant of any principal submatrix of A that includes entries from the first row of A coincides with the determinant of the corresponding submatrix of B and is thus positive. The determinant of any principal submatrix of A with no entries from the first row coincides with a principal minor of $A[\overline{\alpha}]$ and is also positive. Hence A is a P-matrix. □

The following is an algorithmic implementation of the technique suggested by Theorem 8.3 for the P-problem. For a complexity analysis see [48].

ALGORITHM P(A)

1. Input $A = [a_{ij}] \in \mathcal{M}_n(\mathbb{C})$
2. If $a_{11} \not> 0$ output **'Not a P-matrix'** stop
3. Evaluate $A/A[\alpha]$
4. Call P($A(\alpha)$) and P($A/A[\alpha]$)
5. Output **'This is a P-matrix'**

Finally, we provide a Matlab M-file implementing Algorithm P(A).

```
function [r]=ptest(a)
% Return r=1 if 'a' is a P-matrix (r=0 otherwise)
n = length(a);
if ~(a(1,1)>0), r=0;
elseif n==1, r=1;
else
  b=a(2:n,2:n);
  d=a(2:n,1)/a(1,1);
  c=b-d*a(1,2:n);
  % recursively call
  r=ptest(b) & ptest(c);
end
```

REFERENCES

[1] S.M. Fallat, C.R. Johnson, J.R. Torregosa, and A.M. Urbano. P-matrix completions under weak symmetry assumptions. *Linear Algebra and its Applications*, 312, 73-91, 2000.

[2] A. Berman, D. Hershkowitz, and C.R. Johnson. Linear transformations which preserve certain positivity classes of matrices. *Linear Algebra and its Applications*, 68:9-29, 1985.

[3] A. Berman and R. J. Plemmons, *Nonnegative Matrices in the Mathematical Sciences*. SIAM, Philadelphia, 1994.

[4] X. Chen, Y. Shogenji, and M. Yamasaki. Verification for existence of solutions of linear complementarity problems, *Linear Algebra and its Applications*, 324:15-26, 2001.

[5] G. E. Coxson. The P-matrix problem is co-NP-complete. *Mathematical Programming*, 64:173-178, 1994.

[6] G. E. Coxson. Computing exact bounds on elements of an inverse interval matrix is NP-hard. *Reliable Computing*, 5:137-142, 1999.

[7] C.W. Cryer. Some properties of totally positive matrices. *Linear Algebra and Its Applications*, 15:1-25, 1976.

[8] L.M. DeAlba, L. Hogben. Completions of P-matrix patterns. *Linear Algebra and Its Applications*, 319:83-102, 2000.

[9] L. Elsner, R. Nabben, and M. Neumann. Orthogonal bases that lead to symmetric, nonnegative matrices. *Linear Algebra and Its Applications*, 271:323-343, 1998.

[10] C. A. Eschenbach and C. R. Johnson. Sign patterns that require real, nonreal or pure imaginary eigenvalues. *Linear and Multilinear Algebra*, 29:299-311, 1991.

[11] S. Fallat. Bidiagonal factorizations of totally nonnegative matrices. *American Mathematical Monthly*, 108:697-712, 2001.

[12] S. Fallat and M.J. Tsatsomeros. On the Cayley transform of certain positivity classes of matrices, preprint.

[13] M. Fekete. Über ein problem von Laguerre. *Rendiconti del Circolo Matematico di Palermo*, 34:89-100, 110-120, 1913.

[14] M. Fiedler, *Special Matrices and Their Applications in Numerical Mathematics*, Martinus Nijhoff Publishers, 1986.

[15] M. Fiedler and V. Pták. Some generalizations of positive definiteness and monotonicity. *Numerische Mathematik*, 9:163-172, 1966.

[16] S. Friedland, D. Hershkowitz, and H. Schneider. Matrices whose powers are M-matrices or Z-matrices. *Transactions of the American Mathematical Society*, 300:233-244, 1988.

[17] M. Gasca and J.M. Pena. On factorizations of totally positive matrices. In *Total Positivity and Its Applications*, M. Gasca and C.A. Micchelli, editors, Mathematics and Its Applications, Kluwer Academic, 359:109-130, 1996.

[18] R. Grone, C.R. Johnson, E.M. Sa, H. Wolkowicz. Positive definite completions of partial Hermitian matrices. *Linear Algebra and its Applications*, 58:109-124, 1984.

[19] D. Hershkowitz and C.R. Johnson. Linear transformations that map the P-matrices into themselves. *Linear Algebra and its Applications*, 74:23-38, 1986.

[20] D. Hershkowitz and C.R. Johnson. Spectra of matrices with P-matrix powers. *Linear Algebra and its Applications*, 80:159-171, 1986.

[21] D. Hershkowitz and H. Schneider. Matrices with a sequence of accretive powers. *Linear Israel Journal of Mathematics*, 55:344-372, 1986.

[22] L. Hogben. Completions of inverse M-matrix patterns. *Linear Algebra and its Applications*, 282:145-160, 1998.

[23] L. Hogben. Completions of M-matrix patterns. *Linear Algebra and its Applications*, 285:143-152, 1998.

[24] R.A. Horn and C.R. Johnson, *Matrix Analysis*, Cambridge University Press, 1990.

[25] R.A. Horn and C.R. Johnson, *Topics in Matrix Analysis*, Cambridge University Press, 1991.

[26] C. Jansson and J. Rohn. An algorithm for checking regularity of interval matrices. *SIAM Journal on Matrix Analysis and Applications*, 20:756-776, 1999.

[27] C.R. Johnson and B.K. Kroschel. The combinatorially symmetric P-matrix completion problem. *Electronic Journal of Linear Algebra*, 1:59-63, 1996.

[28] C.R. Johnson, M. Neumann, and M. Tsatsomeros. Conditions for the positivity of determinants. *Linear and Multilinear Algebra*, 40:241-248, 1996.

[29] C.R. Johnson, D.D. Olesky, M. Tsatsomeros, and P. van den Driessche. Spectra with positive elementary symmetric functions. *Linear Algebra and Its Applications*, 180:247-262, 1993.

[30] C.R. Johnson and R.L. Smith. The completion problem for M-matrices and inverse M-matrices. *Linear*

Algebra and Its Applications, 241-243:655-667, 1996.

[31] C.R. Johnson and M.J. Tsatsomeros. Convex sets of nonsingular and P-matrices. *Linear and Multilinear Algebra*, 38:233-239, 1995.

[32] R. Kellogg. On Complex eigenvalues of M and P matrices. *Numerische Mathematik*, 19:170-175, 1972.

[33] B. Li, L. Li, M. Harada, H. Niki, and M. Tsatsomeros. An iterative criterion for H-matrices. *Linear Algebra and Its Applications*, 271:179-190, 1998.

[34] O.L. Mangasarian. *Nonlinear Programming*, McGraw-Hill, New York, 1969.

[35] O.L. Mangasarian. Characterization of linear complementarity problems as linear problems. *Mathematical Programming Study*, 7:74-87, 1978.

[36] M. Neumann. A conjecture concerning the Hadamard product of inverses of M-matrices. *Linear Algebra and Its Applications*, 285:277-290, 1998.

[37] J.-S. Pang. Hidden Z-matrices with positive principal minors. *Linear Algebra and Its Applications*, 23:201-215, 1979.

[38] J.-S. Pang. On discovering hidden Z-matrices. *Constructive Approaches to Mathematical Models*, pp. 231-241, Academic Press, 1979.

[39] J.M. Pena. A class of P-matrices with applications to the localization of the eigenvalues of a real matrix. *SIAM Journal on Matrix Analysis and Applications*, 22:1027-1037, 2001.

[40] J. Rohn. Systems of linear interval equations. *Linear Algebra and Its Applications*, 126:39-78, 1989.

[41] J. Rohn. A theorem on P-matrices. *Linear and Multilinear Algebra*, 30:209-211, 1991.

[42] J. Rohn and G. Rex. Interval P-matrices. *SIAM Journal on Matrix Analysis and Applications*, 17:1020-1024, 1996.

[43] S. Rump. Self-validating methods. *Linear Algebra and Its Applications*. 324:3-13, 2001.

[44] S. Rump. On P-matrices. *Linear Algebra and Its Applications*. To appear in the proceedings of the Oberwolfach meeting on Nonnegative matrices, M-matrices and their Generalizations.

[45] G.W. Soules. Constructing nonnegative symmetric matrices. *Linear and Multilinear Algebra*, 13:241-151, 1983.

[46] J.L. Stuart. A polynomial time spectral decomposition test for certain classes of inverse M-matrices. *Electonic Journal of Linear Algebra*, 3:129-141, 1998.

[47] M. Tsatsomeros. Principal pivot transforms: properties and applications. *Linear Algebra and Its Applications*, 300:151-165, 2000.

[48] M. Tsatsomeros and L. Li. A recursive test for P-matrices. *BIT*, 40:404-408, 2000.

[49] H. Väliaho. A polynomial-time test for M-matrices. *Linear Algebra and Its Applications*, 153:183-192, 1991.

[50] B.-Y. Wang, X. Zhang, and F. Zhang. On the Hadamard product of inverse M-matrices. *Linear Algebra and Its Applications*, 305:23-31, 2000.

[51] *Nonnegative matrices, M-matrices and their generalizations*, Oberwolfach, November 26 - December 2, 2000. D. Hershkowitz, V. Mehrmann, and H. Schneider, organizers.

Author's biography

Michael Tsatsomeros was born in Canada and raised in Greece, where he completed high school and a degree in Mathematics at the University of Patras. He then moved to North America and obtained graduate degrees from Concordia University in Montreal and the University of Connecticut. Since then, he has held academic positions in Victoria B.C., Madison Wisconsin, Williamsburg Virginia, Regina Saskatchewan, and is currently an Associate Professor of Mathematics at Washington State University.

In: Focus on Computational Neurobiology
Editor: Lei Li, pp. 133-143
ISBN 1-59033-915-0

THE VISCOSITY METHODS FOR RIEMANN INITIAL-BOUNDARY PROBLEMS OF SCALAR CONSERVATION LAWS*

HONGXIA LIU† AND TAO PAN‡

Abstract. This paper is concerned with global error estimates for the viscosity methods to Riemann initial-boundary problems for scalar conservation laws $u_t + f(u)_x = 0$ on R_+, with the boundary data $u(0,t) = u_-$ and the initial data $u(x,0) = u_+$, where $u_\pm$ are two constants, $u_- \neq u_+$. The error of the viscosity solution to the inviscid solution is bounded by $O(\varepsilon + \varepsilon|\ln\varepsilon|)$ in the L^1-norm for all cases with convex fluxes and some cases with non-convex fluxes, respectively. If there is no central rarefaction wave included in the inviscid solution, the error bound is improved to $O(\varepsilon)$. The proof is given by a matching method and the traveling wave solutions.

Key words. conservation laws, initial-boundary problem, viscosity methods, error estimate

1. Introduction. The viscosity methods play an important role in both theoretical analysis and numerical computation for hyperbolic conservation laws. Studying the accuracy and error bound of viscosity methods to the entropy solution of conservation laws is very important for the development of numerical methods for conservation laws. For piecewise smooth solutions to hyperbolic systems with finitely many non-interacting shocks, $O(\varepsilon)$ local error estimates have been obtained by Goodman and Xin [1], where $\varepsilon > 0$ is viscosity coefficient. Recently, by using a matching method developed by Goodman and Xin [1], Teng and Zhang [2] got an optimal uniform L^1- error bounds of $O(\varepsilon)$ for the viscosity methods to the Cauchy problem of scalar conservation laws with initial data being a finite number of piecewise constants, subject to the initial discontinuities satisfying the entropy conditions. The result is improvement over the half-order rates of L^1-convergence for various approximate methods (see [3-9]). The analysis used in [2] was extended to more general cases for convex fluxes, such as piecewise smooth solutions, with finitely many discontinuities, the L^1-convergence rate of $O(\varepsilon + \varepsilon|\ln\varepsilon|)$ for viscosity methods was established in [10].

For the initial-boundary problems for scalar conservation laws in arbitary space dimensions, vanishing viscosity method proving the existence of the global weak solution was established in [11]. To the best of our knowledge, no global error estimate for the initial-boundary problems of scalar conservation laws has been obtained. We want to establish an L^1-convergence rate for viscosity methods to the initial-boundary problems of scalar conservation laws. By the first step, we consider the case of the following Riemann initial-boundary problems

$$\text{(1.1)} \qquad \begin{cases} u_t + f(u)_x = 0, & (x,t) \in R_+ \times R_+ \\ u(0,t) = u_b(t) := u_-, & t \in R_+ \\ u(x,0) = u_0(x) := u_+, & x \in R_+, \end{cases}$$

where $f \in C^2$, $u_\pm$ are two constants, $u_- \neq u_+$.

*The work for the first author is supported by the National Natural Science Foundation of China [199101012]. The work for the second author is supported by the National Natural Science Foundation of China [10061001] and Guangxi Natural Science Foundation [9912020].

†Department of Mathematics, Jinan University, Guangzhou, 510632, P. R. China (hongxia-liu@163.net). Part of the research was carried out while this author was visiting Academy of Mathematics and System Sciences, Chinese Academy of Science.

‡Department of Mathematics and Information Sciences, Guangxi University, Nanning, 530004, P. R. China, and Laboratory Bioinformation and Food Engineering, Faculty of Bioresources, Mie University, Tsu, Mie, 514-8507, Japan (pan@bife.bio.mie-u.ac.jp).

The viscosity method approaching (1.1) is to solve the parabolic equation with initial-boundary conditions:

$$(1.2)\qquad \begin{cases} (v_\varepsilon)_t + f(v_\varepsilon)=\varepsilon(v_\varepsilon)_{xx}, & (x,t)\in R_+\times R_+,\quad \varepsilon>0 \\ v_\varepsilon(0,t)=u_-, \quad t\geq 0 \\ v_\varepsilon(x,0)=v_0(x)(x\geq 0)\rightarrow u_+(x\rightarrow\infty), \end{cases}$$

and the weak entropy solution u of (1.1) can be constructed as the limit of solutions for (1.2) as $\varepsilon\rightarrow 0+$.

It is well known that under the condition that $v_0(x)\in C^2([0,\infty))$ satisfies the compatibility conditions $v_0(0)=u_-$ and $v_0'(0)=v_0''(0)=0$, and there exists a unique smooth solution v_ε to (1.2) such that v_ε and its first derivative with respect to x are uniformly bounded in $C([0,\infty)\times[0,T])(\forall T>0)$ for ε (See, for instance, [12], or [13]).

Following the arguments of [11, 14, 15], we state the definition of the weak entropy solution to the initial-boundary problems (1.1) as follows.

DEFINITION 1.1 *A bounded and local bounded variable function $u(x,t)$ on $[0,\infty)\times[0,\infty)$ is called a weak entropy solution of the initial boundary problems (1.1), if for each $k\in R$, and for any nonnegative test function $\phi\in C_0^\infty([0,\infty)\times[0,\infty))$, it satisfies the following inequality*

$$(1.3)\qquad \begin{aligned} \int_0^\infty\int_0^\infty & \{|u-k|\phi_t+\operatorname{sgn}(u-k)(f(u)-f(k))\phi_x\}dxdt \\ &+\int_0^\infty |u_0(x)-k|\phi(x,0)dx \\ &+\int_0^\infty \operatorname{sgn}(u_b(t)-k)(f(u(0,t))-f(k))\phi(0,t)dt\geq 0. \end{aligned}$$

For the initial-boundary problems (1.1) with general bounded and measurable initial data and boundary data, the existence and uniqueness of the global weak entropy solution in the sense of (1.3) have been obtained, and the global weak entropy solution satisfies the following boundary entropy condition (1.4) (see also [11, 15]).

LEMMA 1.1 *If $u(x,t)$ is a weak entropy solution of (1.1), then,*

$$(1.4)\qquad \begin{aligned} & u(0,t)=u_b(t)\quad \text{or} \\ & \frac{f(u(0,t))-f(k)}{u(0,t)-k}\leq 0,\quad k\in I(u(0,t),u_b(t)),\quad k\neq u(0,t),\quad \text{a.e. } t\geq 0, \end{aligned}$$

where $I(u(0,t),u_b(t))=[\min\{u(0,t),u_b(t)\},\max\{u(0,t),u_b(t)\}]$.

For the piecewise smooth solution, the following lemma is easy to be proved by Definition 1.1 and Lemma 1.1 (see also [15, 16]).

LEMMA 1.2 *A piecewise smooth function $u(x,t)$ with smooth line discontinuities is a weak entropy solution to (1.1) in the sense of (1.3), if and only if the following conditions are satified:*

(1) $u(x,t)$ satisfies equation $(1.1)_1$ in its smooth domains.

(2) If $x=x(t)$ is a weak discontinuity of $u(x,t)$, then $\frac{dx(t)}{dt}=f'(u(x(t),t))$. If $x=x(t)$ is a strong discontinuity of $u(x,t)$, then

$$\frac{dx(t)}{dt}=\frac{f(u^+)-f(u^-)}{u^+-u^-},\qquad \text{(Rankine -- Hugoniot condition)}$$

and for any u between u^- *and* u^+

$$\frac{f(u^+)-f(u)}{u^+-u} \le \frac{f(u^+)-f(u^-)}{u^+-u^-}, \qquad \text{(Oleinik's entropy condition)}$$

where $u^+ = u(x(t)+0,t)$, $u^- = u(x(t)-0,t)$.

(3) The boundary entropy condition (1.4) holds.

(4) $u(x,0) = u_0(x)$ *a.e.* $x \ge 0$.

Remark 1.1 According to Lemma 1.2, if $U(x,t)$ is the weak entropy solution to the following Riemann problems (initial value problem)

$$(1.5) \qquad \begin{cases} u_t + f(u)_x = 0, & x \in R \\ u(x,0) = \begin{cases} u_-, \\ u_+, \end{cases} & \begin{matrix} x<0 \\ x>0, \end{matrix} \end{cases}$$

then, $u(x,t) = U(x,t)|_{R_+\times R_+}$ is the weak entropy solution to Riemann initial boundary problems (1.1).

But, for the initial-boundary problems of scalar conservation laws with general boundary data and initial data, this constructing method of the weak entropy solution (see Remark 1.1) will be not well posed. Specially, for the cases of including the interaction of elementary waves and the boundary, the structure of the weak entropy solution and the error estimates for the viscosity approximation will be expected in our problems, which will be investigated in the forthcoming paper.

From Remark 1.1, the weak entropy solution $u(x,t)$ to (1.1) does not admit a trace at the boundary, namely, $u(0,t)$ does not always equal to $u_b(t)$. Whereas, as viscosity approximation of the weak entropy solution $u(x,t)$ to (1.1), the solution to the parabolic equation (1.2) with initial-boundary conditions does admit a fixed trace at the boundary. Therefore, it is very interesting to consider the error estimates for the viscosity approximation to the initial-boundary problems of scalar conservation laws.

In this paper, we are concerned with the accuracy of the viscosity methods to the Riemann initial-boundary problems (1.1). More precisely, by applying the matching method used in [1,2,10], we will investigate the L^1-convergence rate for the viscosity methods to the weak entropy solutions of Riemann initial-boundary problems (1.1) with convex and non-convex flux function f, respectively.

Our plan of this paper is as follows. In Section 2, we introduce an L^1-stability lemma, a traveling wave lemma and a stationary solution lemma for the viscosity methods, which play important roles in obtaining the L^1-convergence rate. In the final Section 3, we will state the main results on L^1-convergence rate for the viscosity methods to (1.1).

2. Some basic lemmas. Throughout this paper, the norm $\|\cdot\|$ denotes the standard L^1-norm, $\|\cdot\|_{L^1(R_+)}$. We first introduce an L^1-stability lemma for non-homogeneous viscous equations with initial-boundary conditions.

LEMMA 2.1 *Let* $v^{(i)}(x,t)$ $(i=1,2)$ *be continuous and piecewise smooth solutions of the following equations*

$$(2.1) \qquad (v^{(i)})_t + f(v^{(i)})_x - \varepsilon(v^{(i)})_{xx} = g_i(x,t), \quad x>0,\ t>a\ge 0,\ i=1,2.$$

The above equations hold for all values of $x > 0$ except on some curves $X_m(t)$, $1 \le m \le M$, where $v_x^{(i)}$ may not exist. If $\omega := v^{(1)} - v^{(2)} \to 0$ as $x \to \infty$, then

$$
\begin{aligned}
\|\omega(\cdot,t)\| \le \|\omega(\cdot,a)\| &+ \int_a^t \|g_1(\cdot,\tau) - g_2(\cdot,\tau)\| d\tau \\
&+ \int_a^t \mathrm{sgn}\omega(0,\tau)(f(v^{(1)}(0,\tau)) - f(v^{(2)}(0,\tau)))d\tau + \varepsilon \int_a^t |\omega_x(0+,\tau)| d\tau \\
&+ \varepsilon \sum_{m=1}^{M} \int_a^t |\omega_x(X_m(\tau)+0,\tau) - \omega_x(X_m(\tau)-0,\tau)| d\tau.
\end{aligned} \tag{2.2$_1$}
$$

Especially, when $\omega(0,t) \equiv 0$,

$$
\begin{aligned}
\|\omega(\cdot,t)\| &\le \|\omega(\cdot,a)\| + \int_a^t \|g_1(\cdot,\tau) - g_2(\cdot,\tau)\| d\tau \\
&\quad + \varepsilon \sum_{m=1}^{M} \int_a^t |\omega_x(X_m(\tau)+0,\tau) - \omega_x(X_m(\tau)-0,\tau)| d\tau.
\end{aligned} \tag{2.2$_2$}
$$

Proof. We now prove this Lemma by a similar technique as in [10, 17]. It follows from (2.1) that

$$
\omega_t + (f(v^{(1)}) - f(v^{(2)}))_x = \varepsilon \omega_{xx} + g_1(x,t) - g_2(x,t). \tag{2.3}
$$

If $\omega \ge 0$ or $\omega \le 0$ for all x, then straightforward integration on the above equation gives (2.2). Let $(0 <) p_1(t) < p_2(t) < \cdots$ be the points such that at those points ω changes signs. Let α_j be the sign of ω in $(p_j, p_{j+1}) (j = 0, 1, 2, 3 \cdots, p_0 = 0)$. Multiplying (2.3) by $\alpha_j (j = 1, 2, \cdots)$ and integrating the resulting equation over (p_j, p_{j+1}) gives

$$
\begin{aligned}
\alpha_j \int_{p_j}^{p_{j+1}} \omega_t dx &= \varepsilon(\alpha_j \omega_x(p_{j+1}-0,t) - \alpha_j \omega_x(p_j+0,t)) \\
&\quad + \alpha_j \int_{p_j}^{p_{j+1}} (g_1(x,t) - g_2(x,t)) dx \\
&\quad + \varepsilon \sum_{p_j < X_m < p_{j+1}} \alpha_j (\omega_x(X_m(t)+0,t) - \omega_x(X_m(t)-0,t))
\end{aligned} \tag{2.4}
$$

Since $\omega(p_j,t) = \omega(p_{j+1},t) = 0$ and $\alpha_j \omega \ge 0$ for $x \in (p_j, p_{j+1})$, we have

$$
\frac{d}{dt} \int_{p_j}^{p_{j+1}} |\omega| dx = \alpha_j \int_{p_j}^{p_{j+1}} \omega_t dx.
$$

Moreover, observing that $\alpha_j \omega_x(p_{j+1}-0,t) \le 0$ and $\alpha_j \omega_x(p_j+0,t) \ge 0$ (j=1, 2, ...)(because $\alpha_j \omega_x(p_{j+1}-0,t) = \alpha_j \lim\limits_{x \to p_{j+1}^-} \dfrac{\omega(x,t) - \omega(p_{j+1},t)}{x - p_{j+1}} = \lim\limits_{x \to p_{j+1}^-} \dfrac{\alpha_j \omega(x,t)}{x - p_{j+1}} \le 0$), we obtain from (2.4) that

$$
\begin{aligned}
\frac{d}{dt} \int_{p_j}^{p_{j+1}} |\omega| dx &\le \sum_{p_j < X_m < p_{j+1}} \varepsilon \alpha_j |\omega_x(X_m(t)+0,t) - \omega_x(X_m(t)-0,t)| \\
&\quad + \int_{p_j}^{p_{j+1}} |g_1(x,t) - g_2(x,t)| dx.
\end{aligned}
$$

Since the above inequality is true for all $j \geq 1$, we have

(2.5)
$$\begin{aligned}\frac{d}{dt}\int_{p_1}^{p^*}|\omega|dx \;&\leq \sum_{p_1<X_m<p^*}\varepsilon|\omega_x(X_m(t)+0,t)-\omega_x(X_m(t)-0,t)|\\ &+\int_{p_1}^{p^*}|g_1(x,t)-g_2(x,t)|dx,\end{aligned}$$

where $p^* = \sup_j p_j$. If $p^* < \infty$, using a similar method as above gives

(2.6)
$$\begin{aligned}\frac{d}{dt}\int_{p^*}^{\infty}|\omega|dx \;&\leq \varepsilon\sum_{X_m>p^*}|\omega_x(X_m(t)+0,t)-\omega_x(X_m(t)-0,t)|\\ &+\int_{p^*}^{\infty}|g_1(x,t)-g_2(x,t)|dx.\end{aligned}$$

In obtaining the last inequality, we have used the fact $\omega \to 0$ as $x \to \infty$. In order to get (2.2), we need to estimate $\frac{d}{dt}\int_0^{p_1}|\omega|dx$. Multiplying (2.3) by α_0 and integrating the resultant equation over $(0, p_1)$ gives

$$\begin{aligned}\frac{d}{dt}\int_0^{p_1}|\omega|dx \;&= \alpha_0(f(v^{(1)}(0,t))-f(v^{(2)}(0,t)))+\alpha_0\int_0^{p_1}(g_1(x,t)-g_2(x,t))dx\\ &+\varepsilon(\alpha_0\omega_x(p_1-0,t)-\alpha_0\omega_x(0+,t))\\ &+\sum_{0<X_m<p_1}\alpha_0\varepsilon(\omega_x(X_m(t)+0,t)-\omega_x(X_m(t)-0,t)).\end{aligned}$$

If $\omega(0,t) \equiv 0$, then

(2.7)
$$\begin{aligned}\frac{d}{dt}\int_0^{p_1}|\omega|dx \;&\leq \sum_{0<X_m<p_1}\varepsilon|\omega_x(X_m(t)+0,t)-\omega_x(X_m(t)-0,t)|\\ &+\int_0^{p_1}|g_1(x,t)-g_2(x,t)|dx.\end{aligned}$$

If $\omega(0,t) \not\equiv 0$, then

(2.8)
$$\begin{aligned}&\frac{d}{dt}\int_0^{p_1}|\omega|dx \leq \varepsilon|\omega_x(0+,t)|\\ &+\sum_{0<X_m<p_1}\varepsilon|\omega_x(X_m(t)+0,t)-\omega_x(X_m(t)-0,t)|\\ &+\int_0^{p_1}|g_1(x,t)-g_2(x,t)|dx+\mathrm{sgn}\omega(0,t)(f(v^{(1)}(0,t))-f(v^{(2)}(0,t))).\end{aligned}$$

Using (2.5)–(2.8), we obtain the desired result. □

A traveling wave solution is a smooth solution of viscous scalar conservation laws $(1.2)_1$ in the form $v_\varepsilon(x,t) = V(x-st)$ satisfying $V(-\infty) = u_-$ and $V(\infty) = u_+$, where the shock speed $s = \dfrac{f(u_-)-f(u_+)}{u_- - u_+}$, $u_\pm$ are constants. We have the following existence lemma for the traveling wave solution (see also [2, 18, 19]).

LEMMA 2.2 *Suppose that the constant states u_- and u_+ satisfy the Lax geometric condition*

(2.9)
$$f'(u_+) < s = \frac{f(u_-)-f(u_+)}{u_- - u_+} < f'(u_-)$$

and Oleinik's entropy condition

$$\frac{f(u)-f(u_+)}{u-u_+} < s < \frac{f(u)-f(u_-)}{u-u_-}, \tag{2.10}$$

for all u strictly between u_- and u_+. Then for each $u_m \in (\min\{u_-,u_+\}, \max\{u_-, u_+\})$, there is a unique traveling $V(x-st)$ of $(1.2)_1$, taking on the values $V(-\infty)=u_-$, $V(0)=u_m$ and $V(\infty)=u_+$, which has the following properties:

(1). For $\xi \in R$, $V(\xi)$ is a strictly monotone function.

(2). There are positive constant c_0, c_1 and $c_\pm$ independent of ε, but depending on $u_\pm$, u_m and f such that the following estimates hold

$$|V(\xi)-u_-| \le c_0 e^{-c_-|\xi|/\varepsilon} \qquad \text{for } \xi \le 0, \tag{2.11}$$

$$|V(\xi)-u_+| \le c_0 e^{-c_+|\xi|/\varepsilon} \qquad \text{for } \xi \ge 0, \tag{2.12}$$

and

$$\|H(\cdot)-V(\cdot)\|_{L^1(R)} \le c_1\varepsilon,$$

where

$$H(x) = \begin{cases} u_-, & x<0 \\ u_+, & x>0. \end{cases} \tag{2.13}$$

Now, we turn to establish the stationary solution lemma of $(1.2)_1$ with convex fluxes.

LEMMA 2.3 *Suppose that $f \in C^2$ and $f''>0$. Then, when $u_+ < u_-$ and $f(u_-) \le f(u_+)$, the boundary value problem of the ordinary differential equation*

$$\begin{cases} f(\phi)_\xi = \varepsilon\phi_{\xi\xi}, & \xi > 0 \\ \phi(0)=u_-, & \phi(\infty)=u_+ \end{cases} \tag{2.14}$$

has a unique solution $\phi \in C^3([0,\infty))$ satisfying

$$\phi'(\xi) < 0$$

and

$$|\phi(\xi)-u_+| \le c_2 \exp(-|f'(u_+)|\xi/\varepsilon),$$

where $c_2>0$ is a constant independent of ε, but depends on $u_\pm$ and f.

Proof. From the assumptions, it follows that $f'(u_+)\neq 0$. We take the extension $\widetilde{f}$ of f satisfying $\widetilde{f} \in C^2$, $\widetilde{f}(\phi) \equiv f(\phi)$ for $u_+ \le \phi \le u_-$, and $\widetilde{f}(\widetilde{u}_-) = f(u_+)$ for some $\widetilde{u}_- > u_-$, and $\widetilde{f}''(\phi) > 0$ for $u_- < \phi < \widetilde{u}_-$. Then, by Lemma 2.2, there exists a unique traveling wave $\widetilde{\phi}(\xi)$ with shock speed $\widetilde{s}=0$, which satisfies

$$\begin{cases} \widetilde{f}(\widetilde{\phi})_\xi = \varepsilon\widetilde{\phi}_{\xi\xi} \\ \widetilde{\phi}(-\infty)=\widetilde{u}_-, \quad \widetilde{\phi}(0)=u_-, \quad \widetilde{\phi}(\infty)=u_+. \end{cases}$$

Therefore, we can obtain the desired solution by taking $\phi(\xi) = \widetilde{\phi}(\xi)\,|_{R_+}$. □

3. Main results. Applying the lemmas obtained in Section 2, we are now ready to state and prove the main results of this paper. We divide our problem into two cases: (1) the flux function f is convex, (2) the flux function f is non-convex.

In this section, we always suppose that $v_0(x) - u_+ \in L^1(R_+)$.

3.1. In the case of convex fluxes.

THEOREM 3.1 *Assume that $f'' > 0$ and $u_- < u_+$. Let v_ε be the solution to (1.2) and u be the weak entropy solution to (1.1). If $0 \le f'(u_-) < f'(u_+)$ or $f'(u_-) < 0 < f'(u_+)$, then the following error estimate holds for any $T \ge 0$:*

$$\sup_{0\le t\le T} \|v_\varepsilon(\cdot,t) - u(\cdot,t)\| \le \|v_0(\cdot) - u_+\| + C(T)(\varepsilon + \varepsilon|\ln\varepsilon|). \tag{3.1}$$

If $f'(u_-) < f'(u_+) \le 0$, then the following uniform error bounds are valid for any $T \ge 0$

$$\sup_{0\le t\le T} \|v_\varepsilon(\cdot,t) - u(\cdot,t)\| \le \|v_0(\cdot) - u_+\| + C(T)\varepsilon, \tag{3.2}$$

where $C(T)$ is a positive constant independent of ε.

Proof. When $0 \le f'(u_-) < f'(u_+)$ or $f'(u_-) < 0 < f'(u_+)$ or $f'(u_-) < f'(u_+) \le 0$, according to Remark 1.1, the weak entropy solutions of (1.1) for $t > 0$ are the following centred rarefaction waves and constant state respectively

$$u(x,t) = \begin{cases} u_-, & 0 < x < f'(u_-)t \\ (f')^{-1}(\frac{x}{t}), & f'(u_-)t \le x \le f'(u_+)t \\ u_+, & x > f'(u_+)t, \end{cases} \tag{3.3}$$

or

$$u(x,t) = \begin{cases} (f')^{-1}(\frac{x}{t}), & 0 < x \le f'(u_+)t \\ u_+, & x > f'(u_+)t, \end{cases} \tag{3.4}$$

or

$$u(x,t) \equiv u_+, \quad x > 0. \tag{3.5}$$

By direct computation, we have the following results for (3.3)

$$\begin{aligned} &|u_x| \le \frac{c_3}{t}, \quad |u_{xx}| \le \frac{c_4}{t^2} \text{ as } f'(u_-)t < x < f'(u_+)t, \\ &\text{and } u_x = u_{xx} = 0 \text{ as } 0 < x < f'(u_-)t \text{ or } x > f'(u_+)t, \end{aligned} \tag{A_1}$$

and for (3.4)

$$\begin{aligned} &|u_x| \le \frac{c_3}{t}, \quad |u_{xx}| \le \frac{c_4}{t^2} \text{ as } 0 \le x < f'(u_+)t, \\ &\text{and } u_x = u_{xx} = 0 \text{ as } x > f'(u_+)t, \end{aligned} \tag{A_2}$$

where c_3 and c_4 are positive constants independent of ε and t.

Now, we prove that (3.1) holds for the case $0 \le f'(u_-) < f'(u_+)$. Using (A_1) yields

$$\begin{aligned} &\int_\varepsilon^t |u_x(0+,\tau)|d\tau, \quad \int_\varepsilon^t |u_x(X_l(\tau)+0,\tau)|d\tau, \int_\varepsilon^t |u_x(X_r(\tau)-0,\tau)|d\tau \\ &\le C(T)(1+|\ln\varepsilon|), \end{aligned} \tag{3.6}$$

and

$$\int_{\varepsilon}^{t} \|u_{xx}(\cdot,\tau)\| d\tau = \int_{\varepsilon}^{t} \int_{X_l(\tau)}^{X_r(\tau)} |u_{xx}(x,\tau)| dx d\tau \le C(T)(1 + |\ln \varepsilon|) \tag{3.7}$$

for $0 < \varepsilon < t < T$, where $X_l(t) := f'(u_-)t$, $X_r(t) := f'(u_+)t$. We replace $v^{(1)}(x,t)$, $v^{(2)}(x,t)$ in Lemma 2.1 by $v_\varepsilon(x,t)$, $u(x,t)$, respectively, where $v_\varepsilon(x,t)$ is the solution of (1.2) and $u(x,t)$ is the weak entropy solution of (1.1), defined by (3.3), then we get for $0 < \varepsilon < t < T$,

$$\begin{aligned} \|v_\varepsilon(\cdot,t) - u(\cdot,t)\| &\le \|v_\varepsilon(\cdot,\varepsilon) - u(\cdot,\varepsilon)\| + \varepsilon \int_{\varepsilon}^{t} \|u_{xx}(\cdot,\tau)\| d\tau \\ &+ \varepsilon \int_{\varepsilon}^{t} (|u_x(X_l(\tau)+0,\tau)| + |u_x(X_r(\tau)-0,\tau)|) d\tau. \end{aligned}$$

Applying (3.6) and (3.7) to the above inequality gives

$$\|v_\varepsilon(\cdot,t) - u(\cdot,t)\| \le \|v_\varepsilon(\cdot,\varepsilon) - u(\cdot,\varepsilon)\| + C(T)(\varepsilon + \varepsilon|\ln \varepsilon|). \tag{3.8}$$

Since v_ε and u satisfy the following results,

$$\|v_\varepsilon(\cdot,s_1) - v_\varepsilon(\cdot,s_2)\| \le C|s_1 - s_2|, \qquad \|u(\cdot,s_1) - u(\cdot,s_2)\| \le C|s_1 - s_2|,$$

where $C > 0$ is a constant independent of ε, it follows from (3.8) that for any $0 < t < T$,

$$\|v_\varepsilon(\cdot,t) - u(\cdot,t)\| \le \|v_0(\cdot) - u_+\| + C(T)(\varepsilon + \varepsilon|\ln \varepsilon|),$$

which results in (3.1).

Similarly, using (A_2), Lemma 2.1 and $\mathrm{sgn}(u_- - u(0+,t))(f(u_-) - f(u(0+,t))) < 0$, we can get (3.1) for the case of $f'(u_-) < 0 < f'(u_+)$.

Next, we establish the error estimate (3.2) for the case $f'(u_-) < f'(u_+) \le 0$. We take $v^{(1)}(x,t) = v_\varepsilon(x,t)$, $v^{(2)}(x,t) = u(x,t)$ in Lemma 2.1, where $v_\varepsilon(x,t)$ is the solution of (1.2) and $u(x,t)$ is the weak entropy solution of (1.1), defined by (3.5). Then one can obtain for $0 < t < T$, by using the inequality $\mathrm{sgn}(u_- - u_+)(f(u_-) - f(u_+)) < 0$,

$$\begin{aligned} &\|v_\varepsilon(\cdot,t) - u(\cdot,t)\| \\ &\le \|v_0(\cdot) - u_+\| + \varepsilon \int_0^t |v_{\varepsilon x}(0+,\tau)| d\tau + \int_0^t \mathrm{sgn}(u_- - u_+)(f(u_-) - f(u_+)) d\tau \\ &\le \|v_0(\cdot) - u_+\| + C(T)\varepsilon. \end{aligned}$$

Hence, (3.2) is true. □

Remark 3.1 If we take $v_0(x) \in C^2([0,\infty))$ as follows:

$$v_0(x) = \begin{cases} v_{0\varepsilon}(x), & 0 \le x \le \varepsilon \\ u_+, & x > \varepsilon, \end{cases}$$

where $v_{0\varepsilon}(\cdot) \in C^2([0,\varepsilon])$ satisfies the corresponding compatibility conditions, then, $\int_0^\infty |v_0(x) - u_+| dx < c_3\varepsilon$, c_3 is a constant indepedent of ε. Thus (3.1) and (3.2) are replaced by the followings, respectively:

$$\sup_{0 \le t \le T} \|v_\varepsilon(\cdot,t) - u(\cdot,t)\| \le C(T)(\varepsilon + \varepsilon|\ln \varepsilon|)$$

and

$$\sup_{0\le t\le T} \|v_\varepsilon(\cdot,t)-u(\cdot,t)\| \le C(T)\varepsilon.$$

We can make a similar remark to the succeeding Theorem 3.2-3.4, respectively.

THEOREM 3.2 *Suppose that $f''>0$ and $u_->u_+$. Let v_ε be the solution to (1.2) and u be the weak entropy solution to (1.1). Then the following error estimate holds for any $T\ge 0$:*

$$\sup_{0\le t\le T} \|v_\varepsilon(\cdot,t)-u(\cdot,t)\| \le \|v_0(\cdot)-u_+\| + C(T)\varepsilon, \tag{3.9}$$

where $C(T)$ is a positive constant independent of ε.

Proof. First, we verify (3.9) in the case of $f(u_-)>f(u_+)$. From Remark 1.1, the weak entropy solution of (1.1) for $t>0$ is the following shock wave:

$$\begin{aligned} u(x,t) &= \begin{cases} u_-, & 0<x<st \\ u_+, & x>st \end{cases} \\ &= H(x-st), \qquad (x,t)\in R_+\times R_+, \end{aligned} \tag{3.10}$$

where $s=\dfrac{f(u_-)-f(u_+)}{u_--u_+}$, $H(\cdot)$ is defined in (2.13). By means of the triangular inequality and lemma 2.2, we obtain

$$\begin{aligned} \|v_\varepsilon(\cdot,t)-u(\cdot,t)\| &= \|v_\varepsilon(\cdot,t)-H(\cdot-st)\| \\ &\le \|v_\varepsilon(\cdot,t)-V(\cdot-st)\| + \|V(\cdot-st)-H(\cdot-st)\| \\ &\le \|v_\varepsilon(\cdot,t)-V(\cdot-st)\| + \|V(\cdot)-H(\cdot)\|_{L^1(R)} \\ &\le \|v_\varepsilon(\cdot,t)-V(\cdot-st)\| + c_1\varepsilon, \end{aligned} \tag{3.11}$$

where $V(x-st)$ is a traveling wave solution of $(1.2)_1$, given in Lemma 2.2. Since $V(x-st)$ is also a solution of $(1.2)_1$, from Lemma 2.1 and Lemma 2.2, we can conclude that

$$\begin{aligned} \|v_\varepsilon(\cdot,t)-V(\cdot-st)\| &\le \|v_0(\cdot)-V(\cdot)\| + \int_0^t |f(u_-)-f(V(-s\tau))|d\tau \\ &\quad +\varepsilon\int_0^t (|v_{\varepsilon x}(0+,\tau)|+|V_x(-s\tau)|)d\tau \\ &\le \|v_0(\cdot)-u_+\| + \|V(\cdot)-u_+\| + |f'(u_-)| \\ &\quad \int_0^t |V(-s\tau)-u_-|d\tau + \varepsilon\int_0^t (|v_x(0+,\tau)|+|V_x(-s\tau)|)d\tau \\ &\le \|v_0(\cdot)-u_+\| + C(T)\varepsilon. \end{aligned}$$

Combining the above inequality with (3.11) gives (3.9).

Next, we estimate $\|v_\varepsilon(\cdot,t)-u(\cdot,t)\|$ in the case of $f(u_-)\le f(u_+)$. In this case, the weak entropy solution of (1.1) is the following constant state :

$$u(x,t)\equiv u_+, \qquad (x,t)\in R_+\times R_+.$$

Therefore by using the triangular inequality, Lemma 2.1 and Lemma 2.3, we have

$$
\begin{aligned}
&\|v_\varepsilon(\cdot,t)-u(\cdot,t)\| = \|v_\varepsilon(\cdot,t)-u_+\| \\
&\le \int_0^\infty |v_\varepsilon(x,t)-\phi(x)|dx + \int_0^\infty |\phi(x)-u_+|dx \\
&\le \int_0^\infty |v_0(x)-\phi(x)|dx + \int_0^\infty |\phi(x)-u_+|dx \\
&\le \|v_0(\cdot)-u_+\| + 2\int_0^\infty |\phi(x)-u_+|dx \le \|v_0(\cdot)-u_+\| + C(T)\varepsilon,
\end{aligned}
\tag{3.12}
$$

where $\phi(x)$ is the stationary solution of $(1.2)_1$ given in lemma 2.3. Hence, (3.12) implies (3.9). □

Remark 3.2 For the case $f(u_-) \le f(u_+)$, we can verify (3.9) by using Lemma 2.1 directly.

3.2. In the case of non-convex fluxes. We consider the case in which the flux function f has only one inflection. We have no harm to suppose that $f \in C^2$ satisfies the following inequality

$$
f''(u)\begin{cases} >0, & \text{if } u>0 \\ <0, & \text{if } u<0. \end{cases}
\tag{3.13}
$$

Note that $f(u)$ has a point of inflection at $u=0$.

THEOREM 3.3 *Assume that $u_-\cdot u_+<0$, and that (3.13), (2.10) hold. If $\frac{f(u_-)-f(u_+)}{u_--u_+}>0$ and $f'(u_+)<\frac{f(u_-)-f(u_+)}{u_--u_+}<f'(u_-)$, or $\frac{f(u_-)-f(u_+)}{u_--u_+}\le 0$ and $f'(u_+)\le\frac{f(u_-)-f(u_+)}{u_--u_+}<f'(u_-)$, then the error estimate (3.9) holds for any $T\ge 0$.*

Proof. When $\frac{f(u_-)-f(u_+)}{u_--u_+}>0$ and $f'(u_+)<\frac{f(u_-)-f(u_+)}{u_--u_+}<f'(u_-)$, Theorem 3.3 can be proved in the same way as the first part of proof in Theorem 3.2. When $\frac{f(u_-)-f(u_+)}{u_--u_+}\le 0$ and $f'(u_+)\le\frac{f(u_-)-f(u_+)}{u_--u_+}<f'(u_-)$, by taking $v^{(1)}(x,t)=v_\varepsilon(x,t)$, $v^{(2)}(x,t)=u\equiv u_+$ in Lemma 2.1, we can derive the desired error estimate. We omit the details. □

THEOREM 3.4 *Under the conditions (3.13), $f'(0)<0$ and $u_-<0<u_+$, we further suppose that the Riemann problem for scalar conservation laws (1.5) is resolved by a degenerate shock with speed $\frac{f(u_-)-f(u_*)}{u_--u_*}$ (where $0<u_*<u_+$), connecting u_- and u_*, and a centred rarefaction wave, connecting u_* and u_+. If $f'(u_+)>0$ and $\frac{f(u_-)-f(u_*)}{u_--u_*}\le 0$, then the error estimate (3.1) holds for any $T\ge 0$. If $f'(u_+)\le 0$, then the error estimate (3.2) is valid for any $T\ge 0$.*

Proof. When $f'(u_+)>0$ and $\frac{f(u_-)-f(u_*)}{u_--u_*}\le 0$, or $f'(u_+)\le 0$, in view of Remark 1.1, the weak entropy solutions of (1.1) for $t>0$ are the following centred rarefaction wave and constant state, respectively,

$$
u(x,t)=\begin{cases} (f')^{-1}(\frac{x}{t}), & 0\le x\le f'(u_+)t \\ u_+, & x>f'(u_+)t \end{cases}
$$

or

$$
u(x,t)\equiv u_+, \qquad x>0.
$$

The rest proofs of this Theorem are quite similar to those in Theorem 3.1. The details are omitted. □

Acknowledgments. The authors are grateful to Prof.Jinghua Wang, Prof.Ling Xiao and Prof.Zhenhuan Teng for their valuable discussion and the warm encouragement.

REFERENCES

[1] J.GOODMAN AND X.XIN, *Viscous limits for piecewise smooth solutions to systems of conservation laws*, Arch. Rat. Mech. Anal., 121(1992), pp. 235-265.

[2] Z.H.TENG AND P.W.ZHANG, *Optimal L^1-rate of convergence for viscosity method and monotone scheme to piecewise constant solutions with shocks*, SIAM J. Numer. Anal., 34(1997), pp. 959-978.

[3] D.HOFF AND J.SMOLLER, *Error bounds for Glimm difference approximations for scalar conservation laws*, Trans. Amer. Math. Soc., 289(1985), pp. 611-642.

[4] N.N.KUZNETSOV, *Accuracy of some approximate methods for computing the weak solutions of a first-order quasi-linear equation*, USSR Comput. Math. and Math. Phys., 16(1976), pp. 105-119.

[5] N.N.KUZNETSOV, *On stable methods for solving non-linear first order partial differential equations in the class of discontinuous functions*, Topics in Numerical Analysis III, J. J. H. Miller, ed., Proc. Royal Irish Academy Conference, Academic Press, London, 1977, pp. 183-197.

[6] B.J.LUCIER, *Error bounds for the methods of Glimm, Godunov and Leveque*, SIAM J. Numer. Anal., 22(1985), pp. 1074-1081.

[7] T.TANG AND Z.H.TENG, *The sharpness of Kuznetsov's $O(\sqrt{\Delta x})$ L^1-error estimate for monotone difference schemes*, Math. Comp., 64(1995), pp. 581-589.

[8] T.TANG AND Z.H.TENG, *Error bounds for fractional step methods for conservation laws with source terms*, SIAM J. Numer. Anal., 32(1995), pp. 110-127.

[9] A.TVEITO AND R.WINTHER, *An error estimate for a finite difference scheme approximating a hyperbolic system of conservation laws*, SIAM J. Numer. Anal., 30(1993), pp. 401-424.

[10] T.TANG AND Z.H.TENG, *Viscosity methods for piecewise smooth solutions to scalar conservation laws*, Math. Comp., 66(1997), pp. 495-526.

[11] C.BARDOS, A.Y.LEROUX AND J.C.NEDELEC, *First order quasilinear equations with boundary conditions*, Comm. Partial Diff. Eqs., 4(1979), pp. 1017-1034.

[12] A.FRIEDMAN, *Partial differential equations of parabolic type*, Prentice Hall, New York, 1969.

[13] O.A.LADYZENSKAJA AND N.N.URAL'CEVA, *Boundary problems for linear and quasilinear parabolic equations, I-II*, Izv. Akad. Nauk SSSR, ser. Mat. 26(1964), pp. 2-52, pp. 753-780 = AMS Transl. Ser.2, 47(1965), pp. 217-299.

[14] P.LEFLOCH, *Explicit formula for scalar nonlinear conservation laws with boundary conditions*, Math. Method in Appl. Sci., 10(1988), pp. 265-287.

[15] T.PAN AND L.W.LIN, *The global solution of the scalar nonconvex conservation law with boundary condition I-II*, J. Partial Diff. Eqs., 8(1995), pp. 371-383; 11(1998), pp. 1-8.

[16] E.HOPF, *On the right weak solution of the Cauchy problem for a quasilinear equation of first order*, J. Math. Mech., 19(1969), pp. 483-487

[17] P.D.LAX, *Hyperbolic System of Conservation Laws and the Mathematical Theory of Shock Waves*, SIAM, Philadelphia, 1973.

[18] A.MATSUMURA AND K.NISHIHARA, *Asymptotic stability of traveling waves for scalar viscous conservation laws with non-convex nonlinearity*, Comm. Math. Phys., 165(1994), pp. 83-96.

[19] S.KAWASHIMA AND A.MATSUMURA, *Stability of shock profiles in viscoelasticity with non-convex constitutiverelations*, Comm. Pure Appl. Math., XLXII(1994), pp. 1547-1569.

In: Focus on Computational Neurobiology
Editor: Lei Li, pp. 145-151

ISBN 1-59033-915-0

COMPARISON WITH BLOCKING EFFECT BETWEEN FOUR BASE FUNCTIONS IN DCT METHOD AND OBDCT METHOD

KANAE T. KOBAYASHI* AND HIDEO SAWAMI†

Abstract. When DCT (discrete cosine transform) method as a standard transform coding is used to extend images at higher compression ratio, it is difficult to eliminate degradation of image quality due to blocking effect. We quantify and analyze blocking effect for the DCT and OBDCT(overlapping block DCT) methods corresponding to four bases as degradation of image quality caused by quantization error. We clarify theoretically that the OBDCT method with type-I, III bases show the least blocking effect.

It is concluded that the OBDCT method is more effective transform coding than the DCT method with data compression and image extension since it did not occur blocking effect visually from results of subjective comparison and enough image quality is kept.

Key words. blocking effect, quantization error, extension image, transform coding

1. Introduction. High-resolution images become to be treated generally on computer since high-resolution and high-performance computer display emerged in recent years. Because image data increases greatly according to become higher resolution, we should reduce a great amount of data when applying data compression to save or transmit image data efficiently. However it cannot avoid degradation of image quality whenever images are reconstructed from compressed data. Therefore it is necessary to develop a new transform coding which can eliminate degradation of image quality to the utmost and can be achieved at high compression ratio. By the place, an optimal transform coding must be always determined theoretically after it examined properties of each image. Although processing speed in the present becomes faster, the optimal transform coding needs considerable processing time until an image is reconstructed. Several studies without increase of processing time have been made on methods improving image quality when extension [4]-[6]. The OBDCT method on the same study can regard as the DCT method with a pre-processing which has a weighting window function and a folding process [8]. The OBDCT method can be used to prevent increase of the whole processing time and to improve image quality.

JPEG(joint photographic experts group) is well known as the international standard for color still images and adopts the DCT method as a near optimum transform coding. When JPEG was established, prime purposes of studies was speeding-up of processing and to make smaller hardware. In recent years, one of prime purposes rather became improving of image quality which displayed on high-performance display. By the way, the DCT method has a problem for degradation of image quality which is conspicuous visually by occurring blocking effect when used at higher compression ratio. Blocking effect tends to be more conspicuous when images are extended larger. Therefore it becomes difficult to achieve high quality for reconstructed images if the DCT method is used to extend images at higher data compression. It is necessary to consider image quality in extension case since degradation becomes more conspicuous. It is also well known that four base functions for the DCT method exist as combinations of each sampling coordinate for a signal space and a frequency space. Accordingly, we quantify blocking effect occurring in each basis for the DCT and the OBDCT methods, and specify an excellent transform coding.

*Department of General Education, Kawasaki College of Allied Health Professions, 316 Matsushima Kurashiki, Okayama 701-0194, Japan

†Department of Mathematical Information Science, Faculty of Informatics, Okayama University of Science

2. The DCT Method with Resolution Conversion. In a transform coding, transformation such as DCT for two-dimensional signals is realized by applying one-dimensional transformation to horizontal and vertical directions respectively. In this paper, we discuss transformation by one-dimensional signal for simplicity. One-dimensional DCT of the transform length N and one-dimensional IDCT(inverse DCT) of the transform length M for resolution conversion are as follows.

$$G(k) = d(k)\sqrt{\frac{2}{\mathrm{N}}}\sum_{n=0}^{\mathrm{N}-1} d(n)g(n)\varphi,\ k = 0, 1, \cdots, \mathrm{N}-2, \mathrm{N}-1 \tag{2.1}$$

$$\begin{aligned} g(m) &= \sqrt{\frac{2}{\mathrm{N}}}d(m)\sum_{l=0}^{\mathrm{M}'-1} d(l)G(l)\varphi^{-1},\ m = 0, 1, \cdots, \mathrm{M}-2, \mathrm{M}-1 \\ &\mathrm{M}' = \min(\mathrm{M},\mathrm{N}),\ d(*) = \begin{cases} \sqrt{\frac{1}{2}} & \textit{for} \quad * \textit{ is zero} \\ 1 & \textit{for} \quad \textit{otherwise} \end{cases} \end{aligned} \tag{2.2}$$

$d(*)$ is a coefficient to make uniformity for above operation. The base function φ in DCT and the inverse base function φ^{-1} in IDCT have four types shown in Table 2.1 by combinations on lattice points n, k or on half-shifted points $n+\frac{1}{2}$, $k+\frac{1}{2}$ as sampling points for a signal space n and a frequency space k respectively.

TABLE 2.1
A classification of base functions for DCT

Classification	Base Function φ	Inverse Base Function φ^{-1}
Type-I	$\varphi^{\mathrm{I}} = \cos\frac{nk\pi}{\mathrm{N}}$	φ^{I}
Type-II	$\varphi^{\mathrm{II}} = \cos\frac{(n+\frac{1}{2})k\pi}{\mathrm{N}}$	φ^{III}
Type-III	$\varphi^{\mathrm{III}} = \cos\frac{n(k+\frac{1}{2})\pi}{\mathrm{N}}$	φ^{II}
Type-IV	$\varphi^{\mathrm{IV}} = \cos\frac{(n+\frac{1}{2})(k+\frac{1}{2})\pi}{\mathrm{N}}$	φ^{IV}

3. The OBDCT Method with Resolution Conversion. OBDCT of the transform length N is as follows.

$$f(n) = w(n)y(n),\ n = 0, 1, \cdots, 2\mathrm{N}-2, 2\mathrm{N}-1 \tag{3.1}$$

$$\begin{cases} \overline{y}^{\mathrm{L}}(n) = f(n) + f(\mathrm{N}-n-1), & n = \frac{\mathrm{N}}{2}, \frac{\mathrm{N}}{2}+1, \cdots, \mathrm{N}-2, \mathrm{N}-1 \\ \overline{y}^{\mathrm{R}}(n) = f(n) - f(3\mathrm{N}-n-1), & n = \mathrm{N}, \mathrm{N}+1, \cdots, \frac{3\mathrm{N}}{2}-2, \frac{3\mathrm{N}}{2}-1 \end{cases} \tag{3.2}$$

$$H(k) = c(k)\sqrt{\frac{2}{\mathrm{N}}}\sum_{n=0}^{\mathrm{N}-1} c(n)\overline{y}(n)\varphi, \qquad k = 0, 1, \cdots, \mathrm{N}-2, \mathrm{N}-1 \tag{3.3}$$

Where $\overline{y}(n)$ in eq. (3.3) is a data sequence of the transform length N obtained after applying a pre-processing of eq. (3.1), (3.2). A blocking data in the pre-processing is sampled image data $y(n)$ by the transform length 2N with overlapping $\frac{N}{2}$ to adjacent blocks for the DCT. $\overline{y}(n)$ is obtained from a folding process of eq. (3.2) after applied a window function $w(n)$ of the length 2N in eq. (3.1). IOBDCT(inverse OBDCT) of the transform length M for resolution conversion is as follows.

(3.4)
$$\overline{y}(m) = \sqrt{\frac{2}{N}}c(m)\sum_{l=0}^{M'-1} c(l)H(l)\varphi^{-1}, \quad m = 0, 1, \cdots, M-2, M-1$$
$$M' = \min(M, N), \quad c(*) = \begin{cases} \sqrt{\frac{1}{2}} & for \quad * \ is\ zero \\ 1 & for \quad otherwise \end{cases}$$

(3.5)
$$\begin{cases} f^{L}(m) = \overline{y}(M-m-1) + \overline{y}(m), & m = \frac{M}{2}, \frac{M}{2}+1, \cdots, M-2, M-1 \\ f^{R}(m) = \overline{y}(3M-m-1) - \overline{y}(m), & m = M, M+1, \cdots, \frac{3M}{2}-2, \frac{3M}{2}-1 \end{cases}$$

(3.6)
$$y(m) = W(m)f(m), \ m = 0, 1, \cdots, 2M-2, 2M-1$$

In the same process for inverse transformation, extended images can be presented by an addition of $y(m)$ between adjacent blocks after an unfolding process in eq. (3.5) and applying an inverse window function $W(m)$ in eq. (3.6).

$w(n) = \sin\frac{(n+\frac{1}{2})\pi}{N}$, $W(m) = \sin\frac{(m+\frac{1}{2})\pi}{M}$ are proposed as the adapted window functions to these processing[3]. In this paper, we discuss estimation of distortions for each basis in Table 2.1 in the case of using the DCT and the OBDCT with these window functions.

4. Comparison with Blocking Effect for the DCT. The DCT is applied the blocking without overlapping over adjacent blocks and quantization is applied independently to transform coefficients in each block. It seems that a prime cause of blocking effect is quantization error in the transform coefficients (see reference [7] in detail). We introduce blocking effects for each basis in the DCT and the OBDCT using quantization error in the DC component because of the prime cause of distortion in reconstructed image is depend mainly on quantization error for the DC component.

Error $\hat{g}_i^{DCT-*}(m)$ in respect of a reconstructed data in ith block of the DCT with each basis of type-I to IV are given by applying the IDCT to the quantization error $\hat{G}_i(0)$ for ith block and shown as follows.

(4.1)
$$\hat{g}_i^{DCT-I}(m) = \hat{g}_i^{DCT-II}(m) = \hat{G}_i(0)$$

(4.2)
$$\hat{g}_i^{DCT-III}(m) = \hat{G}_i(0)\cos\frac{\frac{1}{2}m\pi}{M}$$

(4.3)
$$\hat{g}_i^{DCT-IV}(m) = \hat{G}_i(0)\cos\frac{\frac{1}{2}(m+\frac{1}{2})\pi}{M}$$

Coefficients $\sqrt{\frac{2}{N}}, d(*)$ are excluded for simplicity. In the DCT with type-I, II bases, we can interpret that $\hat{G}_i(0)$ is treated as uniform distortion to the interior of each block. An interpretation of distortion in the case of type-III, IV bases is the largest error occurring as the value of the DC component in reconstructed data for each block.

From these results, error $\hat{g}^{\mathrm{DCT}-*}$ at block boundary between ith and $i+1$th blocks are written as follows.

$$\hat{g}^{\mathrm{DCT-I}} = \left|\hat{g}_{i+1}^{\mathrm{DCT-I}}(m) - \hat{g}_i^{\mathrm{DCT-I}}(m)\right| = \left|\hat{G}_{i+1}(0) - \hat{G}_i(0)\right| = \hat{g}^{\mathrm{DCT-II}} \tag{4.4}$$

$$\hat{g}^{\mathrm{DCT-III}} = \left|\hat{G}_{i+1}(0) - \hat{G}_i(0)\cos\frac{\frac{1}{2}(\mathrm{M}-1)\pi}{\mathrm{M}}\right| \approx \left|\hat{G}_{i+1}(0)\right| \tag{4.5}$$

$$\hat{g}^{\mathrm{DCT-IV}} = \left|\hat{G}_{i+1}(0)\cos\frac{\frac{1}{4}\pi}{\mathrm{M}} - \hat{G}_i(0)\cos\frac{\frac{1}{2}(\mathrm{M}-\frac{1}{2})\pi}{\mathrm{M}}\right| \approx \left|\hat{G}_{i+1}(0)\right| \tag{4.6}$$

We define the above as blocking effects occurred at block boundary.

Blocking effects for type-III and IV DCT are equal approximately, however strictly speaking, the blocking effect for type-IV is larger when $\hat{G}_{i+1}(0) - \hat{G}_i(0) = 1$ because $\cos\frac{\frac{1}{2}(\mathrm{M}-1)\pi}{\mathrm{M}} > \cos\frac{\frac{1}{2}(\mathrm{M}-\frac{1}{2})\pi}{\mathrm{M}}$. Therefore it became clear that blocking effects for type-I to IV have the following relation.

$$\hat{g}^{\mathrm{DCT-I}} = \hat{g}^{\mathrm{DCT-II}} < \hat{g}^{\mathrm{DCT-III}} < \hat{g}^{\mathrm{DCT-IV}} \tag{4.7}$$

JPEG is using the basis of type-II DCT. The result mentioned above supports the accepted basis in JPEG uses the DCT method which has the least distortion.

In the next section, we consider blocking effects for each basis of the OBDCT.

5. Comparison with Blocking Effect for the OBDCT. Blocking effects for the OBDCT are estimated from quantization error with the same energy to the DCT. An error occured by quantization for the OBDCT is able to introduce when it is applied with the unfolding processing to the error $\hat{G}_i(0)$ occured by quantization for the DCT, since the OBDCT is the DCT with a pre-processing. Error $\hat{g}_i^{\mathrm{OBDCT}-*}(m)$ included in reconstructed data is computed by applying IDCT (3.4) and the unfolding processing (3.5), (3.6) to $\hat{G}_i(0)$. Variables n, k in Table 2.1 in the case of the OBDCT method correspond on a frequency space and a signal space respectively. The following equations show errors included in reconstructed data when the unfolding processing (3.5), (3.6) are applied to $\hat{\bar{y}}_i^*(m)$ in eq. (3.4).

$$\begin{aligned} \hat{g}_i^{\mathrm{OBDCT}-*,\mathrm{L}}(m) &= W\left(m+\tfrac{\mathrm{M}}{2}\right)\hat{\bar{y}}_i^*(m) + W(\mathrm{M}-m)\hat{\bar{y}}_{i+1}^*(\mathrm{M}-m), \\ & \qquad m = \tfrac{\mathrm{M}}{2}, \tfrac{\mathrm{M}}{2}+1, \cdots, \mathrm{M}-2, \mathrm{M}-1 \end{aligned} \tag{5.1}$$

$$\begin{aligned} \hat{g}_{i+1}^{\mathrm{OBDCT}-*,\mathrm{R}}(m) &= W\left(m+\tfrac{\mathrm{M}}{2}\right)\hat{\bar{y}}_{i+1}^*(m) - W(2\mathrm{M}-m)\hat{\bar{y}}_i^*(\mathrm{M}-m), \\ & \qquad m = 0, 1, \cdots, \tfrac{\mathrm{M}}{2}-2, \tfrac{\mathrm{M}}{2}-1 \end{aligned} \tag{5.2}$$

We note that the point $m = \frac{\mathrm{M}}{2}$ is block boundary. Error $\hat{g}^{\mathrm{OBDCT}-*}$ for type-I to IV OBDCT occured at boundary between ith and $i+1$th blocks are computed as follows.

$$\begin{aligned} \hat{g}^{\mathrm{OBDCT-I}} &= \left|\hat{g}_i^{\mathrm{I,L}}(\mathrm{M}-1) - \hat{g}_{i+1}^{\mathrm{I,R}}(0)\right| \\ &= \Big|\hat{G}_i(0)W(\tfrac{3\mathrm{M}}{2}-1) + \hat{G}_{i+1}(0)W(1) \\ &\qquad - \left\{\hat{G}_{i+1}(0)W(\tfrac{\mathrm{M}}{2}) - \hat{G}_i(0)W(2\mathrm{M})\right\}\Big| \\ &= \left|\hat{G}_i(0)\sin\tfrac{(\frac{3\mathrm{M}}{2}-1)\pi}{2\mathrm{M}} - \hat{G}_{i+1}(0)\sin\tfrac{\pi}{2\mathrm{M}} - \sqrt{\tfrac{1}{2}}\hat{G}_{i+1}(0)\right| \\ &= \hat{g}^{\mathrm{OBDCT-III}} \end{aligned} \tag{5.3}$$

$$\hat{g}^{\mathrm{OBDCT-II}} = \left| \hat{G}_i(0)\cos\frac{\frac{1}{2}(\mathrm{M}-1)\pi}{\mathrm{M}}\sin\frac{(\frac{3\mathrm{M}}{2}-1)\pi}{2\mathrm{M}} + \hat{G}_{i+1}(0)\cos\frac{\frac{1}{2}\pi}{\mathrm{M}}\sin\frac{\pi}{2\mathrm{M}} - \sqrt{\tfrac{1}{2}}\hat{G}_{i+1}(0) \right| \tag{5.4}$$

$$\hat{g}^{\mathrm{OBDCT-IV}} = \left| \hat{G}_i(0)\cos\frac{\frac{1}{2}(\mathrm{M}-\frac{1}{2})\pi}{\mathrm{M}}\sin\frac{(\frac{3\mathrm{M}}{2}-1)\pi}{2\mathrm{M}} + \hat{G}_{i+1}(0)\cos\frac{\frac{3}{4}\pi}{\mathrm{M}}\sin\frac{\pi}{2\mathrm{M}} - \sqrt{\tfrac{1}{2}}\hat{G}_{i+1}(0)\cos\frac{\frac{1}{4}\pi}{\mathrm{M}} \right| \tag{5.5}$$

These are treated as blocking effects occuring at block boundary.

Let M=8, then blocking effects $\hat{g}^{\mathrm{OBDCT-*}}$ are computed concretely as follows.

$$\hat{g}^{\mathrm{OBDCT-I}} = \hat{g}^{\mathrm{OBDCT-III}} = \left|0.037687478\hat{G}_i(0) - 0.703679841\hat{G}_{i+1}(0)\right| \tag{5.6}$$

$$\hat{g}^{\mathrm{OBDCT-II}} = \left|0.037676635\hat{G}_i(0) - 0.703679862\hat{G}_{i+1}(0)\right| \tag{5.7}$$

$$\hat{g}^{\mathrm{OBDCT-IV}} = \left|0.037675031\hat{G}_i(0) - 0.703678849\hat{G}_{i+1}(0)\right| \tag{5.8}$$

The difference appears hardly whichever bases are used, however blocking effects $\hat{g}^{\mathrm{OBDCT-*}}$ have a few relation as follows when $\hat{G}_{i+1}(0) - \hat{G}_i(0) = 1$.

$$\hat{g}^{\mathrm{OBDCT-I}} = \hat{g}^{\mathrm{OBDCT-III}} < \hat{g}^{\mathrm{OBDCT-IV}} < \hat{g}^{\mathrm{OBDCT-II}} \tag{5.9}$$

Bases of type-I and III for the OBDCT are shown as the least distortion.

Compare with blocking effects between the DCT and the OBDCT, the problem for the DCT is conspicuous the blocking effect $\left|\hat{G}_i(0) - \hat{G}_{i+1}(0)\right|$. Blocking effects for the OBDCT does not increase contrarily as much as the DCT even if $\left|\hat{G}_i(0) - \hat{G}_{i+1}(0)\right|$ increases.

In the next section, by using the type-II DCT method and the type-III OBDCT method which have the least distortion respectively, we compare visibly using extended images with data compression.

6. Numerical Results. We use an original image (Fig. 6.1) which is cut off of the center part of 256 pixels × 256 pixels of the standard image Barbara. Reconstructed images in Fig. 6.2(left) which is the square marked part in Fig. 6.1 was extended to eight times using N=8 and M=64 without data compression by the type-II DCT shows the least distortion. The type-III OBDCT appears to be superior as shown in Fig. 6.2(right).

From Fig. 6.2(left), it is shown that the prime cause of degradation of image quality is blocking effect which did not exist in the original image. In contrast to this result, we can find from Fig. 6.2(right) that the OBDCT can reconstruct extended images keeping the continuous property in the original images. Reconstructed images extended by eight times with data compression of $\frac{1}{16}$ times as rate=0.5 bits/pixel using the DCT method and the OBDCT method are shown in Fig. 6.3(left) and 6.3(right) respectively. Fig. 6.3(left) indicates that blocking effect becomes clearer when the DCT is carried with data compression at the high compression rate. Therefore the OBDCT (see Fig. 6.3(right)) is possible to reconstruct the extended image without damaging the continuous property in the original image even if data compression is executed.

In conclusion, it became clear that the OBDCT with type-III is possible to reconstruct high quality images comparatively even if it is applied with data compression at higher extension ratio. This notable feature of the OBDCT method deserves attention and is an important point in case of practical use.

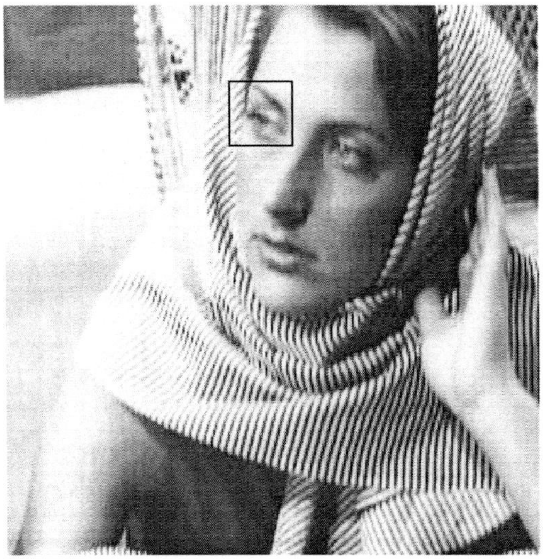

FIG. 6.1. *Original image Barbara (Compare in the square part)*

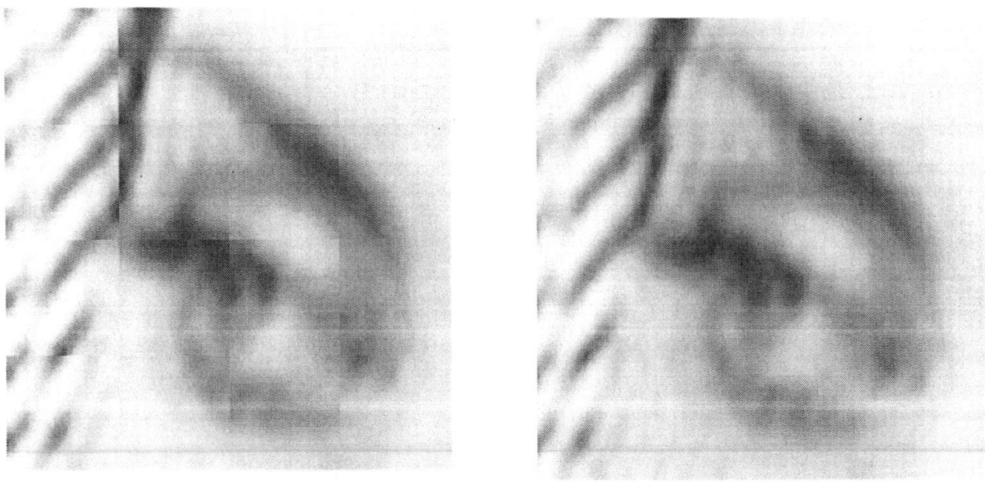

FIG. 6.2. *The left was extended by the DCT method and the right was extended by the OBDCT method as N=8, M=64 with no data compression*

7. Conclusion. In data compression using the DCT, we suppose that the prime cause of degradation of image quality is distortion which was caused by quantization error in the DC component. Thus we quantified blocking effects associated with four bases. In the same way, we quantified blocking effects of the OBDCT with each basis. We note that blocking effects for the OBDCT are evaluated using the post-processing to quantization error occured in the DC component for the DCT. From these results, it became clear theoreticaly that the DCT method with the type-I,II bases and the OBDCT method with type-I,III bases show the least blocking effect respectively. We clarified that the blocking effect for the DCT is also more conspicuous than the OBDCT.

In comparison with two transform coding using the type-II DCT and the type-III OBDCT with data compression and extension, the OBDCT mehod is superior visually than

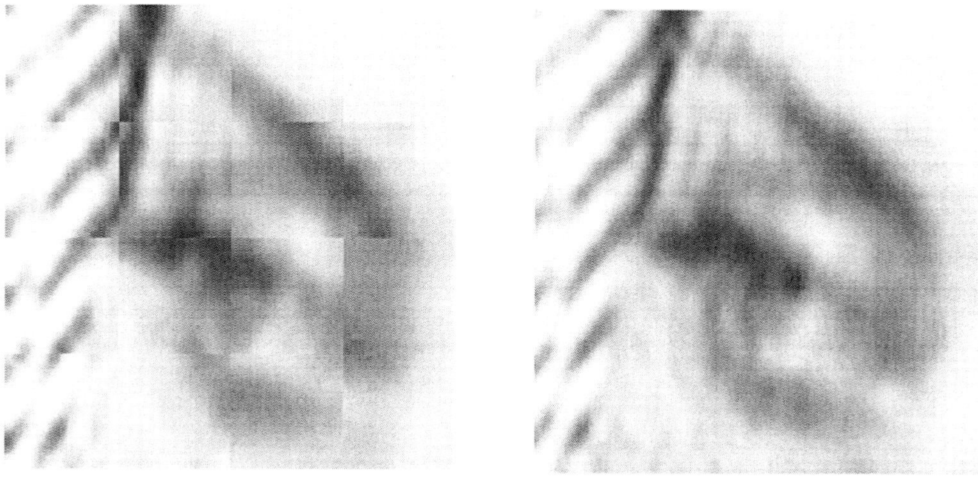

FIG. 6.3. *The left was extended by the DCT method and the right was extended by the OBDCT method as N=8, M=64 with rate=0.5*

the DCT method. These results lead us to the conclusion that the OBDCT method is more effective transform coding than the DCT method when execute extension of image with coding.

REFERENCES

[1] N.ARMED, T.NATARAJAN, AND K.R.RAO, *Discrete cosine transform*, IEEE Trans. Comput., C-25, 1, Jan., (1974), pp.90–93.

[2] H.S.MALVAR AND D.H.STAELIN, *The LOT: Transform coding without blocking effects*, IEEE Trans. Acoust., Speech & Signal Process., 37, 4, Apr., (1989), pp.553–559.

[3] H.SAWAMI, Y.MORIKAWA, AND H.HAMADA, *Overlapping Block Discrete Cosine Transform Coding and Its Fast Algorithm*, Electronics and Communications in Japan, Part 1, Vol. 75, No.4, May., (1992), pp.59–73.

[4] S.MRUETUSATORN, H.KINOSHITA, AND Y.SAKAI, *Resolution Conversion Method with High Image Quality Preservation*, IEICE Trans. Inf. & Syst., Vol. E77-D, No.6, Jun., (1994), pp.686–693.

[5] V.E.DEBRUNNER, LIXIANG CHEN, AND HONG-JIAN LI, *Lapped Multiple Bases Algorithms for Still Image Compression Without Blocking Effect*, IEEE Trans. Image Processing, Vol. 6, No.9, Sep., (1997), pp.1316–1321.

[6] Y.L.LEE, H.C.KIM, AND H.W.PARK, *Blocking Effect Reduction of JPEG Images by Signal Adaptive Filtering*, IEEE Trans. Image Processing, Vol. 7, No.2, Feb., (1998), pp.229–234.

[7] K.T.KOBAYASHI AND H.SAWAMI, *Estimation Method on Quantization Error with Extension of Color Still Image*, Information, Vol. 4, No.1, Jan., (2001), pp.71–80.

[8] K.T.KOBAYASHI AND H.SAWAMI, *Optimization Method for Window Function with Quantization Error*, Information, Vol. 5, No.1, Jan., (2002), pp.7–16.

In: Focus on Computational Neurobiology
Editor: Lei Li, pp. 153-160

ISBN 1-59033-915-0

MICROLOCAL ANALYSIS, SMOOTH FRAMES AND DENOISING IN FOURIER SPACE*

RYUICHI ASHINO†, STEVEN J. DESJARDINS‡, CHRISTOPHER HEIL§, MICHIHIRO NAGASE¶, AND RÉMI VAILLANCOURT||

Dedicated to Yoshinori KAMETAKA *on the occasion of his 60th birthday*

Abstract. Microlocal filtering is performed with adapted orthonormal multiwavelets and smooth frame multiwavelets in $\mathbb{R}^n$. The values of the wavelet coefficients of a function give a rough estimate of its microlocal content, as shown by an example. Multidirectional denoising of images is presented as the action of a pseudodifferential operator which is the product of directional diffusion equations.

Key words. microlocal analysis, smooth frames, wavelet frames, denoising

AMS subject classifications. 42C40, 32A45, 46F15

1. Introduction. Wavelets have proven to be useful decomposition tools in a wide variety of applications throughout mathematics, science, and engineering. For example, the still-image compression standard known as JPEG2000 includes a wavelet option and the next video compression standard, MPEG-4, will be entirely wavelet based.

Hyperfunctions, which were introduced by Sato [13] and extensively developed by the Kyoto school of mathematics, can be considered to be sums of boundary values of holomorphic functions defined in infinitesimal wedges. Microlocal analysis plays an important role in the theory of hyperfunctions, partial differential operators, and many other areas. In this theory, one can define the product of distributions and discuss the partial regularity of multidimensional distributions with respect to any independent variable.

In this paper, we discuss some particular multiwavelet constructions which are suited for microlocal filtering. In particular, expansion of a function in terms of these multiwavelet bases or smooth tight frames gives a rough estimate of its microlocal content, revealing directions of analyticity. The resolution of these multiwavelets in any given direction of analyticity can be made as fine as desired, at the cost of increasing the multiplicity of the multiwavelet basis or frame. We discuss the numerical implementation of these filters and apply them to multidirectional denoising of two-dimensional images.

2. Microlocal Analysis. Our approach to microlocal analysis for Schwartz distributions is based on the theory of hyperfunctions, as introduced by Sato [13] and developed in [12] for the theory of linear partial differential equations with constant coefficients. A more complete treatment of microlocal filtering with multiwavelets can be found in [2]. Other

*This work was partially supported by the Japanese Ministry of Education, Culture, Sports, Science and Technology, Grant-in-Aid for Scientific Research (C), 11640166(2000), 13640171(2001), NSF Grant DMS-9970524, and the Natural Sciences and Engineering Research Council of Canada.

†Mathematical Sciences, Osaka Kyoiku University, Kashiwara, Osaka 582-8582, Japan (ashino@cc.osaka-kyoiku.ac.jp).

‡Department of Mathematics and Statistics, University of Ottawa, Ottawa, ON, Canada K1N 6N5 (desjards@mathstat.uottawa.ca).

§School of Mathematics, Georgia Institute of Technology, Atlanta, Georgia 30332-0160 USA (heil@math.gatech.edu).

¶Department of Mathematics, Graduate School of Science, Osaka University, Toyonaka, 560-0043, Japan (nagase@math.wani.osaka-u.ac.jp).

||Department of Mathematics and Statistics, University of Ottawa, Ottawa, ON, Canada K1N 6N5 (remi@uottawa.ca).

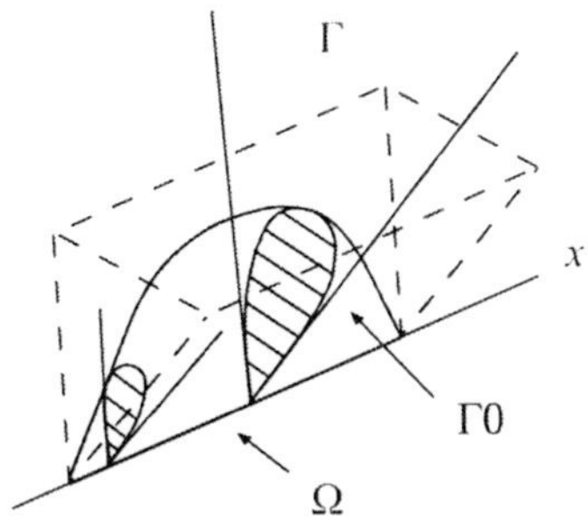

FIG. 2.1. *Infinitesimal wedge* $\Gamma 0$.

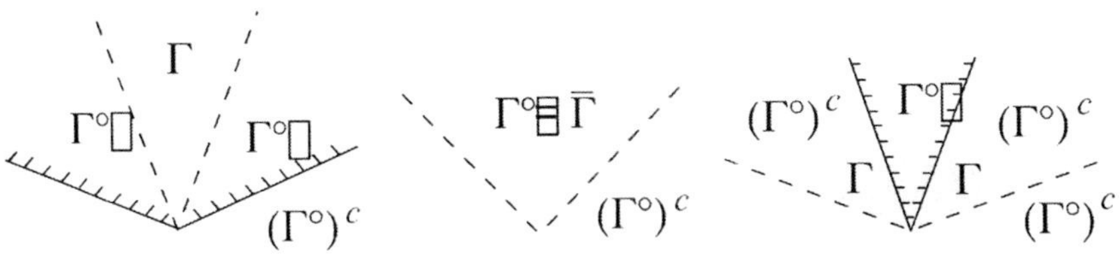

FIG. 2.2. *Open cone* Γ, *dual cone* Γ°, *and complement* $(\Gamma^\circ)^c$ *of dual cone.*

treatments are found in [1] and [3]. A main goal is to find directions in which a function can be continued analytically for every point $x \in \mathbb{R}^n$.

2.1. Hyperfunctions in $\mathbb{R}^n$. A hyperfunction is defined as a sum of general boundary values of holomorphic functions in wedges whose edges are open subsets of $\mathbb{R}^n$. More precisely, a hyperfunction $f : \mathbb{R}^n \to \mathbb{C}$ is defined to be a sum

$$f(x) = \sum_{j=1}^{N} F_j(x + i\Gamma_j 0), \qquad x \in \Omega,$$

of boundary values

$$F_j(x + i\Gamma_j 0) = \lim_{\substack{y \to 0 \\ y \in \Gamma_j 0}} F_j(x + iy)$$

of holomorphic functions $F_j(z)$ in infinitesimal wedges $\Gamma_j 0$ with edge $\Omega \subset \mathbb{R}^n$ (see Fig. 2.1).

2.2. Microanalyticity. To characterize the microanalyticity of a tempered distribution $f \in \mathcal{S}'(\mathbb{R}^n)$ by its Fourier transform, $\widehat{f}$, we introduce the *dual cone*, Γ°, of Γ, defined by

$$\Gamma^\circ := \{\xi \in \mathbb{R}^n \,;\, y \cdot \xi \geq 0 \text{ for every } y \in \Gamma\}.$$

Figure 2.2 shows three examples of cones Γ, their dual cones Γ°, and their complements $(\Gamma^\circ)^c = \mathbb{R}^n \setminus \Gamma^\circ$.

LEMMA 2.1. *Let Γ be an open convex cone. A tempered distribution $f(x)$ can be represented as the limit $f(x + i\Gamma 0)$ of a slowly increasing holomorphic function $f(z)$ in the infinitesimal wedge $\mathbb{R}^n + i\Gamma 0$ if and only if the Fourier transform $\widehat{f}$ of f is exponentially decreasing in every closed proper subcone $\Gamma' \subset\subset (\Gamma^\circ)^c = \mathbb{R}^n \setminus \Gamma^\circ$.*

3. Microlocal Filtering. Given $f \in L^2(\mathbb{R}^n)$, let $f_{jk}(x)$ denote the scaled and shifted function

$$f_{jk}(x) = 2^{nj/2} f(2^j x - k), \qquad j \in \mathbb{Z}, \quad k \in \mathbb{Z}^n.$$

Let D be a finite index set with $\operatorname{card}(D) = (2^n - 1)d$, $d \in \mathbb{N}$. A system

$$\{\psi_{jk}^\delta\}_{\delta \in D, j \in \mathbb{Z}, k \in \mathbb{Z}^n} \subset L^2(\mathbb{R}^n)$$

is called a *multiwavelet tight frame* with frame bound A, and in this case $\Psi = \{\psi^\delta\}_{\delta \in D}$ is called a set of *tight frame multiwavelets*, if

$$f = \frac{1}{A} \sum_{\substack{\delta \in D, \\ j \in \mathbb{Z}, k \in \mathbb{Z}^n}} \langle f, \psi_{jk}^\delta \rangle \, \psi_{jk}^\delta, \qquad \forall\, f \in L^2(\mathbb{R}^n). \tag{3.1}$$

If $\{\psi_{jk}^\delta\}_{\delta \in D, j \in \mathbb{Z}, k \in \mathbb{Z}^n} \subset L^2(\mathbb{R}^n)$ is an orthonormal basis for $L^2(\mathbb{R}^n)$ then it is called an *orthonormal multiwavelet basis*, and in this case $\Psi = \{\psi^\delta\}_{\delta \in D}$ is called a set of *orthonormal multiwavelets*.

Although a tight frame allows the basis-like representations in equation (3.1), a frame need not be an orthonormal or even independent sequence. Frames provide a useful model for obtaining signal decompositions in cases where redundancy, robustness, oversampling, and irregular sampling play a role. We refer to [4], [10], or [11] for basic information on frames and wavelets. It can be shown that Ψ is a set of orthonormal multiwavelets if and only if $\{\psi_{jk}^\delta\}_{\delta \in D, j \in \mathbb{Z}, k \in \mathbb{Z}^n}$ is a multiwavelet tight frame with frame bound $A = 1$ and $\|\psi^\delta\|_{L^2(\mathbb{R}^n)} = 1$ for $\delta \in D$.

Problems.

- Is it possible to construct orthonormal or tight frame multiwavelets $\Psi = \{\psi^\delta\}_{\delta \in D}$ corresponding to each microanalytic direction $\mathbb{S}^{n-1}$?
- Is it possible to obtain information on the microlocal content of $f \in L^2(\mathbb{R}^n)$ from the wavelet coefficients $\langle f, \psi_{jk}^\delta \rangle$?
- Can orthonormal or tight frame multiwavelet filtering separate microlocal contents?

We shall construct orthonormal multiwavelet bases or tight frames which enable us to obtain information on the microlocal content of signals or functions. As this separation of microlocal contents can be considered as a filtering operation, we call it *microlocal filtering*.

3.1. Orthonormal multiwavelets in $\mathbb{R}$. The one-dimensional case is summarized in the following theorem, where $[-2\pi, -4\pi]$ means $[-4\pi, -2\pi]$, and similarly later.

THEOREM 3.1. *Define $\psi^\pm$ by $\widehat{\psi^\pm} = \chi_{[\pm 2\pi, \pm 4\pi]}$* (Fig. 3.1). *Then $\Psi := \{\psi^+, \psi^-\}$ is a set of orthonormal multiwavelets. Define the orthogonal projections $\mathcal{P}_\pm$ by*

$$\mathcal{P}_\pm f := \sum_{j,k \in \mathbb{Z}} \langle f, \psi_{jk}^\pm \rangle \, \psi_{jk}^\pm.$$

Then $\mathcal{P}_\pm f(x)$ can be extended analytically to $\{\operatorname{Im} z > 0\}$ and $\{\operatorname{Im} z < 0\}$, respectively.

Taken individually, $\psi^\pm$ generates an orthonormal wavelet basis for the classical Hardy space $H^2(\mathbb{R}_\pm)$ defined by

$$H^2(\mathbb{R}_\pm) = \{f \in L^2(\mathbb{R}) \,;\, \widehat{f}(\xi) = 0 \quad \text{a.e. } \xi \le (\ge)\, 0\}.$$

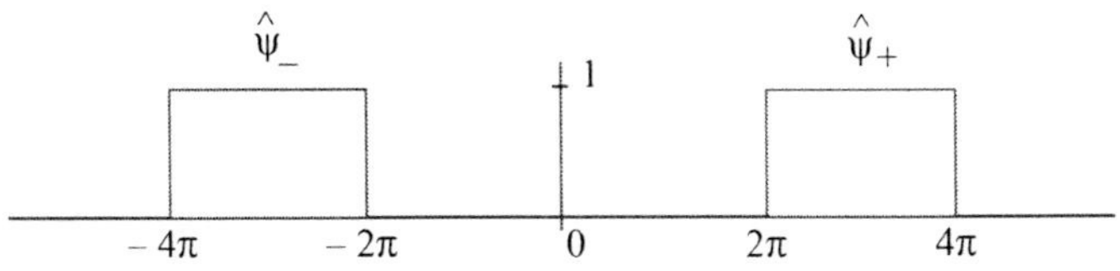

FIG. 3.1. *The Fourier transform of* $\psi_\pm$.

This orthonormal multiwavelet basis was discussed in [5], and smooth tight multiwavelet frames were also constructed there (see also the discussion in [11, Section 8.4]). In the one-dimensional case, there are only two directions of analyticity, while in the n-dimensional case, the set of all microanalytic directions is $\mathbb{S}^{n-1}$, which is an infinite set. In Theorem 3.2, we will give a generalization of Theorem 3.1 to the n-dimensional case. An n-dimensional smooth multiwavelet tight frame will be given in Theorem 3.3. Using an expansion into these bases or frames, it is possible to tell fairly well in which directions f is microanalytic. The price for good angular resolution in $\mathbb{S}^{n-1}$ is the need for many multiwavelets.

3.2. Orthonormal multiwavelets in $\mathbb{R}^n$. The following notation will be used.

- $\eta = (\eta_1, \dots, \eta_n) \in H := \{\pm 1\}^n$.
- $\varepsilon = (\varepsilon_1, \dots, \varepsilon_n) \in E := \{0,1\}^n \setminus \{0\}, \quad j \in \mathbb{Z}_+$.
- $\varepsilon .* \eta := (\varepsilon_1\eta_1, \dots, \varepsilon_n\eta_n)$.
- $\mathcal{Q}_{j,\varepsilon,\eta} := \{\prod_{k=1}^n [\eta_k(\ell_k - 1), \eta_k\ell_k] + 2^j(\varepsilon .* \eta) : 1 \le \ell_1, \dots, \ell_n \le 2^j,\ \ell_1, \dots, \ell_n \in \mathbb{N}\}$.
- $2\pi\mathcal{Q}_{j,\varepsilon,\eta} := \{2\pi Q \ ; \ Q \in \mathcal{Q}_{j,\varepsilon,\eta}\}$.
- $\mathbb{Z}_+^{E\times H}$ is the set of all functions from $E \times H$ to $\mathbb{Z}_+$.

THEOREM 3.2. *Fix $j \in \mathbb{Z}_+$, $\varepsilon \in E$, $\eta \in H$. For $Q \in \mathcal{Q}_{j,\varepsilon,\eta}$, define ψ_Q by*

$$\widehat{\psi_Q} = \chi_{2\pi Q},$$

where $\chi_{2\pi Q}$ is the characteristic function of the cube $2\pi Q$. For $\rho \in \mathbb{Z}_+^{E\times H}$, let

$$\mathcal{Q}_\rho := \bigcup_{(\varepsilon,\eta)\in E\times H} 2\pi\mathcal{Q}_{\rho(\varepsilon,\eta),\varepsilon,\eta}.$$

Then $\Psi := \{\psi_Q\}_{Q\in\mathcal{Q}_\rho}$ is a set of orthonormal multiwavelets.

Figure 3.2 illustrates the 2-D multiwavelets constructed in Theorem 3.2. Multiwavelets are masks in Fourier space — they are characteristic functions of cubes $2\pi Q$. The left part of Figure 3.2 shows 12 multiwavelet functions. For finer resolution in Fourier space, we need a greater number of multiwavelets. The right part of the Figure 3.2 shows 27 multiwavelet functions.

3.3. Smooth tight wavelet frames in $\mathbb{R}^n$. Smooth tight multiwavelet frames are obtained by convolving characteristic functions of cubes πQ so that the support of the smoothed functions have support inside cubes $2\pi Q$. This is achieved by considering the next inside annulus of cubes πQ in the left part of Fig. 3.2.

Let $\vartheta(t)$ be a $C_0^\infty(\mathbb{R})$-function of one variable satisfying

$$\vartheta(t) \ge 0, \qquad \vartheta(t) = \vartheta(-t), \qquad \int_{\mathbb{R}} \vartheta(t)\,dt = 1, \qquad \vartheta(t) = \begin{cases} 1, & |t| \le \frac{1}{3}; \\ 0, & |t| \ge \frac{2}{3}. \end{cases}$$

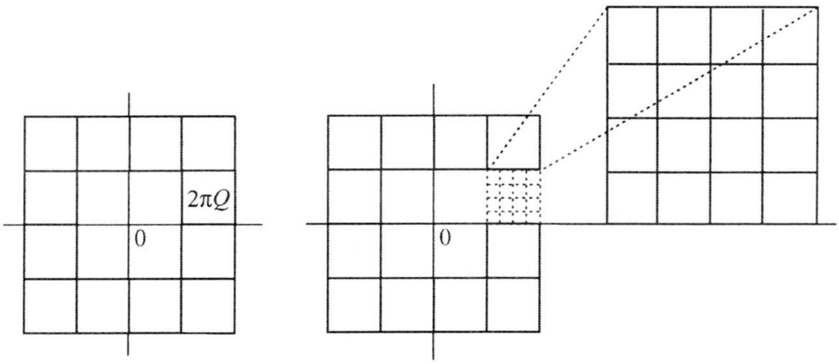

FIG. 3.2. *2-D orthonormal multiwavelet functions in Fourier space.*

For $\alpha > 0$ and $\xi = (\xi_1, \xi_2, \dots, \xi_n) \in \mathbb{R}^n$, let

$$\vartheta_\alpha(\xi) = \frac{1}{\alpha^n} \prod_{j=1}^{n} \vartheta\Big(\frac{\xi_j}{\alpha}\Big).$$

THEOREM 3.3. *Fix $j \in \mathbb{Z}_+$, $\varepsilon \in E$, $\eta \in H$, and $\alpha \in (0, 1/2)$. Define*

$$\lambda_Q(\xi) := (\vartheta_\alpha * \chi_{\pi Q})(\xi) = \int_{\mathbb{R}^n} \vartheta_\alpha(\xi - \zeta)\, \chi_{\pi Q}(\zeta)\, d\zeta, \qquad Q \in \mathcal{Q}_{j,\varepsilon,\eta},$$

where $\chi_{\pi Q}$ is the characteristic function of the cube πQ. For $\rho \in \mathbb{Z}_+^{E\times H}$, let

$$\widetilde{\mathcal{Q}}_\rho := \bigcup_{(\varepsilon,\eta)\in E\times H} \pi \mathcal{Q}_{\rho(\varepsilon,\eta),\varepsilon,\eta}, \qquad \tau_\rho(\xi) := \sum_{j\in\mathbb{Z}, Q\in\widetilde{\mathcal{Q}}_\rho} |\lambda_Q(2^j\xi)|^2,$$

and, for $Q \in \widetilde{\mathcal{Q}}_\rho$, define $\psi_Q(x)$ by

$$\widehat{\psi_Q}(\xi) := \tau_\rho(\xi)^{-1/2}\, \lambda_Q(\xi).$$

Then $\Psi := \{\psi_Q\}_{Q\in\widetilde{\mathcal{Q}}_\rho}$ is a set of tight frame multiwavelets.

Theorem 3.3 follows from Theorem 3.4, which is essentially [9, Theorem 1].

THEOREM 3.4. *$\Psi = \{\psi^\delta\}_{\delta\in D}$ is a set of tight frame multiwavelets with frame bound $A = 1$ if and only if the following two equalities are satisfied:*

$$\sum_{\substack{\delta\in D\\ j\in\mathbb{Z}}} |\widehat{\psi^\delta}(2^j\xi)|^2 = 1, \qquad a.e.\ \xi \in \mathbb{R}^n, \tag{3.2}$$

and

$$t_q(\xi) = 0, \qquad a.e.\ \xi \in \mathbb{R}^n,\ \forall\, q \in \mathbb{Z}^n \backslash (2\mathbb{Z})^n, \tag{3.3}$$

where

$$t_q(\xi) := \sum_{\substack{\delta\in D\\ j\in\mathbb{Z}_+}} \widehat{\psi^\delta}(2^j\xi)\, \overline{\widehat{\psi^\delta}(2^j(\xi + 2\pi q))}, \qquad \mathbb{Z}_+ := \mathbb{N} \cup \{0\}. \tag{3.4}$$

Note that $q \in \mathbb{Z}^n \backslash (2\mathbb{Z})^n$ means that at least one component q_j of q is an odd integer.

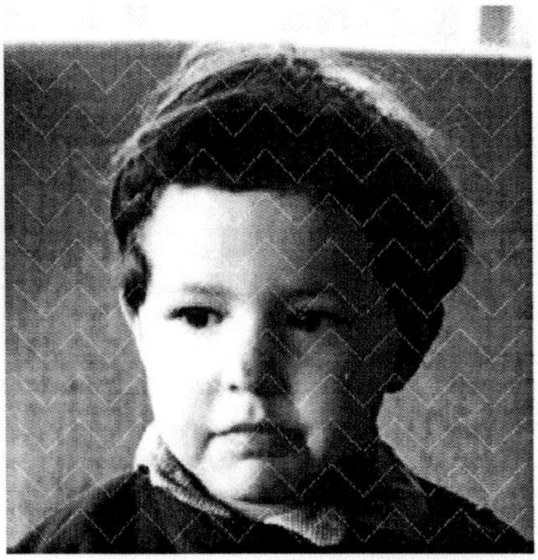

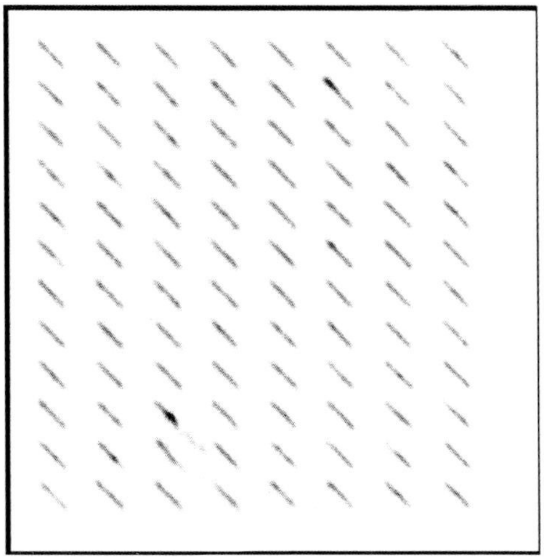

FIG. 4.1. *Left: Positive figure of boy behind an almost invisible zigzag grid. Right: Negative figure localizing the zigzag grid downward singularities.*

4. Numerical applications. Smooth frame wavelets $\{\psi^{\ell}_{j,k}\}$ can locate the singularity of a figure f by filtering $\widehat{f}$ away from the origin, since singularities are associated with high frequencies. Numerically, figures are discretized over rectangular matrices. In the left part of Fig. 4.1, the boy is shown behind a fine zigzag grid. Since the smooth filters consisting of tapered characteristic functions of squares cover a 287×287 matrix [6], the boy image is embedded into the central part of a 287×287 matrix.

The smooth filters consist of tapered characteristic functions of squares covering a 287×287 matrix. By filtering along the secondary diagonal with a smooth frame wavelet with support in the upper right corner of $\widehat{f}$, at a right angle with the downward parts of the grid, these downward parts are localized by means of the frame coefficients

$$\langle f, \psi^{\ell}_{j,k}\rangle = \frac{1}{2\pi}\langle \widehat{f}, \widehat{\psi}^{\ell}_{j,k}\rangle,$$

as can be seen in the right part of Fig. 4.1. The upward parts of the grid can be localized by filtering along the main diagonal in the upper left corner of $\widehat{f}$.

4.1. Multidirectional denoising. Multidirectional filtering by a product filter [7] consists in applying the one-dimensional diffusion operator in several directions with a small step size in Fourier space. This operation removes some random and Gaussian noise without oversmearing edges. Once the filter is constructed for images of a given size, its application on a sequence of noisy images of the same size is very fast.

Diffusion in the x-direction is governed by $u_t = u_{xx}$, in the y-direction by $u_t = u_{yy}$. To diffuse in the direction of a line that makes an angle of θ with the x-axis, the governing equation is

$$u_t = \cos^2\theta\, u_{xx} + 2\sin\theta\cos\theta\, u_{xy} + \sin^2\theta\, u_{yy}.$$

Applying the two-dimensional Fourier transform

$$\widehat{u}(\xi,\eta) = \int_{-\infty}^{\infty}\int_{-\infty}^{\infty} u(x,y)\, e^{-i(\xi x+\eta y)}\, dx\, dy$$

to the diffusion equation, we obtain the equation

$$\begin{aligned}\widehat{u}_t &= -\xi^2 \cos^2\theta\, \widehat{u} - 2\,\xi\,\eta\, \sin\theta\cos\theta\, \widehat{u} - \eta^2 \sin^2\theta\, \widehat{u}\\ &= -[\xi\cos\theta + \eta\sin\theta]^2\, \widehat{u},\end{aligned}$$

whose solution is

$$\widehat{u}(\xi,\eta,t) = \widehat{u}(\xi,\eta,0)\, \exp(-[\xi\cos\theta + \eta\sin\theta]^2\, t).$$

One can diffuse noise in many directions, specified by angles θ_k, by means of the equation

$$u_t = \sum_k [\cos^2\theta_k\, u_{xx} + 2\sin\theta_k\cos\theta_k\, u_{xy} + \sin^2\theta_k\, u_{yy}].$$

In the Fourier domain, this equation becomes

$$\widehat{u}_t = -\left(\sum_k [\xi\cos\theta_k + \eta\sin\theta_k]^2\right)\widehat{u},$$

with solution

$$\widehat{u}(\xi,\eta,t) = \widehat{u}(\xi,\eta,0)\, \exp\left(-\sum_k [\xi\cos\theta_k + \eta\sin\theta_k]^2\, t\right) := \widehat{u}(\xi,\eta,0)\, g(\xi,\eta,t).$$

The denoised image is given by the pseudodifferential operator

$$u(x,y,t) = \frac{1}{(2\pi)^2}\int_{-\infty}^{\infty}\int_{-\infty}^{\infty} e^{i(\xi x+\eta y)}\, g(\xi,\eta,t)\, \widehat{u}(\xi,\eta,0)\, d\xi\, d\eta.$$

Therefore, if $\widehat{u}(\xi,\eta,0)$ is the Fourier transform of a noisy image, then applying the multidirectional operator in the Fourier domain reduces to matrix multiplication with an appropriately chosen value of t.

Signal-to-noise ratio (SNR) is defined by the formula

$$\mathrm{SNR} = \frac{\sum_{i=1}^{m}\sum_{j=1}^{n} u(i,j)^2}{\sum_{i=1}^{m}\sum_{j=1}^{n} [u(i,j) - U(i,j)]^2} = \frac{\|u\|_F^2}{\|u-U\|_F^2}, \tag{4.1}$$

where $[u(i,j)]$ and $[U(i,j)]$ represent the original and noisy images, respectively, as matrices and $\|\cdot\|_F$ is the Frobenius matrix norm. Ideally, if noise were perfectly removed from a noisy image, the result would be $u = U$ and SNR is infinite. In general, a higher SNR value signifies a better result, though visual observation is the true measurement, as two matrices may have the same norm and yet appear completely different when viewed as images.

The boy figure with added random noise of intensity 50, with signal to noise ratio SNR $= 12.7213$, is shown in the left part of Fig 4.2. This noisy image is denoised with the multidirectional filter with 256 directions and $t = 0.0003$. The result, with SNR $= 15.5816$, is shown in the right part of Fig 4.2.

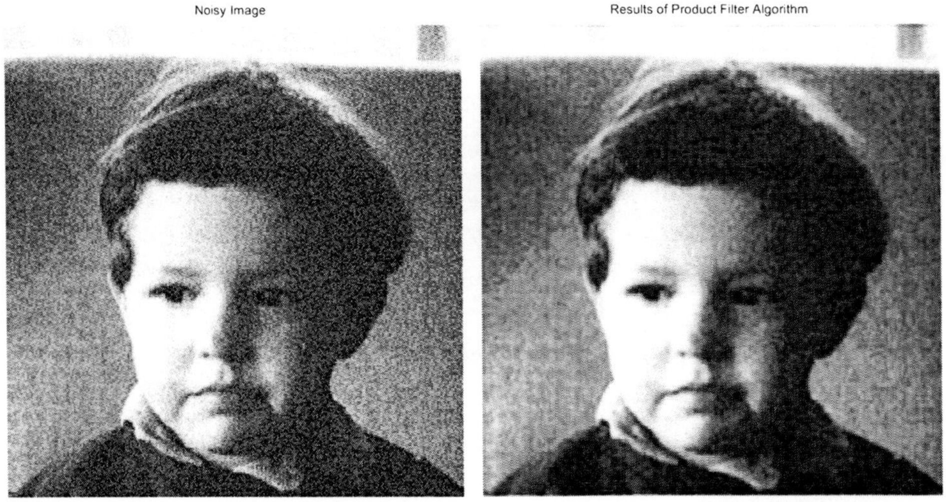

FIG. 4.2. *Left: Noisy figure with SNR = 12.7213. Right: Denoised image with SNR = 15.5816.*

REFERENCES

[1] R. Ashino, C. Heil, M. Nagase, and R. Vaillancourt, *Microlocal analysis and multiwavelets*, in Geometry, Analysis and Applications (Varanasi, 2000), 293–302, R. S. Pathak, ed., World Scientific, River Edge, NJ, 2001.

[2] R. Ashino, C. Heil, M. Nagase, and R. Vaillancourt, *Microlocal filtering with multiwavelets*, Comput. Math. Appl., **41** (2001), pp. 111–133.

[3] R. Ashino, C. Heil, M. Nagase, and R. Vaillancourt, *Multiwavelets, pseudodifferential operators and microlocal analysis*, in Wavelet Analysis and Applications, D. Deng, D. Huang, R.-Q. Jia, and W. Lin eds., AMS/IP Studies in Advanced Mathematics, Vol. 25, American Mathematical Society, Providence, RI, 2002.

[4] I. Daubechies, *Ten Lectures on Wavelets*, SIAM, Philadelphia, 1992.

[5] I. Daubechies, A. Grossmann, and Y. Meyer, *Painless nonorthogonal expansions*, J. Math. Phys., **27**(5) (1986), pp. 1271–1283.

[6] S. J. Desjardins, *Image Analyis in Fourier space*, Doctoral dissertation, University of Ottawa, Ottawa, Ontario, Canada (submitted).

[7] S. J. Desjardins and R. Vaillancourt, *Image de-noising by a multi-directional diffusion equation*, Mathematical Reports Acad. Sci. Canada, to appear.

[8] L. Alvarez, P.-L. Lions, and J.-M. Morel, *Image selective smoothing and edge detection by nonlinear diffusion. II*, SIAM J. Numer. Anal., **26**(3) (1992), pp. 845–866.

[9] M. Frazier, G. Garrigós, K. Wang, and G. Weiss, *A characterization of functions that generate wavelet and related expansion*, J. Fourier Anal. Appl. **3** (1997), Special Issue, pp. 883–906.

[10] C. E. Heil and D. F. Walnut, *Continuous and discrete wavelet transforms*, SIAM Review, **31**(4) (1989), pp. 628–666.

[11] E. Hernández and G. Weiss, *A First Course on Wavelets*, CRC Press, Boca Raton, FL, 1996, Chapter 7 and 8.

[12] A. Kaneko, *Linear Partial Differential Equations with Constant Coefficients*, Iwanami, Tokyo, 1992. (Japanese)

[13] M. Sato, *Theory of hyperfunctions I*, J. Fac. Sci. Univ. Tokyo, Sec. I, **8**(1) (1959), pp. 139–193.

In: Focus on Computational Neurobiology
Editor: Lei Li, pp. 161-166
ISBN 1-59033-915-0

ON THE BOUNDS OF (0,1) MATRIX PERMANENTS

LEI LI* AND WAKANA TAMADA†

Abstract. In this paper, we show some new bounds for the permanent of n-order $(0,1)$ matrices with the row sums and the column sums are all a positive integer k, where $1 \le k \le n$. Especially, for case of (0,1) circulant matrix, we propose some better bounds of the permanent.

Key words. $(0,1)$ matrix, permanent, bound

1. Introduction. An important problem in combinatorial counting methods is computation of (0,1) matrix permanent.

DEFINITION 1.1. *The permanent of an $n \times n$ matrix $A = (a_{ij})$ is defined by*

$$per(A) = \sum_{j_1 j_2 \cdots j_n} a_{1j_1} a_{2j_2} \cdots a_{nj_n}.$$

where $j_1, j_2, \cdots, j_n$ ranges over all permutations of $1, 2, \cdots, n$.

The definition of matrix permanent is similar with the determinant, but half of their items are different. So their computational complexities have great difference. It is obvious that evaluating the permanent needs $O(n!)$ arithmetical operations. Therefore, giving some bounds for guessing the permanent is very important.

Van der Waerden (1926) asked if the permanent of any doubly stochastic $n \times n$ matrix A is at least $\frac{n!}{n^n}$,

$$per(A) \ge \frac{n!}{n^n}. \tag{1.1}$$

which was proved in 1981 by Falikman [3] [4]. When research the permanent of $(0,1)$ matrices, some interesting inequalities and conjectures were presented. If A is a n-order $(0,1)$ matrix, with the row sums and the column sums are all a positive integer k, where $1 \le k \le n$, then M. Hall asserted following inequality is true [1],

$$per(A) \ge k!, \tag{1.2}$$

but as function of variate k, the least value and the greatest value of $per(A)$ not be found yet. Purpose of this paper is to prove M. Hall's inequality and show some new upper bounds and lower bounds for the $per(A)$ by recursive methods. And also will propose some better bounds of the permanent for case of (0,1) circulant matrix especially.

2. Some New Bounds. For every n-order $(0,1)$ matrix A, with the row sums and column sums are all a positive integer k, where $1 \le k \le n$, M. Hall's inequality asserted [1]: $per(A) \ge k!$. Here we first show a sample proof for M. Hall's inequality by using recursive method.

THEOREM 2.1. *Assume that A is a n-order $(0,1)$ matrix with the row sums and the column sums are all a positive integer k, where $1 \le k \le n$, then*

$$per(A) \ge k!.$$

*Faculty of Engineering, Hosei University, Kajino-cho 3-7-2, Koganei, Tokyo 184-8584 Japan (lilei@k.hosei.ac.jp).

†Faculty of Science, Yamaguchi University, Yoshida 1677-1, Yamaguchi 753-8512 Japan

Proof. : We define that the lower bound of the $per(A)$ is $D(n,k)$,

$$D(n,k) = min(per(A)).$$

By developing the first row of A, we know $per(A)$ has k nonzero terms, every nonzero term is a $(n-1)$-order $(0,1)$ matrix with the row sums and the column sums are k or $k-1$, after irresponsibly take away some elements $'1'$, we have following recursive relation,

$$D(n,k) \geq k * D(n-1,k-1) \geq k(k-1)D(n-2,k-2)$$

$$\geq ...... \geq k!D(n-k+1,1) = k!$$

Therefore

$$per(A) \geq D(n,k) \geq k!$$

□

THEOREM 2.2. *Assume that A is a n-order $(0,1)$ matrix with the row sums and the column sums are all a positive integer k, where $1 \leq k \leq n$, then*

$$per(A) \geq \frac{n!k^n}{n^n}. \tag{2.1}$$

Proof. : Because every row sum and column sum of $\frac{1}{k}A$ are all 1, so it is a doubly stochastic matrix. From Van der Waerden Conjecture,

$$per(\frac{A}{k}) \geq \frac{n!}{n^n},$$

$$\frac{1}{k^n}per(A) \geq \frac{n!}{n^n},$$

$$per(A) \geq \frac{n!k^n}{n^n}.$$

□

THEOREM 2.3. *Assume that A is a n-order $(0,1)$ matrix, with the row sums and the column sums are all a positive integer k, where $1 \leq k \leq n$, then*

$$per(A) \leq \frac{k^n k!}{k^k}. \tag{2.2}$$

Proof. : We define that the upper bound of $per(A)$ is $S(n,k)$,

$$S(n,k) = \max(per(A)).$$

By developing the first row of A, we know $per(A)$ has k nonzero terms, every nonzero term is a $(n-1)$-order $(0,1)$ matrix with the row sums and the column sums are k or $k-1$. If extend the row sums and the column sums from $k-1$ to k by adding some 1, then we get following recursive relation,

$$S(n,k) \leq kS(n-1,k) \leq k^2S(n-2,k)$$

$$\leq ...... \leq k^{n-k}S(k,k) = k^{n-k}k! = \frac{k^n k!}{k^k}.$$

Therefore

$$per(A) \leq S(n,k) \leq \frac{k^n k!}{k^k}.$$

□

We can also prove (2.2) by following direct method. Because

$$per(A) = \sum_{j_1 j_2 \cdots j_n} a_{1j_1} a_{2j_2} ... a_{nj_n},$$

and in every row or column, only k numbers are nonzero, so j_1 just can take k positive integers, in the same j_2 just can take also k positive integers, ..., j_p just can take also k positive integers, where p, $1 \leq p \leq n$ is a positive integer. After decided $j_1, j_2, ..., j_p$, the number of permutation $(j_{p+1}, ..., j_n)$ doesn't exceed $(n-p)!$, so

$$per(A) \leq k^p(n-p)!.$$

And for all $1 \leq p \leq n$, this inequality always true, therefore

$$per(A) \leq \min_{1 \leq p \leq n} k^p(n-p)! = k^{n-k}k!.$$

Put Theorem 2.1, 2.2 and 2.3 together, we can get following Theorem.

THEOREM 2.4. *Assume that A is a n-order $(0,1)$ matrix with the row sums and the column sums are all a positive integer k, where $1 \leq k \leq n$, then*

$$max(k!, \quad \frac{n!k^n}{n^n}) \leq per(A) \leq \frac{k^n k!}{k^k}. \tag{2.3}$$

3. Some Examples. Because

$$\frac{n!}{n^n} \leq \frac{k!}{k^k},$$

so when $k \to n$, the upper bound and the lower bound showed in (2.3) gradually approach $per(A)$. And it is obvious to know the lower bound

$$\frac{n!k^n}{n^n}$$

is better than $k!$ when

$$\lim_{n\to\infty} \frac{k}{n} \neq 0.$$

For examples, let $k = 5$, $n = 10$, we have

$$per(A_1) \geq \frac{n!k^n}{n^n} = \frac{10!}{2^{10}} \approx 3544$$

but from Hall's inequality we can get only

$$per(A_1) \geq k! = 5! = 120.$$

Let $k = 8$, $n = 10$, we have

$$per(A_2) \geq \frac{n!k^n}{n^n} = \frac{10!8^{10}}{10^{10}} \approx 389639,$$

but from Hall's inequality we can get only

$$per(A_2) \geq k! = 8! = 40320.$$

From Theorem 2.3, we can also get the upper bounds of the $per(A_1)$ and $per(A_2)$,

$$per(A_1) \leq \frac{5^{10}5!}{5^5} = 375000,$$

$$per(A_2) \leq \frac{8^{10}8!}{8^8} = 2580480.$$

4. A Lower Bound for (0,1) Circulant Matrix. For case of the (0,1) circulant matrix, we have some better bounds. Table 4.1 is showing permanent values of the (0,1) circulant matrix for some n and k.

THEOREM 4.1. *When* $k \geq 1$,

$$Per(A) \geq \frac{(k-1)^{(n-k)(k-1)}}{k^{(n-k)(k-2)}} k!$$

Proof. First, we define that the lower bound of $Per(A)$ is $T(n,k)$,

$$T(n,k) = min(Per(A)).$$

By developing the any low or column of A, we know $Per(A)$ has nonzero term. When $k \geq 1$, comparing $T(n,k)$ with $T(n-1,k)$, T(n,k) has one more row and column than T(n-1,k).

$$\begin{pmatrix} 1 & 1 & 1 & 0 & 0 & 0 \\ 0 & 1 & 1 & 1 & 0 & 0 \\ 0 & 0 & 1 & 1 & 1 & 0 \\ 0 & 0 & 0 & 1 & 1 & 1 \\ 1 & 0 & 0 & 0 & 1 & 1 \\ 1 & 1 & 0 & 0 & 0 & 1 \end{pmatrix} \qquad \begin{pmatrix} 1 & 1 & 1 & 0 & 0 \\ 0 & 1 & 1 & 1 & 0 \\ 0 & 0 & 1 & 1 & 1 \\ 1 & 0 & 0 & 1 & 1 \\ 1 & 1 & 0 & 0 & 1 \end{pmatrix}$$

$T(n,k)$ $\qquad$ $T(n-1,k)$

TABLE 4.1
Permanent values of the (0,1) circulant matrix

$k \backslash n$	1	2	3	4	5	6	7
1	1	1	1	1	1	1	1
2		2	2	2	2	2	2
3			6	9	13	20	31
4				24	44	80	144
5					120	265	579
6						720	1854
7							5040

$k \backslash n$	8	9	10	11	12	13	14
1	1	1	1	1	1	1	1
2	2	2	2	2	2	2	2
3	49	78	125	201	324	523	845
4	264	484	888	1632	3000	5516	10144
5	1265	2783	6208	13909	31337	70985	161545
6	4738	12072	30818	79118	204448	528950	1370674
7	14833	43387	126565	369321	1081313	3182225	9411840
8	40320	133496	439792	1445100	4745952	15610304	51504968
9		362880	1334961	4890741	17855140	65275999	238518181
10			3628800	14684570	59216642	238282730	957841226
11				39916800	176214841	775596313	3407118041
12					479001600	2290792932	10927434464
13						6227020800	32071101049
14							87178291200

Next, we rewrite $T(n,k)$ by an expansion. The expansion of permanents is certain row or column. This is T(6,3) by an expansion in 6th row.

$$\begin{pmatrix} 1&1&1&0&0&0\\ 0&1&1&1&0&0\\ 0&0&1&1&1&0\\ 0&0&0&1&1&1\\ 1&0&0&0&1&1\\ 1&1&0&0&0&1 \end{pmatrix} = \begin{pmatrix} 1&1&1&0&0\\ 0&1&1&1&0\\ 0&0&1&1&1\\ 1&0&0&0&1\\ 1&1&0&0&0 \end{pmatrix} + \begin{pmatrix} 1&1&1&0&0\\ 0&1&1&1&0\\ 0&0&1&1&1\\ 0&0&0&1&1\\ 1&1&0&0&0 \end{pmatrix} + \begin{pmatrix} 1&1&1&0&0\\ 0&1&1&1&0\\ 0&0&1&1&1\\ 0&0&0&1&1\\ 1&0&0&0&1 \end{pmatrix}$$

In consequence, we can get k permanents. And we call these permanents are T'(n,k).

We compare to T(n-1,k) with T'(n,k).

On permanent, (0,1) circulant matrix is largest in all same round robin-formula.

T(n-1,k)

$$\begin{pmatrix} 1&1&1&0&0\\ 0&1&1&1&0\\ 0&0&1&1&1\\ 1&0&0&1&1\\ 1&1&0&0&1 \end{pmatrix}$$

$$Round-robinformura : k^{n-1}$$

T'(n,k)

$$\begin{pmatrix} 1 & 1 & 1 & 0 & 0 \\ 0 & 1 & 1 & 1 & 0 \\ 0 & 0 & 1 & 1 & 1 \\ 1 & 0 & 0 & 0 & 1 \\ 1 & 1 & 0 & 0 & 0 \end{pmatrix}, \begin{pmatrix} 1 & 1 & 1 & 0 & 0 \\ 0 & 1 & 1 & 1 & 0 \\ 0 & 0 & 1 & 1 & 1 \\ 0 & 0 & 0 & 1 & 1 \\ 1 & 1 & 0 & 0 & 0 \end{pmatrix}, \begin{pmatrix} 1 & 1 & 1 & 0 & 0 \\ 0 & 1 & 1 & 1 & 0 \\ 0 & 0 & 1 & 1 & 1 \\ 0 & 0 & 0 & 1 & 1 \\ 1 & 0 & 0 & 0 & 1 \end{pmatrix}$$

$$Round - robinformura : k^{n-k}(k-1)^{k-1}$$

Then

$$T'(n,k) > (\frac{k-1}{k})^{k-1}T(n-1,k)$$

Therefore

$$T(n,k) > k(\frac{k-1}{k})^{k-1}T(n-1,k)$$

We apply this inequality to inductive method,

$$T(n,k) > k(\frac{k-1}{k})^{k-1}T(n-1,k) > k^2(\frac{k-1}{k})^{2(k-1)}T(n-2,k)$$

$$\ldots > k^{n-k}(\frac{k-1}{k})^{(n-k)(k-1)}T(k,k) = k^{n-k}(\frac{k-1}{k})^{(n-k)(k-1)}k!$$

Therefore

$$Per(A) \geq \frac{(k-1)^{(n-k)(k-1)}}{k^{(n-k)(k-2)}}k!$$

□

REFERENCES

[1] H. J. Ryser, *Combinatorial Mathematics*, The Mathematical Association of America, New York, 1963.
[2] K. Yamamoto, *Combinatorial Mathematics*, Asakura Bookstore Publication, Tokyo, 1989.
[3] J. C. Lagarias, *On Van der Waerder Conjecture*, J. of Mathematics Translations, 4(1982), pp. 360–365.
[4] S. Alexander, *Permanents and Edge-Colouring*, Invited Instructional Lectures, CWI and University of Amsterdam, 2000.

In: Focus on Computational Neurobiology
Editor: Lei Li, pp. 167-176

ISBN 1-59033-915-0

LOCALIZATION USING COMBINING SENSORS AND DEAD-RECKONING

ZHAO FENG-JI*, GUO HAI-JIAO†, AND KEN-ICHI ABE‡

Abstract. This paper describes an efficient method for estimating long distance navigation of a mobile robot, by fusing dead reckoning and the combining sensors which consist of sonar and infrared. A corridor with interval convex edges is applied as the mobile robot's moving space, and the convex edges are accepted as good landmarks for robot's position estimation. The robot detects the convex edges using combined sensor system, and navigates in this corridor by fusion the information from the dead reckoning and combined sensor based on the Extended Kalman Filter(EKF). The experimental result has shown that the method is effective for estimating of long distance navigation of the mobile robot.

Key words. mobile robot, Extended Kalman Filter, localization, landmarks

1. Introduction. Mobile robot localization is the problem of determining a robot's pose and position from sensor data. Generally speaking, the robot can always determine its current position and orientation by dead reckoning. However, it is impossible to navigate long distance because the errors of position by dead-reckoning are accumulating gradually. Therefore, to navigate for a long distance, the robot must be able to modify its own estimated position by external sensors. The range sensors, such as sonar and infrared, are often used as external sensors. A lot of works in this field have been conducted so far only in small laboratory environments [1, 10, 14, 9]. The new question of localization is that how these systems will scale up when faced with more complex environments covering much longer distance.

Some methods for navigating in this case have been proposed before [8, 12, 13]. But assuming an environment, such as a big hall, where there is no wall to follow but only pillars which have a shape of convex edge (see Figure 4.1), the robot has to regard these convex edges as landmarks for its navigating.

We describe an efficient method for localizing a mobile robot in such an environment. A mobile robot with a combined sensor system (sonar and infrared) is used in a real environment covering several tens meters, which is called "long distance navigation". We are interested in the long distance navigation of an autonomous mobile robot, such as a corridor in the building. In the corridor environment, a convex edge is a special type of landmark that can be reliably observed in successive sensor measurements. Moreover, the convex edges are stable natural environment features, they are the suitable landmarks for robot navigation. The robot detects the convex edges using combined sensor system, and navigates in this corridor by fusing the information from the dead reckoning and combined sensor based on the Extended Kalman Filter. The experimental result has shown that the method is effective for estimating of long distance navigation of the mobile robot.

2. The Combining Sensors. To operate successfully in indoor environments, mobile robots must be able to localize themselves. In our study, two types of sensors, sonar and infrared are used as a combining sensors to obtain external information for mobile robot.

There are sixteen sonar sensors mounted around the mobile robot which are used to detect obstacles. The reading of sixteen sonar sensors (us_i; $i = 1, 2, ..., 16$) are numbered

*SMC Networks Co., Ltd., Tokyo, Japan. 103-0024 (zhao@smcnetworks.co.jp)
† Department of Electrical Engineering Tohoku University, Sendai 980-8579 Japan.
‡ Department of Electrical Engineering Graduate school of Eng.,Tohoku University, Sendai 980-8579 Japan.

counter-clockwise consecutively beginning with the front of the robot.

The sonar range finder is capable of measuring distance to an object with a resolution of 2.54 cm through a range of 15.24 cm to 647.7 cm. This is accomplished by measuring the time of flight between a transmitted pulse and a returned echo and multiplying by the speed of sound. The sonar sensor has a large beam width, a specular reflections on smooth surfaces, and is influenced by temperature and humidity, it can be used to measure the distance from a convex edge, but the obtained result has poor angular resolution due to its feature above[9, 13].

Moreover, the robot has sixteen infrared sensors, each infrared sensor is composed of two SIEMENS SFH 4343 GaAIAs infrared emitters and a SIEMENS SFH 2030f Siliconpn Photo-diode enclosed in a delrin housing. The two emitters and the receiver are mounted horizontally, the diode between the two emitters. Range to the objects is determined by the intensity of the light from the emitter reflected back to the detector. The intensity of the light is digitally measured using a Voltage Controller Oscillator (VOC), a device which emits a square wave signal with a frequency proportional to its input voltage. The higher the input voltage is, the faster the oscillation.

Infrared sensor emits a plus of near-infrared light and then uses a parabolic dish and a near-infrared detector to sense any returned energy, over a very narrow area. Unlike sonar, the time of flight of light pulse can not be easily measured. The sensor merely indicates whether any returned pulse was detected. So the infrared sensor is not able to measure distance accurately, but has good angular resolution in detecting the feature point of convex edge. The measurement of infrared sensor is influenced by some factors, such as geometry, lighting, color and surface[13]. Therefore, the data of measurement can not be used as the distance information. The main features of infrared sensor are: calibration = 0 20 ... 300 320, dependency = 0, half cone = 10.0 deg, incident = 0.05.

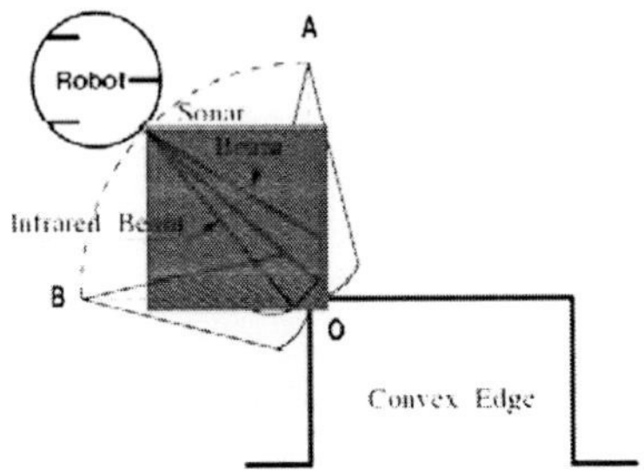

FIG. 2.1. *Fusing of sonar and infrared detecting rang*

It is important to detect a convex edge by combined sensor. Let's denote feature of convex edge as the POE (Peak Of Edge). According to the feature of Time of Flight system, the POE can be detected in the rang of AOB (see Figure 2.1). Consequently, if the robot is not within this range, the real convex edge become very hard to locate. In this range, though the robot can get the distance information from POE to itself, it is difficult to determine robot's position even if the location of a POE is priori known. The robot's position can not be obtained directly. However, the robot is expected to be located on the circumference of a circle which has radius r and a location center O. Then if the robot's location on the circumference is fixed, the orientation of the robot become unique.

A series of experiments have been performed in order to find a way to compensate the recognizing method based on the combined sensors. Firstly, the minimum of measurement is regarded as the distance from robot to POE according to the feature of Time of Flight system. Secondly, the direction which the sensor gets the minimum of measurement is regarded as the direction of the POE. Actually, the data of direction is not unique because of sensor's beam width. Considering the experimental characteristics, the mean value of direction data is regarded as valid direction.

Here as an example, the robot is positioned in front of a convex edge and rotated with an angle, the response data from two sensors are shown in Figure 2.1. It is found that the information of convex edge can be gotten from the sonar for distance and from the infrared for the direction, respectively(see Figure 2.2). This is why we use combining sensor instead of either of them.

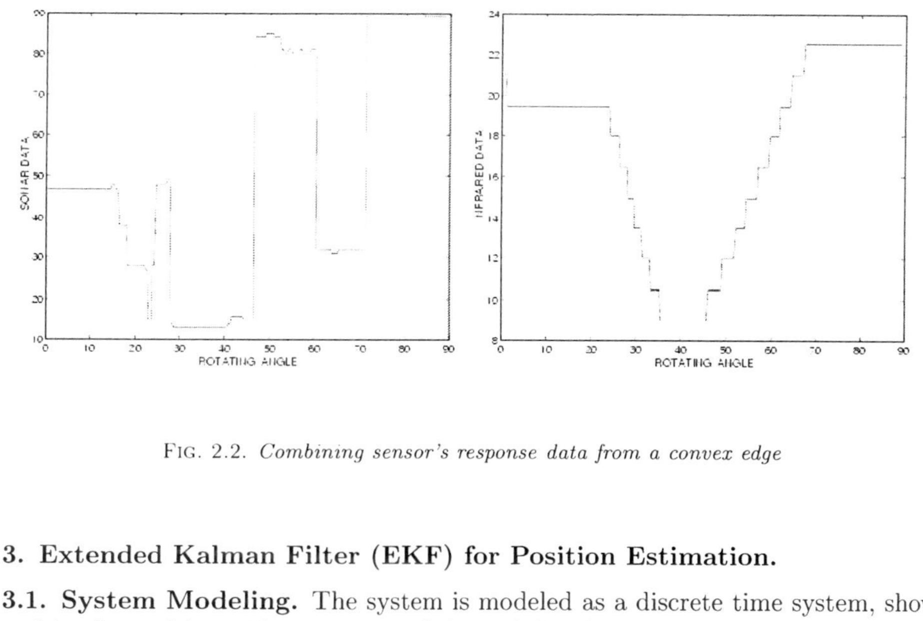

FIG. 2.2. *Combining sensor's response data from a convex edge*

3. Extended Kalman Filter (EKF) for Position Estimation.

3.1. System Modeling. The system is modeled as a discrete time system, shown in Figure 3.1., the position and orientation of the mobile robot at time step k is denoted by the state vector; $\mathbf{x}(k) = [x(k) \quad y(k) \quad \theta(k)]^T$ comprising a Cartesian location and a orientation defined with respect to a global coordinate frame. During a period ΔT, the system modeling is updated as

$$\begin{pmatrix} x(k+1) \\ y(k+1) \\ \theta(k+1) \end{pmatrix} = \begin{pmatrix} x(k) \\ y(k) \\ \theta(k) \end{pmatrix} + \begin{pmatrix} \Delta T v(k)\cos(\theta(k)+\alpha(k)) \\ \Delta T v(k)\sin(\theta(k)+\alpha(k)) \\ \alpha(k) \end{pmatrix}. \tag{3.1}$$

The robot's state $\mathbf{x}(k)$ changes with time in response to a control input $\mathbf{u}(k)$ and a noise disturbance $\mathbf{w}(k)$. The state translation equation can be briefly expressed in general

$$\mathbf{x}(k+1) = \mathbf{f}[\mathbf{x}(k) \quad \mathbf{u}(k)] + \mathbf{w}(k), \tag{3.2}$$

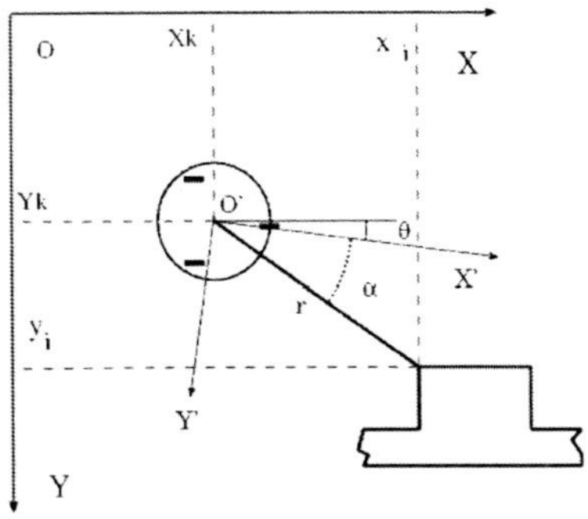

FIG. 3.1. *Configuration of convex edge and robot*

where, $\mathbf{x}(k)$ is the state of the system at time step k, $\mathbf{u}(k) = [v(k) \quad \alpha(k)]^T$, represents external input to the system, here, $\alpha(k)$ and $v(k)$ are the steering angle and the velocity of the driving wheel, it is assumed that the velocity $v(k)$ is disturbed by a zero-mean uncorrelated process. $\mathbf{w}(k)$ is an additive zero-mean process noise and is defined by the covariance matrix $\mathbf{Q}(k)$. $\mathbf{f}$ is the state transition matrix, which relates the state at time step k to the step $k+1$, and includes such parameters as driving function $\mathbf{u}(k)$.

3.2. Estimation of Trajectory Using Dead-reckoning. As shown in Figure 3.1, the mobile robot is assumed to move at all time on the horizontal X, Y-plane, the ground-plane. The robot's position and orientation are specific by the coordinates (x, y, θ), where x, y are the world-frame coordinates of the robot body's center, and θ is the robot's orientation relative to the world X-axis. The robot-centered frame $X'O'Y'$ is defined to have its origin on the ground plane directly under the robot center, with the X'-axis pointing to the front of the robot, Y'-axis to the right. r is the distance from robot to the POE of convex edge and α is the angle between r and X'-axis.

At the starting point, the robot's location in the world frame is defined to be $x = 0, y = 0, \theta = 0$, and the world frame coincides with the robot frame.

3.3. Estimation Errors. For Eq.(3.2), there are errors in estimating the state of the robot at each time step. The errors arise from the fact that the dead reckoning measurements from the wheels are imperfect because of wheels slippage. Let $\hat{\mathbf{x}}(k)$ is the estimated value of $\mathbf{x}(k)$, $\Delta\hat{\mathbf{x}}(k)$ is the error of $\hat{\mathbf{x}}(k)$, $\hat{\mathbf{u}}(k)$ is the measured value of $\mathbf{u}(k)$, and $\Delta\hat{\mathbf{u}}(k)$ is the error of the $\hat{\mathbf{u}}(k)$. Then

$$\begin{aligned} \mathbf{x}(k+1) &= \mathbf{f}\left[\hat{\mathbf{x}}(k) + \Delta\hat{\mathbf{x}}(k) \quad \hat{\mathbf{u}}(k) + \Delta\hat{\mathbf{u}}(k)\right] + \mathbf{w}(k) \\ &\cong \mathbf{f}\left[\hat{\mathbf{x}}(k) \quad \hat{\mathbf{u}}(k)\right] + \mathbf{J}_1(k)\Delta\hat{\mathbf{x}}(k) \\ &\quad + \mathbf{J}_2(k)\Delta\hat{\mathbf{u}}(k) + \mathbf{w}(k) \\ &= \hat{\mathbf{x}}(k+1) + \Delta\hat{\mathbf{x}}(k+1), \end{aligned} \tag{3.3}$$

the error in dead reckoning increase as

$$\Delta\hat{\mathbf{x}}(k+1) = \mathbf{J}_1(k)\Delta\hat{\mathbf{x}}(k) + \mathbf{J}_2(k)\Delta\hat{\mathbf{u}}(k) + \mathbf{w}(k), \tag{3.4}$$

where,

$$\mathbf{J}_1(k) = \frac{\partial \mathbf{f}}{\partial \mathbf{x}}(\hat{\mathbf{x}}(k), \hat{\mathbf{u}}(k)),$$
$$\mathbf{J}_2(k) = \frac{\partial \mathbf{f}}{\partial \mathbf{u}}(\hat{\mathbf{x}}(k), \hat{\mathbf{u}}(k)).$$

By the concept of the error ellipsoid, we can know about degree of the estimation accuracy.

Figure 3.2 shows the simulated trajectory of robot and estimated one by the dead reckoning and error ellipsoid on $X - Y$ plane. The result shows the estimation uncertainty of the dead reckoning system increases as the robot moves. So that it is impossible for the robot to navigate for long distance if it only relies on a dead reckoning system.

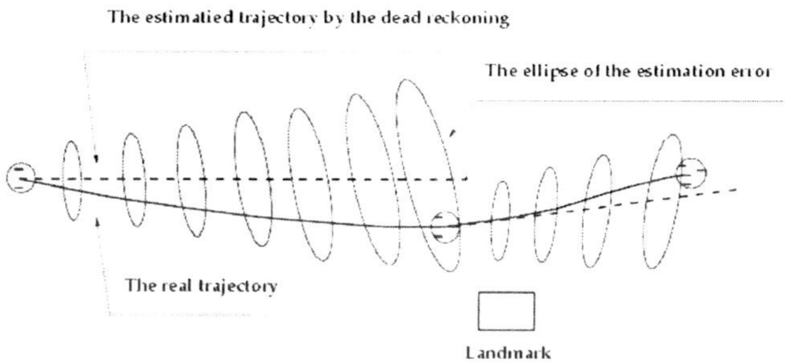

FIG. 3.2. *Estimation error using the dead reckoning*

3.4. Estimation of Trajectory Using EKF. The Extended Klaman filter is a set of mathematical equations that provides an efficient computational solution of the least-squares method. The filter is very powerful in several aspects: it supports estimations of past, present, and even future states, and it can do so even when the precise nature of the modeled system is unknown. Extended Kalman Filtering is a well established technique for estimating the state of a system in the presence of noise. The Extended Kalman filter approach also allows rejection of spurious arrival times which can arise if an indirect path is taken by a pulse from landmarks to receiver. Given that the measurement and state noise is Gaussian, the Extended Kalman filter provides the optimum minimum error variance estimate of position.

The localization problem is treated as a two-stage iterative estimation process. The pose is estimated first and is then available for position estimation. The indirect form of the Kalman filter is developed for attitude estimation when applying gyro modeling. The main benefit of this choice is that complex dynamic modeling of the mobile robot and its interaction with the environment is avoided. The filter optimally combines the attitude rate information from the gyro and the absolute orientation measurements. The proposed implementation is independent of the structure of the mobile robot or the morphology of the ground.

As we described before, when the robot travel distance is small, the error is small and can be ignored. However, if the distance is longer, a larger error is accumulated. For longer distance navigation, if only use dead reckoning, it will leave the planned path due this error, and the robot may collide with objects in the real environment. Therefore, we use the following method to reduce the error before it become large. First, the robot finds the landmark in the real environment and detect its range and direction by using an external sensor embodied with the robot. Secondly, the robot estimate it's position by comparing external sensor data with landmark map which the robot possesses. Then, estimating current position and orientation by dead-reckoning. Finally, combining these estimated positions using EKF technique, and renew estimated position.

A method is found with which the robot's position estimated from dead reckoning can be corrected by the measurements made by landmark detection sensor[12]. The nonlinear observation model is related to the state vector and the landmarks being observed by following observation equation

$$\mathbf{z}(k) = \mathbf{h}\left[\mathbf{x}(k) \quad \mathbf{p}_i\right] + \mathbf{v}(k), \tag{3.5}$$

where $\mathbf{z}(k)$ is the observation vector, $\mathbf{p}_i$ is the convex edge location, $\mathbf{p}_i = [x_i \quad y_i \quad \alpha \quad r]^T$. $\mathbf{h}$ is the observation matrix that transforms the state space vector into observation space, and $\mathbf{v}(k)$ is an additive measurement noise and is defined by the covariance matrix $\mathbf{R}(k)$. The relationship is shown as

$$\mathbf{h}\left[\mathbf{x}(k), \mathbf{p}_i\right] = \begin{bmatrix} (x(k) - x_i) + rcos(\theta + \alpha) \\ (y(k) - y_i) + rsin(\theta + \alpha) \end{bmatrix}. \tag{3.6}$$

It is assumed that the additive process noise vectors $\mathbf{w}(k)$ and measurement noise $\mathbf{v}(k)$ are Gaussian, uncorrelated white sequence.

The true states of the system are not known, and they must be estimated since the process and observation models are disturbed by random processes, the estimation errors are also random variables. However, we can approximate the state and measurement vector without $\mathbf{w}(k)$ and $\mathbf{v}(k)$ as

$$\tilde{\mathbf{x}}(k+1) = \mathbf{f}\left[\hat{\mathbf{x}}(k) \quad \mathbf{u}(k)\right], \tag{3.7}$$

$$\tilde{\mathbf{z}}(k) = \mathbf{h}\left[\tilde{\mathbf{x}}(k) \quad \mathbf{p}_i\right], \tag{3.8}$$

where $\tilde{\mathbf{x}}(k)$ is an approximate of state at time step k, and $\hat{\mathbf{x}}(k)$ is an estimate of state.

When the system non-linearity is not "too serious", the system can be linearized about an operating point, and the linear Kalman filter equations can be applied[6] . In something akin to a Taylor series, we can linearize the equation by writing new governing equations that linearize an estimate about Eqs. (3.7) and (3.8),

$$\mathbf{x}(k+1) \approx \tilde{\mathbf{x}}(k+1) + \mathbf{A}\left[\mathbf{x}(k) - \hat{\mathbf{x}}(k)\right] + \mathbf{B}\mathbf{w}(k), \tag{3.9}$$

$$\mathbf{z}(k) \approx \tilde{\mathbf{z}}(k) + \mathbf{C}\left[\mathbf{x}(k) - \tilde{\mathbf{x}}(k)\right] + \mathbf{D}\mathbf{v}(k), \tag{3.10}$$

where, $\mathbf{x}(k+1)$ and $\mathbf{z}(k)$ are the actual states and measurement vectors, $\tilde{\mathbf{x}}(k+1)$ and $\tilde{\mathbf{z}}(k)$ are the approximated state and measurement vector from Eqs.(3.7) and (3.8), $\hat{\mathbf{x}}(k)$ is an estimate for state at step k, $\mathbf{A}, \mathbf{B}, \mathbf{C}$ and $\mathbf{D}$ are Jacobian matrix, shown as below, respectively.

$$\mathbf{A} = \frac{\partial \mathbf{f}}{\partial \mathbf{x}}(\hat{\mathbf{x}}(k), \mathbf{u}(k)),$$
$$\mathbf{B} = \frac{\partial \mathbf{f}}{\partial \mathbf{w}}(\hat{\mathbf{x}}(k), \mathbf{u}(k)),$$
$$\mathbf{C} = \frac{\partial \mathbf{h}}{\partial \mathbf{x}}(\tilde{\mathbf{x}}(k), \mathbf{p}_i),$$
$$\mathbf{D} = \frac{\partial \mathbf{h}}{\partial \mathbf{v}}(\tilde{\mathbf{x}}(k), \mathbf{p}_i).$$

Now, define a new notation for the prediction error,

$$\Delta\mathbf{x}(k) = \mathbf{x}(k) - \tilde{\mathbf{x}}(k), \tag{3.11}$$

and the measurement residual,

$$\Delta\mathbf{z}(k) = \mathbf{z}(k) - \tilde{\mathbf{z}}(k), \tag{3.12}$$

Using Eqs.(3.11) and (3.12) governing equations can be written for an error process as

$$\Delta\mathbf{x}(k+1) \approx \mathbf{A}(\mathbf{x}(k) - \hat{\mathbf{x}}(k)) + \mathbf{w}'(k), \tag{3.13}$$

$$\Delta\mathbf{z}(k) \approx \mathbf{H}\Delta\mathbf{x}(k) + \mathbf{v}'(k), \tag{3.14}$$

where $\mathbf{w}'(k)$ and $\mathbf{v}'(k)$ represent new independent random variables with zero mean and covariance matrices $\mathbf{BQB^T}$ and $\mathbf{DRD^T}$ as a white noise. Notice that Eqs.(3.13) and (3.14) are linear, which are optimal for linear system.

Now we can use the actual measurement residual $\Delta\mathbf{z}(k)$ in Eq.(3.12) and a second (hypothetical) Kalman filter to estimate the prediction error $\Delta\mathbf{x}(k)$ given by Eq.(3.13). This estimation is denoted as $\hat{\mathbf{x}}(k)$, could then be used along with Eq.(3.11) to obtain a posteriori state estimates for the original non-linear process as

$$\hat{\mathbf{x}}(k) = \tilde{\mathbf{x}}(k) + \Delta\mathbf{z}(k) = \tilde{\mathbf{x}}(k) + \mathbf{K}(k)(\mathbf{z}(k) - \tilde{\mathbf{z}}(k)). \tag{3.15}$$

This equation can now be used for the measurement update in the Eq.(3.9), with $\tilde{\mathbf{x}}(k)$ and $\tilde{\mathbf{z}}(k)$ coming from the Eqs.(3.7) and (3.8). The matrix $\mathbf{K}$ is chosen to be the gain that minimizes the posteriori error covariance, and given by

$$\mathbf{K} = \mathbf{P}(k)\mathbf{H}^T(k)(\mathbf{H}(k)\mathbf{P}(k)\mathbf{H}^T(k) + (\mathbf{V}(k)\mathbf{R}\mathbf{V}^T(k))^{-1}. \tag{3.16}$$

The covariance estimate from times step k to step $k+1$ is given by

$$\mathbf{P}(k+1) = \mathbf{A}(k)\mathbf{P}(k)\mathbf{A}^T(k) + \mathbf{B}(k)\mathbf{Q}\mathbf{B}^T(k), \tag{3.17}$$

where $\mathbf{A}(k)$ and $\mathbf{B}(k)$ are process Jacobian at step k. and $\mathbf{Q}(k)$ is the process noise covariance at step k. By calculating the covariance estimates at a suitable interval, we can know about degree of the estimation accuracy and which direction the estimation error extends to.

We state the Extended Kalman Filter equations without derivation and refer to [4, 6] for more details.

3.5. Simulations of Trajectory Estimation. Figure 3.3 shows the simulated trajectory of robot, the estimated trajectory by the dead reckoning and the error ellipse in the working space. When the robot uses the dead-reckoning system, the error between the estimated position and the real position tended to spread as the robot moves, and the accuracy of estimation decreased. After the landmarks came into the view of the robot, combined sensor provided a measurement information for the robot to correct the estimated position, therefore, the error ellipse was decreased and the robot moved towards the goal. The sensor noise covariance was assumed to be 0.6 and process noise covariance was 0.8. The information was updated every sampling interval 1*meter* in length.

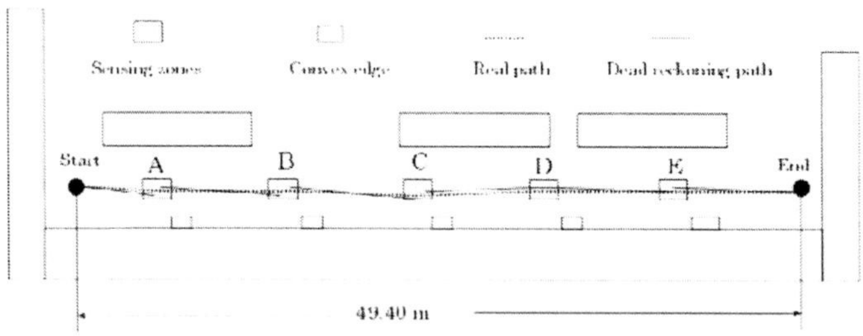

FIG. 3.3. *Simulation of trajectory estimation*

4. Navigation Experiment. The experiment was performed in a corridor with some convex edges, which are along to the corridor with suitable intervals 8 *meters*(see Figure 4.1). When the robot moved, it can know the moment for detecting the convex edge by its dead reckoning system, the place is called sensing zones whose locations are known in advance as a map information. The robot moved along the planned path according to the dead reckoning from start to a sensing zone, it rotated the sensors an angle to get the information of sensors as it moved.

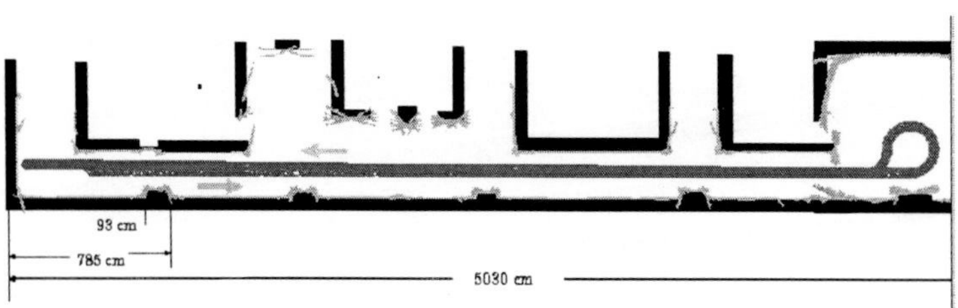

FIG. 4.1. *The experiment for different edge and pole*

The navigation is divided into following steps:

1) The planning path from current point to next sensing zone is a straight path. Navigating the robot between these two points is performed based on dead reckoning.

2) Detecting a landmark by combined sensor, the robot obtains the position and the direction information of a convex edge as a landmark from an environmental map, and

calculates the expected distance and direction of the convex edge from the robot. Using these parameters, the convex edge detection sensor tries to face the convex edge and measure the distance and direction.

3) After detecting a convex edge, the robot fuses the measured values and the dead reckoning information to correct its estimated position by the proposed method.

When gotten estimated position, the robot updates the dead reckoning by this information, then, regards next sensing point as sub-goal to make a new path plan.

Let the sensed convex edge be located at (x_i, y_i), the relation between the robot's and convex edge is illustrated in Figure 3.1. r is the distance and α is the angle of the detected sensor with respect to the robot front, the relation can be shown as

$$r = \sqrt{(x(k) - x_i)^2 + (y(k) - y_i)^2} \tag{4.1}$$

$$\theta = \tan^{-1} \frac{y(k) - y_i}{x(k) - x_i} - \alpha \tag{4.2}$$

Referring to Eq.(3.6) the information from the combined sensor can be rewritten as

$$\mathbf{h}\left[\mathbf{x}(k), \mathbf{p}_i\right] = \left[(y(k) - y_i) - (x(k) - x_i)\tan(\theta(k) + \alpha)\right] \tag{4.3}$$

According to Eq.(3.8) we can calculate the estimated position and the covariance matrix with the proposed method, the parameters used in the equation are obtained from following equations,

$$\tilde{\mathbf{z}}(k) = (\tilde{y}(k) - y_i) - (\tilde{x}(k) - x_i)\tan(\tilde{\theta}(k) - \tilde{\alpha}) \tag{4.4}$$

$$\mathbf{B} = \frac{\partial \mathbf{h}}{\partial \mathbf{x}} = \begin{bmatrix} -\tan(\tilde{\theta}(k) + \tilde{\alpha}) & 1 & \frac{\tilde{x}(k) - x_i}{\cos^2(\tilde{\theta}(k) - \tilde{\alpha})} \end{bmatrix} \tag{4.5}$$

$$\mathbf{D} = \frac{\partial \mathbf{h}}{\partial \mathbf{v}} = \begin{bmatrix} \tan(\tilde{\theta}(k) + \tilde{\alpha}) & -1 & \frac{\tilde{x}(k) - x_i}{\cos^2(\tilde{\theta}(k) - \tilde{\alpha})} \end{bmatrix} \tag{4.6}$$

By combining two estimations, dead reckoning and external sensor, the robot position becomes more accurate than either of estimations, individually. The calculation for more accurate estimation was performed using Eq.(3.9). Then the robot updates the dead reckoning using the result of Eq.(3.9). From Figure 4.1, we can know that the dead reckoning was updated at every sensing point.

In the experiment, the robot was always controlled to follow the given path. By correcting the estimated position, the robot changed its path in following order: firstly, the robot ran a straight distance 47.4 meters along with four convex edges as landmarks; secondly, the robot turned back along an arc, 3 *meters* in radius, and then went back to the start point using the same landmarks. So the robot was able to return back to the starting point within about 10cm, the 0.2% of the total distance traveled.

5. Discussion and Conclusions. In this paper, we have described the robot position estimated by dead reckoning, then the correction of robot position by the observation of landmarks based on extend Kalman Filter was introduced. In addition, the results of tests were carried out with EKF over a long distance, where a mobile robot was controlled to follow a route of over 100m in length. This system used convex edges as landmarks and combined sensor based on self-guide. The result shows that natural landmarks such as convex edges are useful to correct the robot position by the proposed method.

Acknowledgments. Part of this research was done while the author was visiting Robotic Intnstitute, Carnegie Mellon University, PA, USA. The author is also supported by AOKI scholarship, Tokyo, Japan. The author would like to express his thanks to the members of Laboratory of Control Theory, Tohoku University, for their great collaboration while the research was doing in there.

REFERENCES

[1] K. Kidono, J. Miura, and Y. Shirai, *"Autonomous Navigation of a Mobile Robot Using a Human-Guided Experience"*, Proc.Asian Conf. on Computer Vision, pp. 449-454, Jan. 2000.

[2] I. Moon, J. Miura, and Y. Shirai, *"On-line Selection of Stable Visual Landmarks under Uncertainty"*, Proc. 1999 IEEE/RSJ Int. Conf. on Intelligent Robots and Systems, pp. 781-786, Kyongju, Korea, Oct. 1999.

[3] I. Moon, J. Miura, and Y. Shirai, *"Automatic Extraction of Visual Landmarks for a Mobile Robot under Uncertainty of Vision and Motion"*, Proc. 2001 IEEE Int. Conf. on Robotics and Automation, pp. 1188-1193, Seoul, Korea, May 2001.

[4] Roumeliotis S.I. and Bekey G.A., *"Bayesian estimation and Kalman filtering: A unified framework for Mobile Robot Localization"*, In Proc. 2000 IEEE International Conference on Robotics and Automation, San Francisco, CA, April 22-28, pp. 2985-2992.

[5] Goel P., Dedeoglu G., Roumeliotis S.I., and Sukhatme G.S., *"Fault Detection and Identification in a Mobile Robot Using Multiple Model Estimation and Neural Network"*, In Proc. 2000 IEEE International Conference on Robotics and Automation, San Francisco, CA, April 22-28, pp. 2302-2309.

[6] Jun M., Roumeliotis S.I., and Sukhatme G.S., *"State Estimation via Sensor Modeling for Helicopter Control using an Indirect Kalman Filter"*, In Proc. 1999 IEEE/RSJ International Conference on Intelligent Robots and Systems, Kyongju, Korea, Oct. 17-21, pp. 1346-1353.

[7] Schultz, A., Adams, W., and Yamauchi, B., *"Integrating Exploration, Localization, Navigation and Planning With a Common Representation"*, Autonomous Robots, v6 n3, May(1999), IEEE Press, pp. 293-308.

[8] Zhao, Fengji, Guo, Hai-jiao and Abe, Ken-ichi, *"Position Location for a Mobile Robot Using Sonar Sensors"*, IEEE International Conference on Intelligent Engineering Systems Vienna, Austria, pp. 130-135, Sept., 1998.

[9] H.R.Beom, K.I.Koh and H.S.Cho, *" The improvement of sonar-based mobile robot localization method by multiple beacons"* , IFAC 13th Triennial World Congress, San Francisco, USA, 1996, pp. 199-204.

[10] H.R.Beom and H.S.Cho, *"Mobile robot localization using a single rotating sonar and two passive cylindrical beacons"*, Robotica, vol. 13(1995), pp. 243-252.

[11] Bozma and Roman Kuc, *" Building a sonar map in a specular environment using a single mobile sensor"*, IEEE Trans. Pattern Anal. Machine Intel, vol. 13, no. 1991, 12, pp. 1260-1269.

[12] Zhao, Fengji, Guo, Hai-jiao and Abe, Ken-ichi, *"A Mobile Robot Localization Using Ultrasonic Sensors in Indoor Environment"*, Proceeding of 6th IEEE International Workshop on Robot and Human Communication, Sendai, Japan, pp. 52-57, Oct., 1997.

[13] Zhao, Fengji, Guo, Hai-jiao and Abe, Ken-ichi, *"Precise Localization for a Mobile Robot with Sonar and Infrared Sensors"*, IASTED International Conference Robotics and Manufacturing Banff, Canada, pp. 8-12, July, 1998.

[14] Matthies,L.,Elfes,A., *"Integration of sonar and stereo range data using a grid-based representation"*, Proc. of IEEE Conference on Robotics and Automation, 1998, pp. 727-733.

In: Focus on Computational Neurobiology
Editor: Lei Li, pp. 177-189

ISBN 1-59033-915-0

SUPPORT SOFTWARE EVOLUTION WITH ABSTRACTION RULES AND PROGRAMMING KNOWLEDGE PATTERNS

GUIFA TENG* AND XIAODONG LIU†

Abstract. This paper advocates that reengineering is an effective means of legacy system evolution. Extracting formal specification semantically consistent to the original legacy system will facilitate further redesign and forward engineering greatly. The key technology is abstraction, which is often interpreted as the act of hiding irrelevant details.

Programming knowledge refers to the "technique" or "convention" that a programmer used to implement an application. The structure of an existing program was heavily affected by this kind of knowledge. A set of programming knowledge patterns are developed to discover the programming knowledge embedded in legacy systems. Implementation details can be eliminated effectively with these patterns and relevant abstraction rules.

A unified reengineering approach with a focus on reverse engineering is proposed. The approach is based on three points: the construction of a wide spectrum language based reengineering framework, the development of abstraction rules and programming knowledge patterns.

Key words. software evolution, system reengineering, reverse engineering, abstraction, programming knowledge, time critical systems.

1. Introduction. Software reengineering is considered as an effective means of the evolution of legacy systems, that is, correction and improvement of these systems. Its importance and popularity increase as more and more successful computing systems become legacy systems. However, the following problems often prevent existing reengineering approaches from success: a) ambiguity and incorrectness in recovered specification and design; b) ambiguity, lack of proof and incorrectness in reengineering process and rules; c) lack of automation.

The above weaknesses will inevitably result in unsuccessful reengineering. The reengineering products, for example, improved computing systems, will be incompatible to requirements or not workable. Without automatic support, reengineering will be intolerably slow, costly in manpower and only feasible for small-scaled legacy systems.

This paper proposes a formal unified approach for software reengineering, which is designed to facilitate effective and more automatic reengineering process. A supporting tool is built to speed and scale up practical reengineering.

It is natural to assume that forward engineering part of reengineering can be carried out by borrowing an existing suitable software development method which has been well developed. Therefore, our reengineering research mainly focuses on the reverse engineering part, i.e., how to understand an existing system or how to obtain design/specification from an existing system.

The key techniques in the approach are abstraction rules and programming knowledge patterns. A set of abstraction rules are developed to tackle how to identify the key functionality of legacy systems from their source code, which is often the only reliable information source for these systems. Programming knowledge refers to the "technique" or "convention" that a programmer used to implement a program for real applications. The structure of an existing program was heavily determined by this kind of knowledge during implementation. A set of programming knowledge patterns are developed to identify the programming

*Department of Computer Science, Agricultural University of Heibei, Baoding, China. (tguifa@heinfo.net).

†School of Computing, Napier University, Edinburgh, UK. (x.liu@napier.ac.uk).

knowledge embedded in legacy source code. The identified programming knowledge is then applied in specification extraction with relevant abstraction rules.

Our approach is based on the construction of a wide spectrum language, known as Reengineering Wide Spectrum Language (RWSL), the development of a set of abstraction rules and programming knowledge patterns, all of which enjoy a sound formal semantics.

Besides sequential non-time systems, the proposed approach aims at time critical systems with parallelism. This is a particular challenging research area because within such a system the functional behavior and non-functional timing requirement are combined, implicit and very difficult to recover.

Case studies are used for experiments with the approach and the prototype tool. Conclusion is drawn based on analysis, which shows that the proposed approach is feasible and promising in its domain.

2. The Approach.

2.1. An Integrated Reengineering Framework. Our previous study has shown [12] that using a wide spectrum language is one of the most suitable and efficient approach to the reengineering of computing systems because of its various abstraction levels and the integrity of these levels.

In our approach, a wide spectrum language is constructed as the representation platform of legacy systems. The wide spectrum language is known as RWSL and enjoys a sound formal semantics. RWSL is a multi-layered wide spectrum language with sound formal semantics. Due to the distinct advantage of Interval Temporal Logic (ITL) [13, 4], we use it as the semantic foundation of RWSL.

Figure 2.1 shows the architecture of RWSL. The top part is the object-oriented section, which includes three layers, namely ITL Specification, Object-Oriented Temporal Agent Model (ObTAM) and Common Object-Oriented Language (COOL). ObTAM is an extension of Temporal Agent Model (TAM) language [14] with object-oriented features. The most concrete layer of the object-oriented section is Common Object-Oriented Language, which provides structures as those in an ordinary OO language.

The bottom part is the structural (procedural) section, which also includes three layers: ITL Specification, Timed Guarded Command Language (TGCL) and Common Structural Language (CSL). TGCL is an extension of Dijkstra's Guarded Command Language [7, 8] with time and concurrency feature. Both TGCL and CSL are at the code level, while in CSL operators and concepts are implemented in common programming elements, such as shunts.

Both the object-oriented and procedural systems will be specified with ITL formulae. The semantics of other layers of RWSL, together with the abstraction and object extraction rules will be defined in ITL.

Figure 2.2 shows the possible process when using RWSL to reengineer legacy systems. The approach may be used as follows: the source code of a legacy system is first translated into CSL through a translator.[1] Such a translation ensures standardization, since legacy systems may have come in various languages, such as C, Modula or COBOL. This is followed by transformation to TGCL through successive application of correctness-preserving transformation rules.

There are three possible paths for reengineering:

[1] The "universal translator", as shown in Figure 2.1, translates between a source/target language to/from RWSL (e.g., a COBOL-to-RWSL Translator). This translator must be written for each source/target language and is simply a one-to-one mapping, to ensure semantics equivalence.

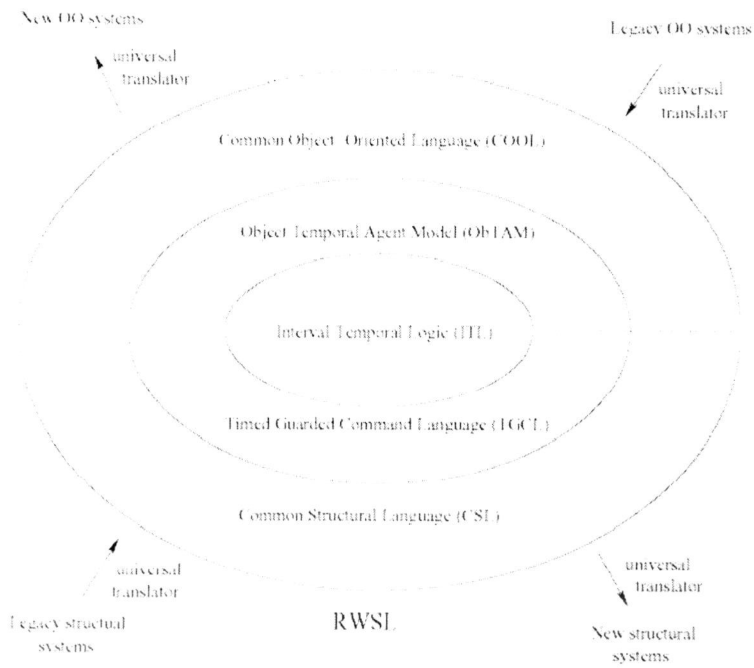

FIG. 2.1. *General architecture of RWSL.*

1. TGCL code can be improved/extended by adding the required extra functionalities. The TGCL code can be then transformed into an equivalent programming language (either through transformation or straight forward translation). In this path, the procedural nature of the legacy system is kept.
2. If Object Oriented paradigm is sought, object extraction is performed to obtain an equivalent ObTAM code. Then the ObTAM code is extended/improved. Subsequently, this is transformed to an Object Oriented language, such as ADA, JAVA and C++.
3. If high level of abstract specification is needed, then following the construction of TGCL code or/and ObTAM code, the semantics calculation is performed to produce an ITL specification. This will be subsequently used as a basis for forward engineering through refinement.

In this paper, we focus on the reverse engineering part, i.e., how to engage formal abstraction technology to extract formal specifications from legacy source code.

Interested readers may refer to [16] for the detailed syntax and semantics of RWSL.

2.2. Abstraction Rules. Central to our approach is a set of **abstraction rules**. In our approach, abstraction is performed *stepwise* at both data and structural levels in such a way that the underlying computation is not disturbed whilst functional abstraction is also performed, that is, some functionality considered "trivial" is abstracted away from the code. Here, "stepwise" means to stepwise abstract the sub-systems of the target system first and

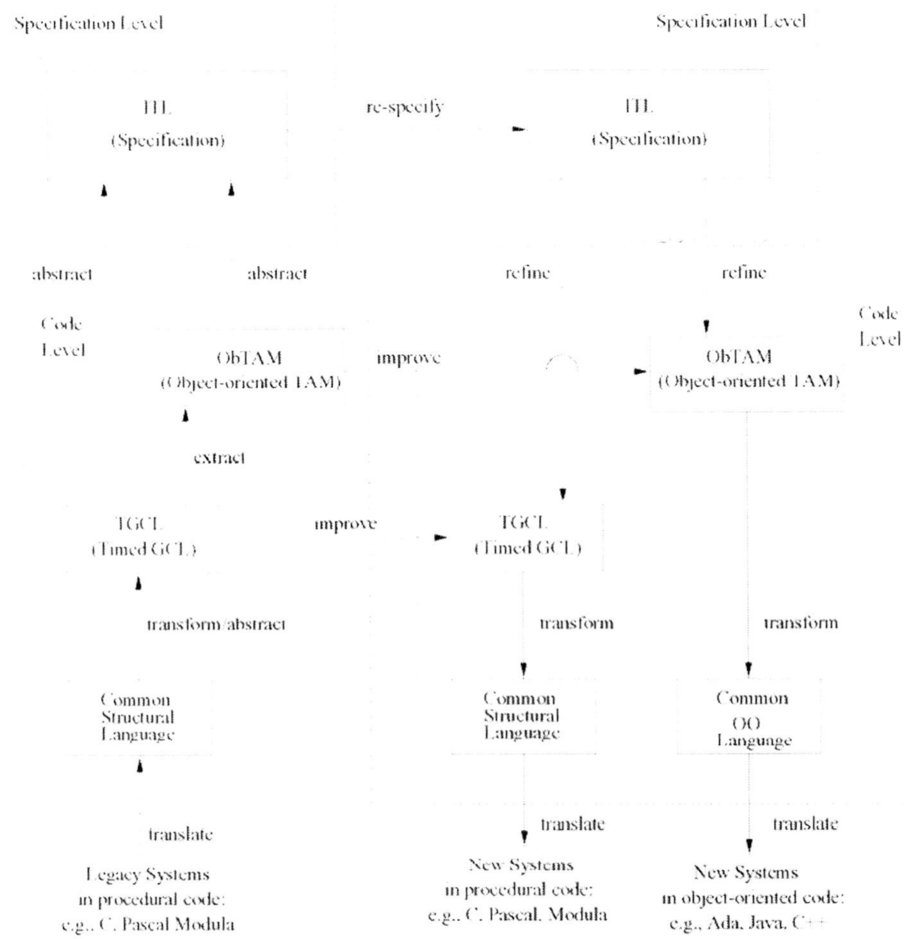

FIG. 2.2. *Working process of RWSL in reengineering.*

then to further abstract the higher level view of the sub-systems into the full view of the target system.

The *correctness* is achieved through the soundness of the abstraction rules.

An implementation (code), a design and a specification of a software system are usually at different levels of abstraction. To move from code to design and then to specification involves a process of crossing levels of abstraction. A specification is more abstract than its implementation, and therefore the above process can be also represented as:

$$\textit{concrete} \rightarrow \textit{less abstract} \rightarrow \textit{more abstract}$$

Abstraction is defined as semantics weakening of system representations. The implementation of a software system is known as the concrete form of the system, e.g., source code, and the specification is known as the abstract description. To unify terminology, we use the term *representation* for both abstract and concrete forms. An abstraction relation $\succeq$ is defined as a function relating two representations of one single system. A representation $\mathcal{B}$ is an abstraction of representation $\mathcal{A}$, written as $\mathcal{A} \succeq \mathcal{B}$ is defined as:

$$\mathcal{A} \succeq \mathcal{B} \stackrel{\wedge}{=} [\![\mathcal{A}]\!] \Rightarrow [\![\mathcal{B}]\!]$$

which means that $\mathcal{B}$ is an abstraction of $\mathcal{A}$ on the condition that the semantics of $\mathcal{A}$ implicates that of $\mathcal{B}$. Obviously, abstraction is the *inverse of functional refinement.*

A formal notation is used to describe abstraction rules in our study. We have classified the abstraction rules obtained through our study into two categories: *elementary abstraction rules*, rules to abstract source statements into logic formulae, which may be very redundant and specific; and *further abstraction rules*, which extract a more concise and abstract specification from the formulae through compositions and semantics weakening.

Elementary Abstraction Rules. *Elementary abstraction rules* aim to abstract the statements in TGCL and ObTAM to formulae in ITL (the resultant formulae may be redundant, or even "too specific") and these rules can transform source statements into logic formulae, which is a kind of specification.

The statements in TGCL and ObTAM consist of two sets: *simple statements* such as assignment, input and output, and *composite statements* which are a composition of simple statements and composite statements through composition structures, such as a condition, a loop and a procedure. Therefore, elementary abstraction rules fall into two sets correspondingly: the first set named *Primitive Abstraction Rule* converts simple statements to ITL formulae, and the second set named *Compound Abstraction Rule* deals with composite statements.

Primitive Abstraction Rule. The formal definition is as follows:

$$S \succeq LOG(S)$$

where S denotes an uncomposite statement in source code, LOG gives the semantics definition of S in logical form.

Here are two sample instances of primitive abstraction rules.

1. Assignment
   $x := e \succeq x = e$
   This rule extracts a logic formula of the assignment statement which assigns the value of expression e to variable x.
2. Delay
   $delay\ n \succeq len = n$
   Delay means doing nothing during the specified period. This rule extracts a logic formula of the delay statement.

Compound Abstraction Rule. The formal definition of is as follows:

$$\frac{S_i \succeq \Phi_i}{\mathcal{C}(S_i) \succeq f_{\mathcal{C}}(\Phi_i)}$$

where $f_{\mathcal{C}}$ denotes logical construction corresponding to composition operator $\mathcal{C}$, and S_i denotes agents which can be simple statements or composite statements.

Here we give a few instances of compound abstraction rules as examples.

1. Conditional Statement

$\mathcal{A}_i \succeq \Phi_i$ (for all $i \in I$)

$if\ _{i\in I} g_i\ then\ \mathcal{A}_i\ fi \succeq (\bigvee_{i\in I}(g_i \wedge \Phi_i)) \vee (\bigwedge_{i\in I} \neg g_i)$

This rule extracts a logic formula of a conditional statement.

2. Procedure Definition

$\mathcal{A}' \succeq \Phi$

$proc\ P(In\ pin_i : T_i,\ Out\ pout_j : T_j')\{\mathcal{A}'\} \succeq \Phi \wedge (pin_i)$

A procedure definition is abstracted into a separate agent with its input parameters stable and output parameters possibly instable.

3. Parallel

$\mathcal{A} \succeq \Phi,\ \mathcal{B} \succeq \Psi$

$parbegin\ \mathcal{A} \parallel \mathcal{B}\ parend \succeq (\Phi \wedge \Psi)$

Two concurrency or parallel agents can be abstracted separately and the results are combined through the conjunction operator.

Further Abstraction Rules. *Further abstraction rules* aim to extract more concise and abstract specifications from the formulae obtained through applying elementary abstraction rules. Logic composition and semantics weakening are the basis of further abstraction, and during the abstraction domain knowledge may be applied by software engineers.

A few sample instances of further abstraction rules are given as follows.

1. Sequence Folding

$[\![\mathcal{A}\ ;\mathcal{B}]\!] \Rightarrow [\![\mathcal{A} \wedge \mathcal{B}]\!]$

$\mathcal{A}\ ;\mathcal{B} \succeq \mathcal{A} \wedge \mathcal{B}$

If no contradiction is caused when substituting the sequential relation between two agents to conjunction relation, then the sequence can be folded through conjunction.

2. Specification Combination

4.1 $(W_1 : \Phi_1) \wedge (W_2 : \Phi_2) = (W_1 \cup W_2) : \Phi_1 \wedge \Phi_2$

4.2 $(W_1 : \Phi_1) \vee (W_2 : \Phi_2) \succeq (W_1 \cup W_2) : \Phi_1 \vee \Phi_2$

Two specifications with conjunction or disjunction relation can be combined to one single specification.

3. Weakening

$\mathcal{A} \succeq \Phi$

$\Phi \Rightarrow \Psi$

$\mathcal{A} \succeq \Psi$

Any semantics weakening that does not contradict the healthiness condition and makes a better specification of the system can be applied. Semantics weakening is often used together with programming knowledge patterns to eliminate inessential information.

2.3. Programming Knowledge Patterns. Unlike transformation which preserves the semantics of programs unchanged, abstraction endeavors in weakening the original semantics of system implementation. Implementation details which are not directly related with system functions and other key system features, should be abstracted away. However, the identification of these parts irrelevant to specification is one of the most difficult tasks in reengineering, because it requires certain knowledge of the program structure and semantics.

To solve this problem, *programming knowledge patterns* are proposed as an means to describe and identify programming knowledge existing in legacy source code. And then abstraction will be performed with the aid of the identified programming knowledge and relevant abstraction rules.

Programming knowledge, which could be defined as the "technique" or "convention" that a programmer used to implement a program for real applications. The structure of a program was heavily influenced by programming knowledge during implementation. If the programming knowledge embedded in the program could be discovered, it will help to clarify which part of information contained in a program is unnecessary in high-leveled specification.

Programming knowledge can be classified and then described in various patterns. A set of programming knowledge patterns are developed as means to describe and discover programming knowledge in legacy code. Working with further abstraction rules, these patterns play a key role in specification extraction.

Programming knowledge patterns appear in RWSL representation as *pattern assertions.* Based on the diversity of programming knowledge, the patterns are classified into the following categories:

- State Test and Exception Handling. They are often used in programs to assure smooth execution. Although they may be important in system implementation, these details do not involve the crucial functionality of the system. Therefore, in high-level specification, these details are unnecessary and should be abstracted away.
- User Interface Format. Almost all computing systems have to pay some attention to the format of its interface with the user. There are three sorts of so called user interface format: Input Format, Output Format and Graphic User Interface (GUI). For some systems, a rather big part is devoted to making a better user interface format. However, these format-related parts are not involved in the function core of the system and could be left out in specification.
- Semantic Core. The semantic core of a program is the part which covers the program's key functions. In this pattern, if the semantic core could be identified, further abstraction will keep the core but omit other parts of the program.
- Domain Function. Domain functions give more scientific and concise descriptions of the functionality of target systems. If one program part is identified as an implementation of certain domain function, then it should be abstracted back to the domain function in further abstraction. This will make the specification more abstract and concise. For example, $\{x, y\} : (x > 0 \wedge y = y * x \; ; x = x - 1)^{x-1}$ implements $y = x!$. So, it can be abstracted to $\{x, y\} : y = x!$.
- Efficiency-Improving Details. The implementation is often cluttered with information/details to improve the efficiency of the system. These details are normally not function related, and could be abstracted away in high-level specification. For example, use of register variable is to improve the system's efficiency, and therefore the related parts are classified as efficiency-improving details.

3. Case Study. A resultant semi-automatic tool has been developed. Case studies have been carried out with the proposed approach and the tool. Here we use "A Mine Drainage System", a typical case study in real time domain to demonstrate the proposed approach.

Background. The mine drainage system concerns the software necessary to manage a simplified pump control system for a mining environment. The system is used to pump mine water, which collects in a sump at the bottom of the shaft, to the surface. The main safety requirement is that the pump should not be operated when the level of methane gas in the mine reaches a high value due to the risk of explosion. A simple schematic diagram of the system is given in Figure 3.1.

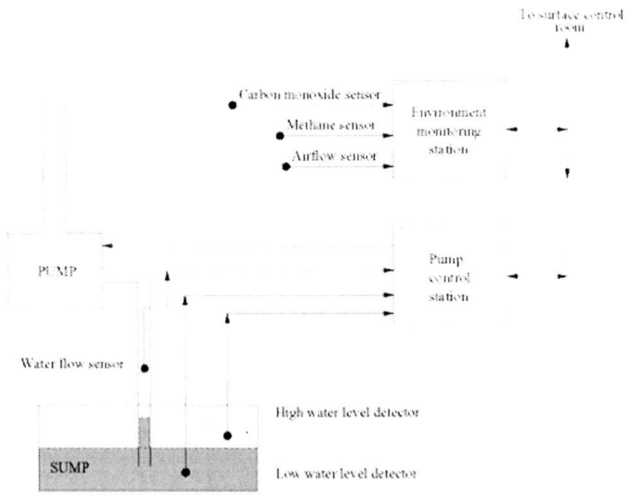

FIG. 3.1. *A mine drainage control system*

The functional specification of the system is divided into four components: the pump operation, the environment monitoring, the operator interaction, and system monitoring.

The required behavior of the pump is that it monitors the water levels in the sump. When the water reaches a high level, the pump is turned on and the sump is drained until the water reaches the low level. At this point, the pump is turned off. A flow of water in the pipe can be detected if required. The pump should be allowed to operate only if methane level in the mine is below a critical level.

The environment must be monitored to detect the level of methane in the air; there is a level beyond which it is not safe to cut coal or operate the pump. The monitoring also measures the level of carbon monoxide in the mine and detects whether there is an adequate flow of air. Alarms must be signaled if gas levels or air-flow become critical.

The non-functional requirements includes three components: timing, dependability and security. This case study is mainly concerned with the timing requirements, which appear as monitoring periods, pump shut-down deadline and operator information deadline.

The complete case study is given in [11]. For conciseness, we use the pump module as an example.

Extracting the Specification. The system is implemented in ADA. As preliminary process, we translated this implementation into CSL.

```
proc motor-unsafe()
  {
     if motor-status=On
     then
        duration in 5ms sw:=Off end;
        motor-status:=Off;
        motor-log(In "motor-stopped")
     fi;
     motor-condition:=Disabled;
     motor-log(In "motor-unsafe")
  };

proc motor-safe()
  {
     if motor-status=Off
     then
        duration in 5ms sw:=On end;
        motor-status:=On;
        motor-log(In "motor-started")
     fi;
     motor-condition:=Enabled;
     motor-log(In "motor-safe")
  };

proc set-pump(In pump-status: Boolean;)
  {
     if pump-status=On
     then if motor-status=Off
          then if motor-condition=Disabled
                 then err-msg(In "pump-not-safe")
                 fi;
                 if ch4-status=Motor-safe
                 then motor-status:=On;
                   duration in 5ms sw:=On end;
                   motor-log(In "motor-started")
                 else err-msg(In "pump-not-safe")
                 fi
          fi
     else if motor-status=On
          then motor-status:=Off;
                 if motor-condition=Enabled
                 then
                   duration in 5ms sw:=Off end;
                   motor-log(In "motor-stopped")
                 fi
          fi
     fi
  };
```

As the first step, we abstract the three procedures separately into ITL specification by applying elementary abstraction rules:

$$motor\text{-}unsafe() \triangleq motor\text{-}status = On \wedge (sw := Off \wedge len \leq 5ms motor\text{-}status := Off$$
$$motor\text{-}log('motro\text{-}stopped'))motor\text{-}condition := Disabled motor\text{-}log('motor\text{-}unsafe')$$

$$motor\text{-}safe() \triangleq motor\text{-}status = Off \wedge (sw := On \wedge len \leq 5ms motor\text{-}status := On$$
$$motor\text{-}log('motor\text{-}started'))motor\text{-}condition := Enabled motor\text{-}log('motor\text{-}safe')$$

$$set\text{-}pump(pump\text{-}status) \triangleq$$

$(pump\text{-}status = On \wedge$
$(motor\text{-}status = Off \wedge$
$(motor\text{-}condition = Disabled \wedge err\text{-}msg('pump\text{-}not\text{-}safe'))$
$(ch4\text{-}status = Motor\text{-}safe \wedge (motor\text{-}status := Onsw := On \wedge len \leq 5ms$
$motor\text{-}log('motor\text{-}started')))$
$\vee(ch4\text{-}status = Motor\text{-}unsafe \wedge err\text{-}msg('pump\text{-}not\text{-}safe'))))$
$\vee(pump\text{-}status = Off \wedge$
$motor\text{-}status = On \wedge (motor\text{-}status := Off$
$motor\text{-}condition = Enabled \wedge (sw := Off \wedge len \leq 5ms motor\text{-}log('motor\text{-}stopped'))))$

In the above specification, there are several things need to abstract. Firstly, some "chop" operator could be replaced by logic conjunction, and therefore resulting in further logic composition. Secondly, there are quite a lot exception test and handling detail in the specification. For example, when methane level is not safe or motor condition is disabled the system gives out error message and take no action. A "state test and exception handling" programming knowledge pattern is identified by recognition of the condition branch and error message reporting. In high level specification, this kind of description is considered as implementation-related details and therefore be abstracted away with further abstraction rules (in this case, sequence folding and weakening). A more abstracted specification is given as follows:

$motor\text{-}unsafe() \triangleq motor\text{-}status = On \wedge (sw := Off \wedge len \leq 5ms motor\text{-}status := Off$
$\wedge motor\text{-}log('motro\text{-}stopped'))motor\text{-}condition := Disabled \wedge motor\text{-}log('motor\text{-}unsafe')$

$motor\text{-}safe() \triangleq motor\text{-}status = Off \wedge (sw := On \wedge len \leq 5ms motor\text{-}status := On$
$\wedge motor\text{-}log('motor\text{-}started'))motor\text{-}condition := Enabled \wedge motor\text{-}log('motor\text{-}safe')$

$set\text{-}pump(pump\text{-}status) \triangleq$
$(pump\text{-}status = On \wedge motor\text{-}status = Off \wedge ch4\text{-}status = Motor\text{-}safe \wedge$
$(motor\text{-}status := Onsw := On \wedge len \leq 5ms motor\text{-}log('motor\text{-}started')))$
$\vee(pump\text{-}status = Off \wedge motor\text{-}status = On \wedge$
$(motor\text{-}status := Off motor\text{-}condition = Enabled \wedge (sw := Off \wedge len \leq 5ms$
$motor\text{-}log('motor\text{-}stopped'))))$

The log function is not directly related with system function. A "semantic core" pattern could be discovered with expert intervene, and then the log-related part is abstracted away:

$motor\text{-}unsafe() \triangleq motor\text{-}status = On \wedge (sw := Off \wedge len \leq 5ms motor\text{-}status := Off)$
$motor\text{-}condition := Disabled$

$motor\text{-}safe() \triangleq motor\text{-}status = Off \wedge (sw := On \wedge len \leq 5ms motor\text{-}status := On)$
$motor\text{-}condition := Enabled$

$set\text{-}pump(pump\text{-}status) \triangleq$
$(pump\text{-}status = On \wedge motor\text{-}status = Off \wedge ch4\text{-}status = Motor\text{-}safe \wedge$
$(motor\text{-}status := Onsw := On \wedge len \leq 5ms))$
$\vee(pump\text{-}status = Off \wedge motor\text{-}status = On \wedge$
$(motor\text{-}status := Off motor\text{-}condition = Enabled \wedge sw := Off \wedge len \leq 5ms))$

The final specification is precise and concise. Through it, it is easier to understand the functional behavior of the program. The involved time constrain is the switch on/off operation of the pump should be accomplished within 5 milliseconds. This specification can then be used as the foundation of further system improvement and forward engineering.

4. Related Work. Existing research closely related to our work (formal and informal) on software abstraction for reverse engineering has been studied when our approach and tool were developed. Here only several most related projects are briefly discussed.

Transformation-based Maintenance Model (TMM) is a method proposed in [1] for recovering abstractions and design decisions that were made during implementation. The abstractions and design decisions of software must be recovered first before the software is re-implemented. [9] proposed "A Concept Recognition-Based Program Transformation System", whose characteristic is its use of concept recognition, the understanding and abstraction of high-level programming and domain entities in programs, as the basis for transformations. Four understanding levels are defined: the text level, the syntactic level, the semantic level, and the concept level. The program transformation system depends on its program understanding capabilities up to the concept level. The key component is a concept library which contains the knowledge about programming and application domain concepts, and concept recognition is done by pattern matching. REFORM project developed a tool named the Maintainer's Assistant to assist the human maintainer, handling assembler and Z in an easy to use way [3, 15]. One of the most important successes of Maintainer's Assistant is that it is based on a wide spectrum language whose syntax and semantics are formally defined. Maintainer's Assistant focused on transformation rather than abstraction. It involved little in how to use multi-leveled abstractions and relevant abstraction rules to reach a good system reengineering, especially reverse engineering. The Wide Spectrum Language in Maintainer's Assistant is sequential and non-timed, which limits its application domains. Research in University of California at San Diego [10] based their approach to reverse engineering on abstraction, and identified three kinds of abstractions: problem domain, structural, and logical. This work is not formalized and did not have multiple abstraction levels with an integrated formal semantics. These may limit the accuracy and power of their approach. PRISME is a reverse engineering tool based on functional abstraction [2] but the abstraction in PRISME is function-based instead of semantics-based. It does not engage a mature formal method to specify the target system, and PRISME extracts "signatures" as pieces of outline description of the system, instead of complete specification. AUTOSPEC project [5, 6] involves a two-phase approach to reverse engineering that integrate a process for abstracting formal specifications from program code with a technique for identifying candidate objects in program code. A prototype tool was built. This project deals with the first abstraction step of reverse engineering, i.e., it extracts lowest level specifications, in the form of predicate logic as a notation of the source code.

To summarize, although many aspects of reengineering have been researched into, using formal abstraction rules together with programming knowledge to extract formal specifications from code is rarely addressed. The above listed studies solved some closely-related problems, such as transformation and part of informal abstraction. However, none of them engages in extracting semantics-consistent formal specifications from source code through abstraction. Abstraction levels are not clearly defined. Abstraction to be used in a "real-time" system has been rarely addressed. Techniques for coping with crossing levels of abstraction covering all abstraction levels need close research. Where genuine crossing of levels of abstraction occurs, this is done manually.

5. Conclusion. A formal reengineering approach with an emphasis on reverse engineering using program abstraction is proposed. Programming knowledge is discovered through relevant patterns to facilitate program abstraction. A supporting tool based on the approach is developed to scale and to speed up practical reengineering. A formal framework based on ITL semantics was developed and it is implemented in a wide spectrum language, RWSL. We have formalized program abstraction within a reengineering environment in such a way that a semi-automatic tool is feasible. The abstraction problem has been addressed by software engineering researchers for years but dedicated approaches used in a reengineering environment with both concurrency and real-time features have been non-existent.

The specification produced is then understood and used as basis of enhanced specification for forward engineering the system. Before proceeding, the specification may be changed and/or extended with extra non-functional requirement(s) that we require (e.g. reliability, dependability, limited resources, etc.)

Through the discussion in this paper, it can be concluded that program abstraction together with programming knowledge patterns is a powerful means for reverse engineering and a systematic approach of reengineering, together with an intelligent supporting tool, such as the one proposed in this paper will help reengineering and software evolution.

REFERENCES

[1] Arango, G., Baxter, I., Freeman, P., and Pidgeon, C. TMM: Software maintenance by transformation. *IEEE Software* (May 1986), 27–39.

[2] Balmas, F. Prisme: Formalizing programming strategies as a way to understand programs. In *Eighth International Conference on Software Engineering and Knowledge Engineering* (Lake Tahoe, Nevada, June 1996), IEEE Computer Society.

[3] Bennett, K. H., Bull, T., and Yang, H. A transformation system for maintenance — turning theory into practice. In *IEEE Conference on Software Maintenance-1992* (Orlando, Florida, November 1992).

[4] Cau, A., and Zedan, H. Refining interval temporal logic specifications. In *the 4th AMAST Workshop on Real-Time systems, Concurrent, and Distributed Software (ARTS'97)* (Mallorca, Spain, May 1997).

[5] Cheng, B. H. C. Applying formal methods in automated software development. *Journal of Computer and Software Engineering 2* (Feburary 1994), 137–164.

[6] Cheng, B. H. C., and Jeng, J. J. Reusing analogous components. *IEEE Transactions on Knowledge and Data Engineering* (November 1994).

[7] Dijkstra, E. W. *A Discipline of Programming*. Prentice-Hall, Englewood Cliffs, New Jersey, 1976.

[8] Dijkstra, E. W., and Scholten, C. S. *Predicate Calculus and Program Semantics*. Springer-Verlag, 1990.

[9] Engberts, A., Kozaczynski, W., and Ning, J. Concept recognition-based program transformation. In *IEEE Conference on Software Maintenance-1991* (Sorrento, Italy, 1991), pp. 73–82.

[10] Howden, W. E., and Pak, S. Problem domain, strutural and logical abstractions in reverse engineering. In *Proceedings of the International Conference on Software Maintenance 1992* (November 1992), IEEE Computer Society Press, pp. 214–224.

[11] Liu, X. Abstraction: A notion for reverse engineering. *PhD Thesis, De Montfort University* (1999).

[12] Liu, X., Yang, H., and Zedan, H. Formal methods for the re-engineering of computing systems. In *the Proceedings of The 21st IEEE International Conference on Computer Software and Application (COMPSAC'97)* (Washington, D.C., August 1997), IEEE Computer Society, pp. 409–414.

[13] Moszkowski, B. *Executing Temporal Logic Programs*. Cambridge University Press, Cambridge UK, 1986.

[14] SCHOLEFIELD, D., ZEDAN, H., AND HE, J. A specification-oriented semantics for the refinement of real-time systems. *Theoretical Computer Science 130* (August 1994).

[15] YANG, H., AND BENNETT, K. H. Aquairing entity-relationship attribute diagrams from code and data through program transformation. In *IEEE International Conference on Software Maintenance (ICSM '95)* (Nice, France, October 1995).

[16] YANG, H., LIU, X., AND ZEDAN, H. Tackling the abstraction problem for reverse engineering in a system re-engineering approach. In *the proceedings of the IEEE Conference on Software Maintenance (ICSM'98)* (Metropolitan, Washington D.C., USA, November 1998), IEEE Computer Society.

[17] M. GOOSSENS, F. MITTELBACH, AND A. SAMARIN, *The LaTeX Companion*, Addison-Wesley, Reading, MA, 1994.

[18] N. J. HIGHAM, *Handbook of Writing for the Mathematical Sciences*, Society for Industrial and Applied Mathematics, Philadelphia, PA, 1993.

[19] L. LAMPORT, LaTeX: *A Document Preparation System*, Addison-Wesley, Reading, MA, 1986.

[20] R. SEROUL AND S. LEVY, *A Beginner's Book of* TeX, Springer-Verlag, Berlin, New York, 1991.

In: Focus on Computational Neurobiology
Editor: Lei Li, pp. 191-205

ISBN 1-59033-915-0

AN AGENT ORIENTED APPROACH FOR DIAGNOSIS AND SUPERVISION OF INDUSTRIAL PROCESSES

AZIZ EL FAZZIKI*

Abstract. Generally, an IPCS should reconcile two contradictory properties: reacting in real time to the solicitations of the environment and operating out some evolved reasoning in order to meet these solicitations. This paper, proposes an approach where the system is considered as composition of three sub-systems. A reactive sub-system taking into account the control, the surveillance of the IP. An evaluating sub-systems that watch out for the functioning safety and the breakdowns prediction. A supervising sub-system taking into account the diagnosis and the supervision of the IP. This approach proposes a diagnosis architecture using the Data Mining techniques. These techniques enable to answer different tasks of the diagnosis such as the selection of pertinent indicators, the generation of breakdown cases, the prediction and more particularly, the temporal and spatial dependencies of the IP.

Key words. industrial process, reactive sub-system, evaluating sub-system, supervising sub-system, Data Mining, temporal dependencies, spatial dependencies

1. Introduction. The complexity of the industrial processes (IP) [1] and their requirements (security, flexibility, availability, etc.) can be considered as constraints to satisfy. Generally, an industrial process control system(IPCS) will be to link between two opposite properties : to react in continuously real time to the evolution of the process environment, and to react intelligently through an evolved

reasoning in order to answer some complex and unpredictable situations. The actions of a classic IPCS are based on the analysis of measurements according to some predefined patterns. This way of operating is very rigid and leads sometimes to some out of place reactions. To introduce more flexibility in the IPCS, some tools coming from the Artificial Intelligence (AI) were introduced. For instance the Expert Systems (ES), are used especially in diagnosis. An IPCS is endowed with a reasoning and a deliberation before any reaction. This approach didn't enjoy an important success, because of the limited adaptability of the ES to the dynamic environment [2].

1.1. The available approaches. In order to correct the weakness of the IPCS, several approaches were used. These approaches are of two categories:

- Approaches based on numeric modeling: they are based on modeling the states of a system according to different ways of which we can quote for, instance:
- physical Modeling : this approach is quite practical when the system is simple and the equations of the states are known. However, this approach cannot be used when the system is too complex to be modeled with simple equations. Sometimes these equations can't even be identified [3].
- Modeling by classes of states : it concerns the classification of the states in progress as a set of predefined classes. Then, it is necessary to recognize the state of the system thanks to the measured variables among the different states. This approach is typical to some Patterns recognition (PR) and can be used in the setting of diagnosis also. Mourot, Bousghiri and Boar [4] applied the methods of Patterns recognition (PR) to the diagnosis of technological systems.
- Approaches based on reasoning : These are approaches based on the expert systems: the use of the ESs for the industrial processes diagnosis offers many more opportu-

* Faculty of Sciences Semlalia-Department of computing BP 2390 Marrakech Morocco Email : elfazziki@ucam.ac.ma

nities for solving a problem of precise diagnosis. Moreover, their maintenance and updating increase the cost of their exploitation. The bigger reproach that could be addressed to these approaches is that they are rarely real IPCSs [5].

- Approaches based on the cooperative ES : the cooperative ESs have the particularity of generating some trees of hypothesis for their diagnosis. This approach uses a kind of cooperation where the results are basically shared. That allows accelerating the process of diagnosis and produces some more detailed results [2]. It could be improved by using some cooperative information systems. These systems remind the software databases management that offer some general searching engines that are a little bit different from the inference engine of the ES and could be used with a slight modification [4].

1.2. The main characteristics of an IPCS. The previous works and analyses of approaches led us to think that, in order to carry out its mission an IPCS, should be characterized by the following properties [6] :

- The system reactivity toward its governed environment. That is to say, the system has the ability of reacting continuously to the events that could occur uncertainly.
- The system punctuality toward the fixed deadlines. These deadlines could be dynamic in the phase of exploitation and this property requires from the IPCS the ability of adapting itself dynamically to new deadlines.
- The behavioral predictability of the IP. That is to say the ability to foresee its potential behavior according to the environment behavior and thereafter, the possibility of proving the logical and temporal correction of the IP.
- The surveillance could be defined as a succession of operations aiming the detecting and diagnosing of the internal and external shortcomings as well as the abnormal modes of unusual operating of an IP.
- The supervision, in presence of shortcomings, should allow managing the (multicriteria) compromises between the exploitation and the maintenance which is indeed opposite to exploitation and production imperatives. The decision of the maintenance leads to the interruption of the mission in order to restore the process and fix it in a surely operating state [7].

1.3. Objectives and organization. This paper proposes an agent-based architecture permitting the control and the supervision of the industrial processes. An IPCS should answer two opposite needs: reacting in real time to the solicitations of the environment and building an evolved reasoning in order to answer these solicitations. To this end, this work distinguishes three kinds of agents : the reactive agents that implement the logical and temporal control of the system, the evaluating agents and supervising agents (cognitive agents) that implement the functions and some complex techniques of reasoning and of diagnosis. The remainder of this paper is organized as follows. Section 2 presents the different stages of diagnosis and of prediction. Section 3 presents the approach used. Sections 4, 5 and 6 describe the different types of agents of the system with their functionality. Finally section 7 concludes the paper and presents some perspectives.

2. Diagnosis and Prediction.

2.1. The diagnosis. The IPs are more and more complex, it is necessary to supervise them permanently so that they could warn out of any incident, detect the breakdowns and maintain a high service quality. Therefore, the diagnosis of an IP is an important but difficult task. It could be defined through quoting tree levels (cf Fig. 2.1) : generation of alarms (abnormal states of the IP) from measurements on an IP (observing : the detection of disrupted states in the IP); the filtering and the interpretation of alarms (understanding : the processing of alarms for a better understanding of the phenomenon taking place) and commands the process (Acting : how to put the system back in its normal state)[8][9].

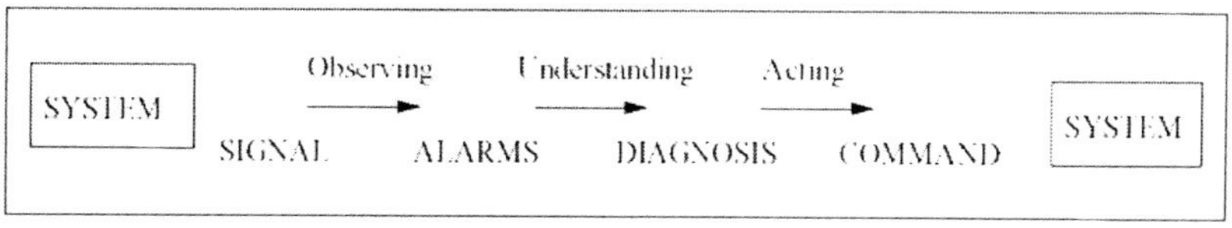

FIG. 2.1. *Diagnosis steps applied to an IP*

2.1.1. The Observing step. The goal of this first step is to generate some alarms corresponding to the anomalous states of the IP, starting from the signal processing (the variable) measured on this IP. The first problem consists in identifying the existing abnormal states. This knowledge is often well provided by the experts in the domain, but we should note that certain systems of diagnosis can take into account automatically the occurring of new unsettled states. Another problem consists in determining, if possible, what is the applicable variable in order to detect the unsettled states. Most of the cases, it comes to selecting the most applicable variable and to eliminating the useless or redundant variables among those already existing. The last problem is the alarms generation. Thus, there exists two kinds of approaches. The first one is the modeling and detection approach (it is necessary to represent the different states of the system first). The second is the approach through direct discrimination among the different states of the IP (it is necessary to recognize directly the state of the IP thanks to the measured variable [4].

2.1.2. The understanding step. As soon as some anomalous situations are detected in a complex IP, several alarms are generated in different places of the IP. Now it is necessary to determine what is the reason behind such alarms and what breakdown took place and where?. This task is held on different operations of the filtering. The alarms could come from the same origin at different instants (temporal filtering) and / or from different origins (spatial filtering) [10]. Several techniques can be used to deal with these different operations :

- Symbolic Training : Some methods as the case based reasoning allows to sort the most important alarms in order to find the source of the breakdown. These approaches are often associated to the methods of alarm generations by modeling [11].
- Bayesian Networks (BN) : the alarms and the breakdowns are considered as some events tied through some conditional probabilities in a causal graph. Therefore, it is possible to infer the probabilities of the different breakdowns to leave some probabilities of alarms and some conditional probabilities. The BNs are used in many domains. We can quote for example, the system Visa [12] developed by Microsoft for the NASA. This system allows the interpretation of the telemetry in real time and gives an opinion on the verisimilitude of different breakdowns in the propulsion systems of the space shuttle. Morjaia and Al [12] also uses the BN in

the diagnosis of electric energy stations.
- The statistical methods: as the Neural Networks (NN) or the Patterns of Markov chains (MC) allow to take into account the information contained in the temporal sequences of numeric alarms [12].

2.1.3. The Acting step. As soon as the disruption is known and localized thanks to the different alarms, it is often necessary to act on the system and propose an adequate correction (command) so that the system resumes its normal state. When the system is supervised and ordered by an operator, it is also possible to provide some complementary information. This information allows to determine quickly the adapted order (command). At this level, there exist several approaches again in automation [5][10]. In this work, we will not deal with the reactive part of IPCS.

2.2. Forecasting / Prediction. The forecasting of an event is often expressed most as the probability that an event occurs (Knowing the causes, what will be the effects?). However, this forecasting could vary according to external events. The prediction goes farther than the forecasting since it specifies its time. The interest of the prediction in matter of diagnosis is to predict as far as possible the coming date of a breakdown and to anticipate the breakdowns as possible in order to save time to reorganize and update the system. This is about the seeking to predict the future evolution of a temporal set from a limited sequence of measurements (sizes measured on the IP) done at the end of regular time intervals. Say X(1), X(2)., X(n), where X(i) corresponds to the measured value at the i instant. The laws that govern the system generating these data are unknown. In this case the system needs to know the cases of the breakdowns before it becomes able to recognize them while the system is operating.

3. The used approach.

3.1. General Profile. The aim of our work is the setting up of an architecture and of a solution based on a multi-agents framework that allows to weave the reactive system by an assessing and a supervising system. Each reactive agent is coupled to two cognitive agents (cf. Fig. 3.1) : The first one is an evaluating agent and the second one is a supervising agent. The coupling of these agents allows to preserve the autonomy and can easily integrate the pre-existing systems. In our approach, we advocate the use of such a multi-agents system where the co-operation is based on the exchange of possible breakdowns cases. This kind of co-operation proves out to be very efficient and more general than those of ESs [14]. We consider a breakdown case as a list of breakdown characteristic symptoms and a list of measurements. The co-operation among agents is achieved by the exchange of possible breakdown cases. This requires the elaboration of some exchange mechanisms and tests in a distributed manner. So, an IPCS is composed of tree sub-systems: a reactive sub-system in charge of the control and the surveillance of the IP: an evaluating sub-system in charge of the functioning safety, the prediction of the breakdowns; a supervising sub-system ensuring the diagnosis and the supervision of the IP.

3.2. Multi-Agents Systems.

3.2.1. Definition. An agent [13] is a physical or abstract entity that is able to act on itself and on its environment. It arranges a partial representation of this environment and can communicate with other agents. It realizes an individual objective and its behavior is the consequence of its observations, knowledge, expertise and interactions that it can have with other agents and with the environment. In an IPCS, an agent is composed mainly

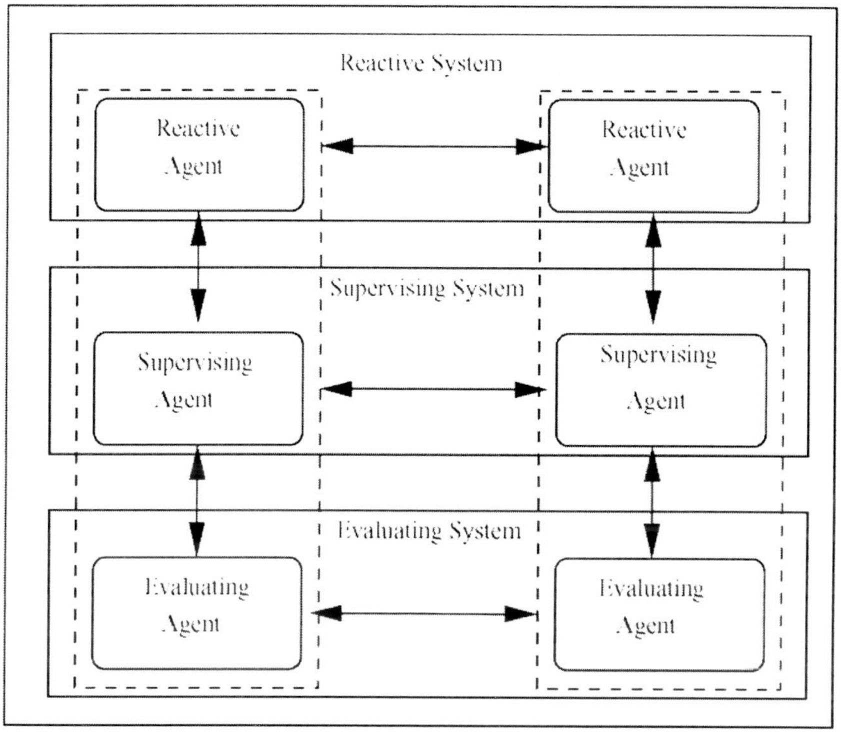

FIG. 3.1. *Global architecture of an IPCS*

of two kinds of tasks: the control tasks (resources control) and the generic tasks (its own execution control, communication with the environment, communication with the other agents, updating of certain variables, the breakdowns diagnosis, supervision of the process) [1][13]. A MAS for the industrial process control is a set of agents permitting to assure the surveillance, the control and the supervision of a physical phenomenon. It distinguishes itself of the other computer systems by the fact that it is in interaction with the real world. It must permit the expression of all concepts characterizing an IP and should satisfy the constraints that it imposes.

3.3. Distinctive characters of a MAS. Generally, in the theory of AMAS (Adaptive multi-agents systems) [14], an agent is endowed with competence, possibilities of communication or interaction with the other agents and with its environment, of belief on some other agents of the system, capacities to argue, and of a social attitude based on cooperation. Each agent behavior is specified in such a way that it should trie to reach its own objective while keeping cooperative interactions with the others. Before any action, the agent analyzes locally if it is or not in cooperative interactions. More exactly, it checks whether there exist non cooperative situations, and if that was the case, tries to eliminate them to return to a cooperative state. Cooperation is the social attitude which drives the each agent behavior in accordance with local criteria. Thus, An agent has two essential roles : The first one is to realize the function for which it was specified and the second is, if it meets no cooperative situations, it should act on the internal organization of the system, with the aim of returning to cooperative state. We can distinguish two kinds of MAS; firstly, the agent structure is reduced much as possible and it is essentially functional. It is the domain of the reactive agents, simulating intelligent real- time mechanisms of surveillance [15][16]. Secondly, the agent structures are complex and we consider these as endowed with knowledge and meta-knowledge. They are said cognitive agents. The construction of these agent systems can be made by leaning partially on the object paradigm. There is then an elementary level of the system entities in which these are permanent and regular. It is the components level that can be completely seen as objects. Thus, the agent level corresponds to an organizational and functional modeling over objects, where those are admitted to form entities in the variable behavioral dynamics [15]. Generally, most IPCS modeling approaches are not sufficient to conceive IPCS by multi-agent systems, they do not take into account the main agent characteristics : autonomy and sociability as well as the complexity of interactions and the system dynamic. That is why, much research work nowadays focuses concerning the designing methods are oriented agents [17], [18], [19] and [20].

3.4. The proposed Approach. In our approach, we propose a classification of the various IPCS tasks into the following three component categories [1][5][16] :

- Basic entities, which establish(constitute) the elementary components of the IPCS, which are going, once ordered, to form its basic structure (reactive agents). These agents react to the external stimuli by elaborating immediate answers. Their main tasks are the control and the surveillance of the PI. Considering the natural distribution of the sensors and the functions of treatment which characterize all IPCS, these agents implement the logical and temporal control of the system. Among their main characteristics we can quote : the ability to react, the punctuality, the adaptability and the priority.
- Entities having in charge the analysis and the evaluating of the various variables of the IP (evaluating agents). These evaluating agents are in charge of the functioning safety and the possible breakdown prediction.
- Entities having in charge the supervision and the effectual means of spatial and temporal action on the environment (supervisor agent). These agents allow the substratum of the IPCS to have an active behavior to reach their objectives. Contrary to the reactive agents, the supervisor agents implement functions and complex techniques (reasoning, diagnosis, supervision) [5]. These three agent categories form the substratum of an IPCS. They allow it to put its identical action in its environment. Therefore, the whole system will be organized in a set of communicating agents. The cooperation between agents is realized by the exchange of possible breakdowns cases. This requires the elaboration of exchange mechanisms and test in a distributed way. So, every site of the IPCS will consist of a sub-system constituted with a reactive agents having in charge the control and the surveillance, evaluating agents having in charge the functioning safety and the prediction of possible breakdowns and an supervisor agent having in charge of the diagnosis and the supervision of the PI. To carry out their tasks, we propose on the one hand, the use of Data Mining techniques (cf Fig. 3.2) for the tasks of prediction, diagnosis and supervision. Others part the active use of data base for the control and the surveillance.

3.5. Data Mining. The objective of using the Data Mining Techniques [21][22] is to improve the knowledge and get the pertinent information in order to undertake an action to be carried out, in analyzing facts and translating them into data. Data Mining is used

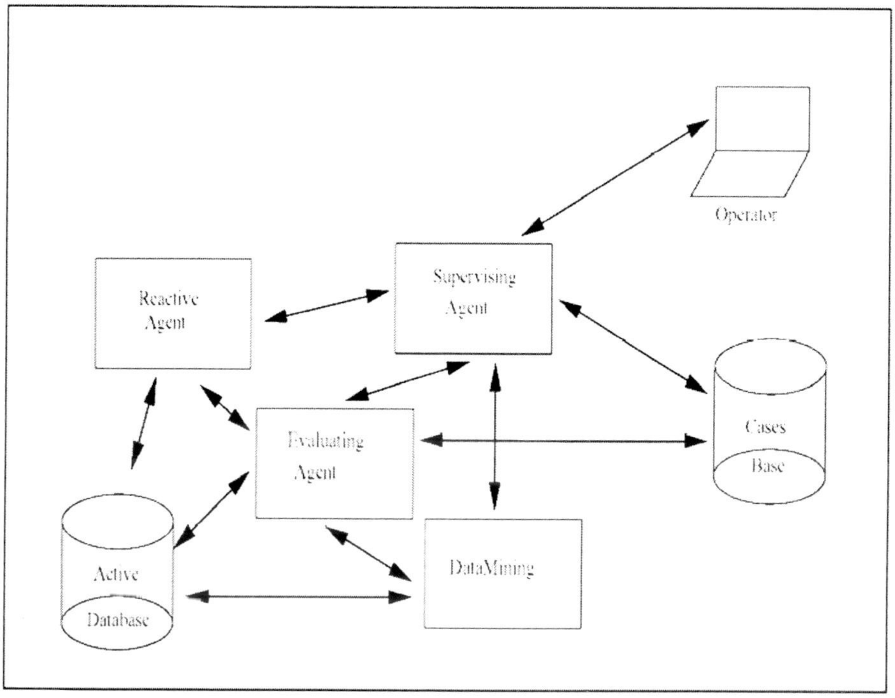

FIG. 3.2. *A site architecture*

in : exploring, analyzing, diagnosing, proposing some corrections following the evolution and collecting new data. Most Data Mining Techniques are complementary. They are very often used together in order to improve the quality of the predictions. In our approach, we propose the use of different Data Mining methods (Bayesian Networks, Neural Networks, Case based Reasoning, Decision Trees and tools of analysis and selection of variables).

3.6. Active Databases and IPCS.

3.6.1. Active Database. Contrarily to the usual data bases (so-called passive), the only operation allowed on an active database is the insertion of news relations [23]. In our system, an active relation could be created by an operator or a reactive agent. For each passive relation, the agents create some active relations containing respectively some inserted, suppressed or modified relations. In addition to the concept of active relations, there is the concept of active definite requests on the active relations. Contrarily to a passive request which is executed on the relations in the state during the request, an active request continues acting as progressively as new relations are inserted in the active relations. An active request concerns the past, present and future data while a passive request is concerned only with the past or present data. Each active relation is associated with a set of triggers. The trigger model could be a model with an immediate coupling of both the event and the condition as well as different models of coupling between condition and action. To be noted are [24] :

- A temporal coupling which ascertains if the action is executed in a synchronous or asynchronous way with regard to the initial transaction.
- Assertional Coupling which specifies if the execution of the action is immediate or deferred to the end of the transaction (solely compatible with a temporal synchronous coupling). A condition is a predicate that could bear upon any relation that is active or non-active. These different data bases with their systems of management constitute a co-operative information system for the control and the supervision of industrial process. This information system is constituted of two subsystems:
- A static subsystem : The co-operative information system is a network of interconnected knowledge bases. A request is transmitted by an agent to the network and the objective is here of grouping the facts and basic rules of knowledge in order to answer the request.
- A dynamic subsystem : The co-operative information system is a network of expert systems disposing each one of causal rules allowing to predict the behavior of the IP. The objective is of grouping these causal rules in order to answer to a problem of temporal projection. The modeling of this co-operative information system could be perceived by using an approach based on the negotiation and the explanations among system agents. The different components (databases) of co-operative system are managed by the reactive agents that communicate and cooperate among them with a view of satisfying their solicitations as well as those of the operators.

3.6.2. Environment of an IPCS. Generally, an IP could be described and characterized by the following concepts (variable, action, chain of actions, causal relations or laws of command) [1] :

- A variable is a size measure of the process, that gives account of the process state at a given time by means of data value.
- An action is an applied elementary operation to the IP, either directly or indirectly, through the intermediary of an operator.
- A chain of actions is a set of necessary actions to the realization of a process objective. The absence of one action of this set puts to risk the realization of this objective.
- A law of command is a relation set among variables and triggering of actions that express the temporal evolution of actions and secure the evolution conditions of activities as well as processing pertaining to each condition. Its general expression is of the kind "in coming of every message and if a condition is satisfied, trigger the corresponding actions".

The whole IPCS environment is composed by [1] :

- Inputs that are messages from the environment towards it, they correspond to the taking into account the variables of the IP.
- Outputs that are messages from the IPCS toward the environment that can result in operations on the IP.
- Communication among IPCS components(agents).
- Temporary and persistent variables.

3.6.3. Active Databases and IPCS analogy. Formally, an IPCS (S), could be described as : S = (E, R(E, S),S) with E set of inputs, S a set of outputs, R a causal relation among the system inputs and outputs. As example : If $e \in E$, $s \in S$, and $r \in R$, if e r s and the corresponding law of command is satisfied then execute s (r: causal relation between e and s) [1]. In order to take into account the mechanism of the rules, it is necessary to take into accounts the way in which a rule is modeled and the way in which it is executed. The modeling rule concerns [23][24]: 1- the specification of the events, some conditions (rule structures), 2- the part of the database that the rule can referee (the rule associate context) and 3- the way in which the concept of rule is included in the database mode. The execution concerns the activation of the rule, that is to say the detection of an event occurrence, followed by the assessment of conditions on the data base and eventually by the execution of actions if its conditions are satisfied. An active rule could be modeled by the formalism (event, condition, actions) (ECA) [23][24]. Thus, we could define the correspondence between the formalism (E,C,A) and the formalism(E,R(E,S),S). An input corresponds to an event, an output corresponds to an action and the causal relations correspond to the conditions.

4. The evaluating agent (EA).

4.1. Functionality.. The main function of the evaluating agent is to take into account the functioning safety imperatives through the identification of the breakdown scripts. However, the EA allows to take into account the appearance of shortcomings and their features in order to adjust the data in the evaluating quantitative models of the functioning safety. It uses some tools (Data Mining) of characterization and of generalization of the different variables characterizing the IP evolution in time. These different variables are stored on an active data base. It uses the experience feedback consisting of a collection of information to put forward the system behavior (expert opinion, the functioning observations). Therefore, the development of methods allowing to synthesize the feed back of the experience and to take out some pertinent information seem to be necessary for the setting up of preferment studies of the functioning safety [5]. In order to use these tools fully, the evaluating agent should

prepare and analyze the data, represent, refine and propose some hypothesis of breakdown cases (predicted cases) to the supervising agent for a potential validation.

4.2. Prediction steps. In order to predict a case, the evaluating agent proceeds by steps (cf Fig. 4.1):

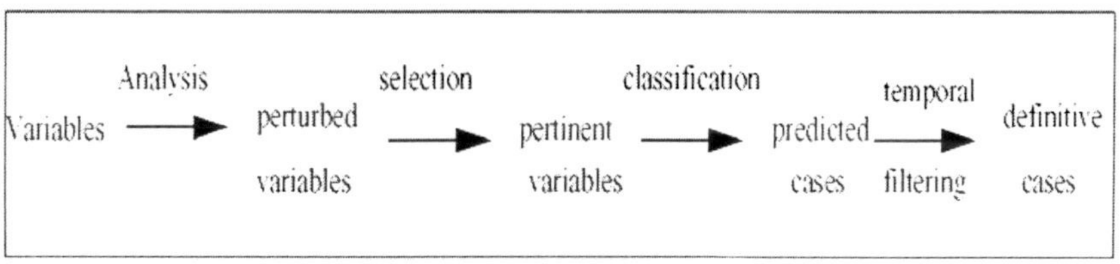

FIG. 4.1. *prediction steps*

4.3. Analysis and selection of variables. To detect the abnormal situations, the EA uses a Data Mining tool [21][22]. The AE proceeds to the analysis of the different variables of the process stored in a temporal data base in order to determine the unsettled variables and the pertinent ones. The constitution of a breakdown case predicted is decided with the help of Neural Networks (NN) already trained by the expert on the known breakdowns in the domain. This NN takes into account the breakdown cases occurring while operating and that are not foretold in the practice.

4.4. Classification by Neural Networks. The NN takes as inputs a list of the tackled variable values at the t instant (cf. Fig. 4.2) and provides a list of breakdown cases. Say, X1, X2..Xn the selected measurable variable and Xi (t): measurement of Xi at the instant t. Actually, we get at the output a list of weights that are interpreted as some

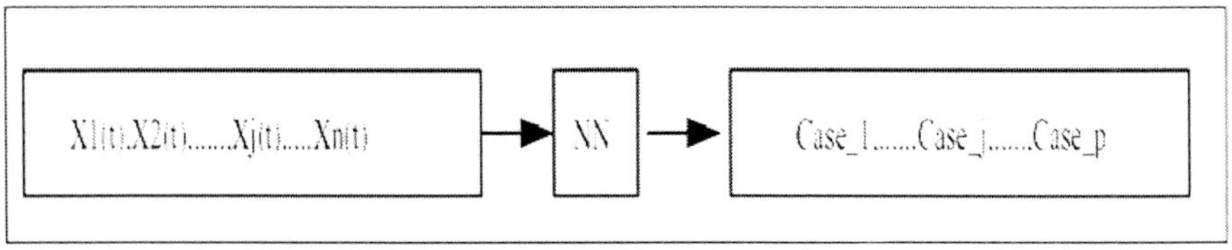

FIG. 4.2. *Neural Networks for the classification of the possible breakdown cases*

evaluations on the breakdown cases. The decision of a breakdown case is taken according to two rules: 1) If p ((casej)) (t) ¿ (tolerated) then casej is a possible breakdown case. 2) If p (casej) increases with time then (casej) is a possible breakdown case. P ((casej)) (t) : output value of NN for (casej) at the instant t.

5. The supervising agent (SA).

5.1. Functionality. The SA is characterized by some functions and relations among the SA and other agents of the IPCS. It has two essential goals:

- in case of a breakdown, to find out the reasons and act according to these reasons starting from the case base. This base is built on the basis of some breakdowns provided by experts in the domain [6].
- To foresee the happening of a breakdown according to the information coming from different sources. The evaluating agent feeding this SA. This feeding is performed through some analyzed data that could be the source of a possible breakdown case. The feeding is done from all the messages provided by other supervising agents, reactive agents and the operator orders also. According to the quoted goals, the SA operates in two states:
- Emergency state : the SA detects the reasons why a real breakdown happens and is quoted by the reactive agent. The breakdown can stop partially or completely the functioning of the system. The SA should act quickly in order to solve the problem.
- Current state : the SA receives the information as a hypothesis of possible breakdowns that can happen a posteriori. Actually, in this situation the task of the SA becomes helpful or even necessary since the problem consists in fixing the IP at first and thus avoiding the freezing situation. Another interesting consequence is to warn out the operator about the possible breakdowns through listing the conditions and finding the appropriate conclusions. Thus, we have adopted a Data Mining tool that is the case based reasoning (CBR) [5][21].

5.2. Diagnosis steps. To every solicitation by the reactive agent or the evaluating agent (quoted or predicted breakdown case), the SA establishes the list of the most similar breakdown cases relevant to the studied case (cf. Fig. 5.1). These cases are classified by order of a similarity degree. A solution is proposed for each case. The results obtained for each case are expressed in terms of similarity percentage for each symptom and of percentage of global similarity. In order to identify the suitable solution, the SA selects the closest case. If the solution turns inadequate, the SA could select an other case within the list. Once applied and adopted, the solution is added to the case base. When the number of the processed cases reaches a certain rate of the initial case base, it is recommended to restart a new phase of indexing. The search for similarities is built starting from the identification of keywords. That can lead to two kinds of problems:

- the case is indexed with several key words. Each case will look as a possible diagnosis.
- on the contrary, the case is indexed with few key words. In this situation, the case can never be identified. The selection of the key words is therefore fundamental. For example, a breakdown referring to oil leaking can be associated with the key words heat, noise, loss of strength but also temperature and jingling. The risk of a strong degradation of the CBR performances increases with
  the dimension of indexing (several key words). The successive addition of new indexing keys, leads necessarily to reducing the efficiency of the RBC. In order to correct this problem, one of the present issues of research consists in rebuilding the indications of indexing in an automated way using some techniques of the decision trees [5].

5.3. Local Diagnosis and RBC. The generation of breakdown cases is done in two steps : the SA determines first what are the indicators of the most relevant breakdowns in order to recognize the cases of these breakdowns. Then, it uses these relevant variables in order to look for the closest cases. It proceeds with a CBR in order to solve some problems through the comparison of breakdown cases withdrawn from the case base. With this resolution method, if a confirmed breakdown case and a new situation is similar enough, all the solutions applied to the breakdown remain valid and could be applied to the new situation. The supervising agent follows a procedure of research in order to compare the descriptive of the case to be processed with those contained in the internal base. Thus, the capacity of resolution increases with the measurement of the addition of new examples in the base of credential. As the number of examples increases, the SA will be more able to find a closest case, or rather a similar one. Unlike the expert system witch distinguishes the knowledge base and the case base, the CBR maintains the training and the reasoning in a constant relation. The expert systems correspond to a static vision of reasoning. This vision requires some regular updating of the knowledge base. Thus, the RBC seems to be a good answer (pragmatic and evolutive) to many problems of the breakdowns diagnosis and of operators assistance.

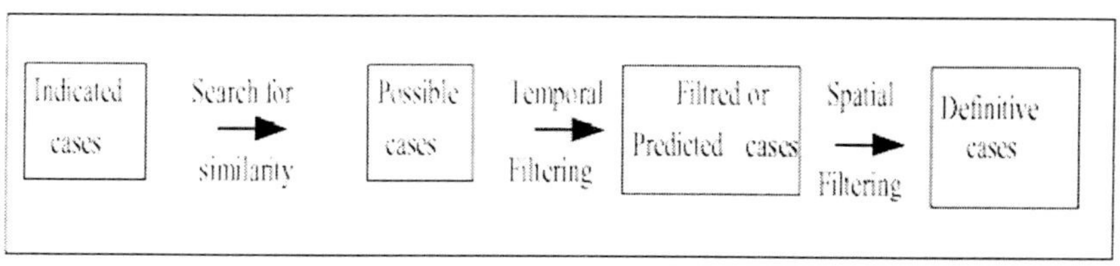

FIG. 5.1. *Diagnostic steps*

5.4. Temporal dependencies among different breakdown cases. For the temporal filtering of the IP breakdown cases, we propose the use of an NN in order to take into account the temporal inter- relationships existing among the different cases of the previously occurring breakdowns. In order to calculate the best evaluation at the instant t, we propose the formula : C(t)= F (C (t n)) .. C (t), W) where C(t) is the result of the combination, C(t-i) is the result of the local classification at the instant (t-i) and F is a NN depending from the parameters W coming from the variables. The evaluation at the instant t depends on the previous evaluations at the instant (t-n) to t [6][12][25].

5.5. Spatial dependencies among different breakdown cases. To improve the performances of our diagnosis architecture, the SA takes into account the existing spatial dependencies among the different sites of the IP. To achieve this, we propose the use a Bayesian Networks (BN) for the spatial filtering [25]. BN possesses more knowledge prior to the task to be solved. It is defined by :

- the qualitative description of some relationships of dependence among its variables (the causal graph).
- the quantitative description of these relationships (the matrix of conditional probabilities).
- and a method of reasoning using these descriptions (the inference analysis). The steps of building a BN consist in : the definition of the variables, the definition of the conditional probabilities matrixes, the definition of the variables of each graph and the definition of the causal graph. The goal of spatial filtering is to calculate the probability of the breakdown impact at the level of a site on the other sites and on the whole IP. The easiest way of building the causal graph (cf. Fig. 5.2), i.e the ties among the different variables (the variable system represents the whole system, Sitei represents a site and Csiteij represents the component j of a sitei), consists in using some properties of the BNs and the criterion of separation distance. This distance remains in the conditional dependence among variables [26]. We could show that the variables System and the Sitei are conditionally dependent (when the variable system is known, the states of the Sitei variables are linked), and thus links them as in figure 7. In the same way, every variable Sitei is conditionally depending on the local components Csiteij achieved in this site. It gives us as example (cf. Fig. 5.2) for the sitei.

In order to define completely the causal graph, it is necessary to calculate the conditional probability matrix P ((node) / father) for each node of the graph. Once the graph built, the using of BNs remains on the inferring algorithm that gives the probability of each variable from a certain number of values set in advance. In our case, the BN is a tree that allows to use the simplest inferring algorithm proposed by PEARL [7][10]. The power of BN is to insert some qualitative knowledge on the causal relations among the variables. So the BN are relevant for the explanation of a phenomenon, they give information of a high level, like the exploration of the variables leading to the result.

6. The operator. In our system, we consider the operator as an agent having a role to play in the community of the agents [27]. He is endowed with a knowledge which makes him able to interfere in a class of problems. An expert operator will be, for example, able to manage most of the reasoning, he will use a cooperation mode which will make him more or less present in the resolution of a problem. The current situation gather, a set of information on the chronological account of the resolution. In some circumstances, a mode of cooperation should be put into question if it is not suitable. This will occur for example,

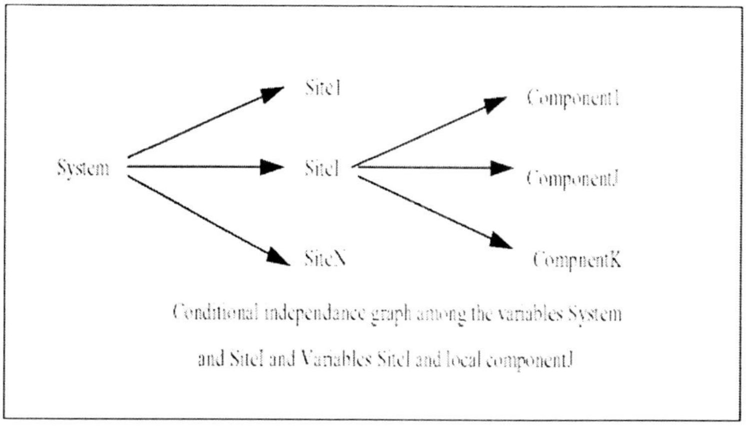

FIG. 5.2. *Graph of conditional independence for the spatial filtering*

when the operator puts systematically into question the results of the system or when the system is stuck. According to the fixed objectives, the operator may want in some different cases, to take the hand for some precise stages of resolution and leave it for some others. If he wants to analyze a particular case, the operator will ask to be solicited for all the stages of decision and of validation.

7. Conclusion and perspectives. The idea in this paper comes from an established fact that the use of intelligent control becomes imperative for the IPCS. It is therefore necessary to deal with these systems from new approaches so much for the surveillance as that of the functioning safety and the supervision. Thus, we propose an architecture using agent framework and Data Mining Techniques (Alliance MAS Data Mining tool Box) for the IPCS. The main idea of this paper is to consider the system formed as a composition of :

- a set of basic entities that constitutes the elementary component of the IPCS that, once arranged, are going, to form its structure (reactive system of control).
- a set of entities responsible for the analysis and the evolution of the different sizes characterizing the process (system of analysis and assessment of the different sizes of the IP).
- a set of entities responsible for the supervision and means of the efficient spatial and temporal action on the environment, that allows the substratum to actively include itself to reach some of the auto-defined goals

The architecture proposed in our approach doesn't lie on a hierarchical rigid organization, but, on the contrary, on some semi autonomous entities AGENTS. This allows to avoid neck strangling resulting from some hierarchical controls, to keep the autonomy of the different agents, to integrate easily some preexistent systems and of aiming at the security of exploitation (tolerances to the breakdowns) as well as that of the users (risky industrial installations). This hybrid architecture is robust and could be used for any complex IP propertied spatial and temporal dependencies.

Our perspectives are: the applicability evaluation of the concepts introduced by our approach to any kind of structural organization of the exploitation functions of an automated system and the application of our approach on some pilot application.

REFERENCES

[1] A. El fazziki and M.Sadgal, *An agent oriented method for analysis and design for industrial processes contro*, the Second International Workshop on Software Agents and Workflows for Systems Interoperability proceeding , p 21-29,London, Ontario, Canada,12,14 Jully 2001.

[2] *Systeme a agents multiples pour le controle de l'accelerateur du CERN*, http://www.epfl.ch/SIC/publications/FI96/f1-sp96/page96.html

[3] J. Sjoberg, Q. Zhang, L. jung, A. Benveniste, B. Deylon, P.Y. Glorennec, H. Hjalmarsson, and A. Juditsky, *Nonlinear Black Box Modeling in System*, 1995.

[4] G. Bousghiri and J. Ragot, *Pattern recognition for diagnosis of technological Systems: Review*, IEEE International Conference on Systems, Man and Cybernetics 5 :275- 283.1993.

[5] A. El fazziki and M.Sadgal, *Agent-based systems for diagnosis and supervision of industrial processes*, Prpceeding, 14 th International Conference on Computer Applications in Industry and Engineering (CAINE-2001), Las Vegas USA, 27-29 Novembre 2001.

[6] P. Gallinari, S. Thiria,; Y. Lechevalier, O. Gascuel, and S. Canus, *Methodes neuronales de descrimination.Ch3 de statistiques et methodes neuronales*, eds Dunods.1997.

[7] F. Jensen, *Introduction to Bayesian Network*, Springer Verlag. 1996.

[8] M. Basseville and M.O. Cordier, *Surveillance et diagnostic de systemes dynamiques : approches complementaires du Traitement de Signal et de l'Intelligence Artificielle*,Rapport de Recherche INRIA 2861.1996.

[9] M. Basseville and M.O. Cordier, *surveillance d'installation industrielles:demarche generale et conception de l'algorithmique*,Rapport interne IRISA PI 1010. 1996.

[10] P. Leray and P. Gallinari, *Une architecture neuro-baysienne pour le traitement spatio-temporel d'alarmes. Application au diagnostic dans le reseau telephonique*, , Proceedings of NMR'99.R1999.

[11] L. Miclet, *structural Methods for the recognition of the shapes*, Eyrolles.1994.

[12] M.A. Morjaia, J. Rink, W.D. Smith, G. Klempner, C. Burns, and J. Stein, *Commercialization of EPRI's Generator Expert Monitoring System (GEMS)*,Expert system application for the electric power industry.1993.

[13] F.M.T. Brazier , B. Duninkelicz, N. Jenning and J. Treur, *DESIRE : Modelling multi-agent systems in compositional formal framework*, Int Journal of cooperative Information systems, 6 (1), 67-94, 1997.

[14] C. Bernon, V. Camps, M.P. Gleize, P. Gleize, *La conception des Systemes adaptatifs ? Contraintes et specificites. Atelier de Methodologie et Environnement pour les systemes Multi-agents (SMA 2001)*, Plate-forme AFIA, Grenoble du 25 au 28 Juin 2001.

[15] M-P. Gleizes and P. Marcenac, *Ingenierie des SMA et Application*, Actes des septiemes journees francophones d'Intelligence Artificielle Distribuee et Systemes Multi-agents - - Editions Hermes 1999.

[16] A. Cardon and Z. Guessoum, *Systemes multi-agents adaptatifs*, Actes des huitiemes journees francophones d'Intelligence Artificielle distribuee et Systemes Multi-agents - Edition Hermes, Novembre 2000.

[17] A. Collinot, A. Drogoul, P. Benhamou, *Agent oriented Design for a Soccer Robot Team*, p 41-47, Proceedings of ICMAS'96, 1996.

[18] A. TveitT, *A survey of agent-oriented software engineering*, NTNU Computer Science Graduate Student Conference. Norwegian University of Science and Technology, May 2001.

[19] M. Woolridge and P. Ciancarini, *Agent-oriented software engineering : the state of the art*, AOSE'00, LNCS n 1957, Springer Verlag, Berlin, January 2000.

[20] M. WOOD and S. DELOACH, *An overview of the multiagent systems engineering methodology*, AOSE'00, LNCS n 1957, Springer Verlag, Berlin, January 2000.

[21] *Data Mining and Knowledge Discovery*, http://www.research.microsoft.com/research/datamine.

[22] R. Lefebure and G. Venturi, *Le Data Mining*, Eyrolles 1999.

[23] S. Imad, *Les base de donnees avancees*, Edition Hermes 1992.

[24] E. Simon, J. Kiernan, C. Maindreville, *Unifying Deductive and Active Databases*, Conference sur la nouvelle generation des bases de donnees : du modele relationnel au modele objet, universite Paris VIII 30/09 au 02/10 1992.

[25] S. Bengio, *Prediction de series temporelles par reseau de neurones*, http://www.iro.umontreal.ca/

ebengio/prediction.html.

[26] J. Pearl, *Probabilistic Reasoning in Intelligent systems : Network of plausible inference*, ed. Morgan Kaufmann 1988.

[27] F.Regis, *Rôles et mode de cooperation dans les systemes a base de connaissances cooperatifs*, universite de Montpelier II Doctorat d'universite 1996.

In: Focus on Computational Neurobiology
Editor: Lei Li, pp. 207-210 ISBN 1-59033-915-0

A FACTORING ALGORITHM USING JACOBI'S SYMBOL*

TSUTOMU ANSAI†, TAKAHIRO HAYATA‡, AND KUNIKATSU KOBAYASHI§

Abstract. We show a factoring algorithm based on a new idea that using Jacobi's symbol in regard to the composite number of $n = p^2q$. The complexity of this method is about $\mathbf{O}(n^{1/3.7})$.

Key words. factoring algorithm, Jacobi's symbol, $n = p^2q$, complexity

1. Introduction. The factoring problem for large composite numbers has been studied as hard problem since old days [1], [2], [3], [4], and recently, even in terms of clarifying the security of the RSA cryptosystem that depends on the factoring problem being difficult, researches on the complexity required for factoring are being made [5].

In this paper, we show a factoring algorithm using Jacobi's symbol in regard to the composite number of $n = p^2q$[6]. Then, we discuss the complexity of this algorithm. Because the value of the Jacobi's symbol of $n = p^2q$ for arbitrary prime number p_i is equal to the Legendre's symbol of q for the prime number p_i, whether a prime factor q is a quadratic residue or not is known by calculating the value of the Jacobi's symbol and remainder candidates of prime factor q for prime number p_i are obtained (narrowing down to half of the possible remainder candidates). In other words, the candidates of $q \pmod{p_i}$ are obtained. Accordingly, the value of $q \pmod{p_i}$ is obtained each having the value of prime number p_i varied from 2 on in order until the product of prime number p_i is over $\sqrt[3]{n}$ and prime factor q is obtained by combination of these by the Chinese remainder theorem. The complexity of this method is about $\mathbf{O}(n^{1/3.7})$. The problem of this method is, however, that much memory is required.

2. An algorithm of factoring using Jacobi's symbols. The Jacobi's symbol for the composite number of $n = p^2q$ type is, regarding prime number p_i when $\mathrm{GCD}(p_i, n) = 1$,

$$\left(\frac{p_i}{n}\right) = \left(\frac{p_i}{p}\right)^2 \left(\frac{p_i}{q}\right) = \left(\frac{p_i}{q}\right) \tag{2.1}$$

and, this is equal to the Legendre's symbol of prime factor q. And, by calculation of the Legendre's symbol of $n \pmod{p_i}$ for prime number p_i, whether prime factor q for prime number p_i is a quadratic residue or not, is known from

$$\left(\frac{n \bmod p_i}{p_i}\right) = \left(\frac{p \bmod p_i}{p_i}\right)^2 \left(\frac{q \bmod p_i}{p_i}\right) = \left(\frac{q \bmod p_i}{p_i}\right) \tag{2.2}$$

and remainder candidates of prime factor q for p_i are obtained. In other words, $(p_i - 1)/2$ values of $q \pmod{p_i}$ are obtained.

When $p > q$, from $q < \sqrt[3]{n}$, having prime number p_i varied from 2 on, and the product of these prime numbers is first over $\lfloor \sqrt[3]{n} \rfloor$, that is, when the below is valid,

$$\prod_{i=1}^{\max} p_i > \lfloor \sqrt[3]{n} \rfloor \tag{2.3}$$

---

*This work was supported in part by the Grant-in-Aid for Science Research of the Ministry of Education, Science and Culture of Japan under Grant (C)(2) 12650360.

†Yamagata University,Yonezawa-shi,Japan(tr386@dip.yz.yamagata-u.ac.jp)
‡Yamagata University,Yonezawa-shi,Japan(hayata@yz.yamagata-u.ac.jp)
§Yamagata University,Yonezawa-shi,Japan(kobayash@yz.yamagata-u.ac.jp)

the maximum value of p_i is $p_{\max}$. Next, the value of $q \pmod{p_i}$ for each prime number p_i is obtained, and by combination of these values by the Chinese reminder theorem, q $(\bmod \prod_{i=1}^{\max} p_i)$, that is, prime factor q, is obtained.

The p of prime factor when 4 is the modulus number, with k as the arbitrary integer, is expressed by either

$$(2.4) \qquad p = 4k + 1 \quad \text{or} \quad p = 4k + 3$$

and, either case is

$$(2.5) \qquad p^2 \equiv 1 \pmod 8.$$

In other words, when $n = p^2q$,

$$(2.6) \qquad \begin{aligned} n &\equiv q \pmod 3 \\ n &\equiv q \pmod 8 \end{aligned}$$

and each remainder of n when each modulus is 3 and 8 is equal to the remainder of prime factor q with each modulus is 3 and 8. In other words, the remainder of q is defined uniquely with 24 as the modulus.

The factoring algorithm using Jacobi's symbol is shown below.

Step 1. First, the remainder of q in modulo 24 is obtained by calclation of the remainder of n in modulo 24.

Step 2. When p_i are defined to be prime numbers over 5, and the product of multiplying all of p_i in order from smallness by 24 first satisfies the following (2.7), the maximum value, $p_{\max}$ of p_i is obtained.

$$(2.7) \qquad 24 \prod_{i=1}^{\max} p_i > \lfloor \sqrt[3]{n} \rfloor$$

Step 3. The Legendre's symbol of $n \pmod{p_i}$ for prime number p_i from $p_1 = 5$ on in order is calculated and $(p_i - 1)/2$ remainder candidates of prime factor q for prime number p_i are obtained depending on whether the values are quadratic residue or not.

Step 4. By combination of the remainder candidates of prime factor q for each prime number p_i using the Chinese remainder theorem, the candidates of the q with the modulus of $24 \prod_{i=1}^{\max} p_i$ are obtained.

Step 5. The q is obtained calculating GCD of the n from values below $\lfloor \sqrt[3]{n} \rfloor$ among the candidates of the q with the modulus of $24 \prod_{i=1}^{\max} p_i$.

A simple example is shown below.

In the case of $n = 68374556539$:

Step 1. From $n \equiv 19 \pmod{24}$, $q \equiv 19 \pmod{24}$.

Step 2. From $24 \times 5 \times 7 \times 11 = 9240 > \lfloor \sqrt[3]{n} \rfloor = 4089$, $p_{\max} = 11$D

Step 3. When $p_1 = 5$, from $n \pmod 5 \equiv 4, (\frac{4}{5}) = 1$, $q \pmod 5 =$ either 1or 4.
When $p_2 = 7$, from $n \pmod 7 \equiv 2, (\frac{2}{7}) = 1$, $q \pmod 7 =$ either one of $1, 2$ or 4.
When $p_{\max} = 11$, from $n \pmod{11} \equiv 3, (\frac{3}{11}) = 1$, $q \pmod{11} =$either one of $1, 3, 4, 5$ or 9.

Step 4. From

$$\begin{cases} q \equiv 19 & \pmod{24} \\ q \equiv 1, 4 & \pmod 5, \end{cases}$$

TABLE 2.1
The complexity of this algorithm

n	$\lfloor \sqrt[3]{n} \rfloor$	$p_{\max}$	$24\prod_{i=1}^{\max} p_i$	number of remainder	candidates of q
4.9×10^{60}	1.7×10^{20}	59	7.7×10^{21}	3.9×10^{15}	8.5×10^{13}
8.1×10^{70}	4.3×10^{23}	61	4.7×10^{23}	1.2×10^{17}	1.1×10^{17}
5.7×10^{80}	8.3×10^{26}	71	2.2×10^{27}	1.4×10^{20}	5.0×10^{19}
4.9×10^{90}	1.7×10^{30}	79	1.3×10^{31}	1.9×10^{23}	2.5×10^{22}
8.1×10^{100}	4.3×10^{33}	89	9.5×10^{34}	3.4×10^{26}	1.6×10^{25}
5.1×10^{110}	8.0×10^{36}	97	9.2×10^{36}	1.7×10^{28}	1.4×10^{28}
4.9×10^{120}	1.7×10^{40}	103	9.6×10^{40}	4.2×10^{31}	7.4×10^{30}
8.1×10^{130}	4.3×10^{43}	109	1.1×10^{45}	1.2×10^{35}	4.7×10^{33}
5.9×10^{140}	8.4×10^{46}	113	1.3×10^{47}	6.8×10^{36}	4.5×10^{36}
4.9×10^{150}	1.7×10^{50}	131	2.1×10^{51}	2.8×10^{40}	2.2×10^{39}

$q \equiv$ either 19 or 91 (mod 120).
From

$$\begin{cases} q \equiv 19, 91 & \pmod{120} \\ q \equiv 1, 2, 4 & \pmod{7} \end{cases}$$

$q \equiv$ either one of $211, 331, 379, 499, 571$ or $739 \pmod{840}$. From

$$\begin{cases} q \equiv 211, 331, 379, 499, 571, 739 \pmod{840} \\ q \equiv 1, 3, 4, 5, 9 \pmod{11} \end{cases}$$

, $q \equiv$ either one of $331, 379, 499, 1171,$
$1219, 1411, 2011, 2179, 2731, 3019, 3259,$
$3859, 3931, 4579, 5191, 5251, 5371, 5611,$
$5779, 6451, 6931, 7099, 7219, 7291, 7771,$
$7891, 8299, 8611, 8779, 9139 \pmod{9240}$.

Step 5. Value $q = 3019$ is obtained from calculation of GCD of the n and 13 pieces of the candidates of the q with $\lfloor \sqrt[3]{n} \rfloor \le 4089$.

When seen in the example how number of candidate T of prime factor q decreases by each step, first, begins with $T = 4089$ since $q < \lfloor \sqrt[3]{n} \rfloor$, comes to $T \approx 4089/24 \approx 170$ at stage step 1, and stage step 3, comes to $\frac{4089}{24} \times \frac{2}{5} \times \frac{3}{7} \times \frac{5}{11} \approx 13$.

Thus, determining whether prime factor q for each prime number is quadratic residue or not, decreases the number of the candidates of q to less than 1/2 that so far. Provided, however, that the remainder candidates of q with $\prod p_i$ combined using the Chinese remainder theorem as the modulus increase by $(p_i - 1)/2$ times that so far as the number of prime number p_i increases, and the problem is the requirement of a large memory. And, it is also a problem that the complexity requires for obtaining for the remainder candidates of the q by the Chinese remainder theorem increases by $(p_i - 1)/2$ times that so far as the number of prime number p_i increases.

TABLE 2.1 shows, for some number of n, the number of remainder candidates of prime factor q for modulus $24\prod_{i=1}^{\max} p_i$ and the number of candidates of prime factor q at the time. As seen in TABLE 2.1, the memory required by the algorithm, that is, the number of the remainder candidates when $24\prod_{i=1}^{\max} p_i$ is the modulus, is about $\mathbf{O}(n^{1/3.7})$. And, the complexity required for obtaining prime factor q is almost in the same order.

3. Conclusion. In this paper, we proposed a method to obtain prime factor q for a composite number of $n = p^2q$ type using Jacobi's symbols. The method is, by judging whether prime factor q for small prime number p_i is a quadratic residue or not, a method to repeat narrowing down of the candidates of the q to about half that up to then, and the memory necessary for the algorithm is about $\mathbf{O}(n^{1/3.7})$. The complexity required for obtaining prime factor q is almost in the same order.

REFERENCES

[1] N. Ikeno and K. Koyama, *Modern Cryptographic Theory*, Institute of Electronics, Information, and Communication Engineers, 1986.

[2] H. Wada, *Computers and Factorization* , Yuuseisya Press, 1987.

[3] Y. Kida and I. Makino, *Computer Number Theory Based on UBASIC*, Nihonhyoronsya Press, 1994.

[4] T. Okamoto, K. Ohta, *Cryptography, Zero-Knowledge Interactive Proofs, and Number Theory*, Kyoritsu Shuppan, 1995.

[5] Y. Kida, *On the Latest Integer Factorization Methods*, Sophia Kokyuroku in Mathmatics, No.35, 1992.

[6] T. Ansai, T. Hayata and K. Kobayashi, *A Few Considerations on Factoring Algorithms*, Technical Report of IEICE, ISEC, May, 2001.

Index

H

I

J

L

M

N

O

P

Q

R

S

T

V

W

Y